CARNEGIE LEARNING

LONG + LIVE + MATH

High School Math Solution

Algebra II

Student Edition

Volume 1

Sandy Bartle Finocchi and Amy Jones Lewis

with Josh Fisher, Janet Sinopoli, and Victoria Fisher

501 Grant St., Suite 1075
Pittsburgh, PA 15219
Phone 888.851.7094
Customer Service Phone 412.690.2444
Fax 412.690.2444

www.carnegielearning.com

Cover Design by Anne Milliron

ISBN: 978-1-60972-326-2
Student Edition, Volume 1

Printed in the United States of America
4 5 6 7 8 9 BB 21

LONG + LIVE + MATH

ACKNOWLEDGMENTS

High School Math Solution Authors
- Sandy Bartle Finocchi, Senior Academic Officer
- Amy Jones Lewis, Director of Instructional Design
- Josh Fisher, Instructional Designer
- Victoria Fisher, Instructional Designer
- Janet Sinopoli, Instructional Designer

Foundational Authors
- William S. Hadley, Co-Founder
- David Dengler
- Mary Lou Metz

Vendors
- Lumina Datamatics, Ltd.
- Mathematical Expressions, LLC

Images
www.pixabay.com

Special Thanks

- Alison Huettner for project management and editorial review.
- Jacyln Snyder for her contributions to the Teacher's Implementation Guide facilitation notes.
- Harry Lynch for his contributions and review of the Statistics and Probability strand.
- Madison Kalo for her design contributions.
- The members of Carnegie Learning Cognitive Scientist Team—Brendon Towle, John Connelly, Bob Hausmann, Chas Murray, and Martina Pavelko—for their insight in learning science and collaboration on MATHia® Software.
- John Jorgenson, Chief Marketing Officer, for all his insight and messaging.
- Carnegie Learning Education Services Team for content review and providing customer feedback.
- The entire Carnegie Learning staff for their hard work and dedication to transforming math education.
- The families of the authoring team for their continued support.

"Mathematics is so much more than memorizing rules. It is learning to reason, to make connections, and to make sense of the world. We believe in Learning by Doing(TM)—you need to actively engage with the content if you are to benefit from it. The lessons were designed to take you from your intuitive understanding of the world and build on your prior experiences to then learn new concepts. My hope is that these instructional materials help you build a deep understanding of math.

Sandy Bartle Finocchi, Senior Academic Officer

"You have been learning math for a very long time—both in school and in your interactions in the world. You know a lot of math! In this course, there's nothing brand new. It all builds on what you already know. So, as you approach each activity, use all of your knowledge to solve problems, to ask questions, to fix mistakes, and to think creatively.

Amy Jones Lewis, Director of Instructional Design

"At Carnegie Learning we have created an organization whose mission and culture is defined by your success. Our passion is creating products that make sense of the world of mathematics and ignite a passion in you. Our hope is that you will enjoy our resources as much as we enjoyed creating them.

Barry Malkin, CEO, Carnegie Learning

Volume 1 Student Edition

Module 1: Analyzing Structure

Topic 1: Exploring and Analyzing Patterns

Topic 2: Composing and Decomposing Functions

Topic 3: Characteristics of Polynomial Functions

Module 2: Developing Structural Similarities

Topic 1: Relating Factors and Zeros

Topic 2: Polynomial Models

Volume 2 Student Edition

Module 3: Inverting Functions

Topic 3: Exponential and Logarithmic Equations

Topic 4: Applications of Growth Modeling

Module 4: Investigating Periodic Functions

Topic 1: Trigonometric Relationships

Module 5: Relating Data and Decisions

Topic 1: Interpreting Data in Normal Distributions

Topic 2: Making Inferences and Justifying Conclusions

© Carnegie Learning, Inc.

Each lesson has the same structure. Key features are noted.

1. Learning Goals
Learning goals are stated for each lesson to help you take ownership of the learning objectives.

2. Connection
Each lesson begins with a statement connecting what you have learned with a question to ponder.

Return to this question at the end of this lesson to gauge your understanding.

Planting the Seeds
Exploring Cubic Functions

3

Warm Up
Use the Distributive Property to rewrite each expression.

1. $a(2a - 1)(5 + a)$

2. $(9 - x)(x + 3)$

3. $b^2(10 - b) + b^2$

4. $(w - 2)(w + 3)(w + 1)$

Learning Goals
- Represent cubic functions using words, tables, equations, and graphs.
- Interpret the key characteristics of the graphs of cubic functions.
- Analyze cubic functions in terms of their mathematical context and problem context.
- Connect the characteristics and behaviors of a cubic function to its factors.
- Compare cubic functions with linear and quadratic functions.
- Build cubic functions from linear and quadratic functions.

Key Terms
- cubic function
- relative maximum
- relative minimum

 You have calculated the volume of various geometric figures. How can you use what you know about volume to build an algebraic function?

3. Getting Started

Each lesson begins with a Getting Started. When working on the Getting Started, use what you know about the world, what you have learned previously, or your intuition. The goal is just to get you thinking and ready for what's to come.

③ **GETTING STARTED**

Our Business Is Growing

The Plant-A-Seed Planter Company produces planter boxes. To make the boxes, a square is cut from each corner of a rectangular copper sheet. The sides are bent to form a rectangular prism without a top. Cutting different sized squares from the corners results in differently sized planter boxes. Plant-A-Seed takes sales orders from customers who request a sized planter box.

It may help to create a model of the planter by cutting squares out of the corners of a sheet of paper and folding.

Each rectangular copper sheet is 12 inches by 18 inches. In the diagram, the solid lines indicate where the square corners are cut, and the dotted lines represent where the sides are bent for each planter box.

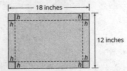

1. Complete the table given each planter box is made from a 12 inch by 18 inch copper sheet. Include an expression for each planter box's height, width, length, and volume for a square corner side of length h.

Square Corner Side Length (inches)	Height (inches)	Width (inches)	Length (inches)	Volume (cubic inches)
0				
1				
2				
3				
4				
5				
6				
7				
h				

...idth

Ask yourself:

What patterns do you notice in the table?

...box

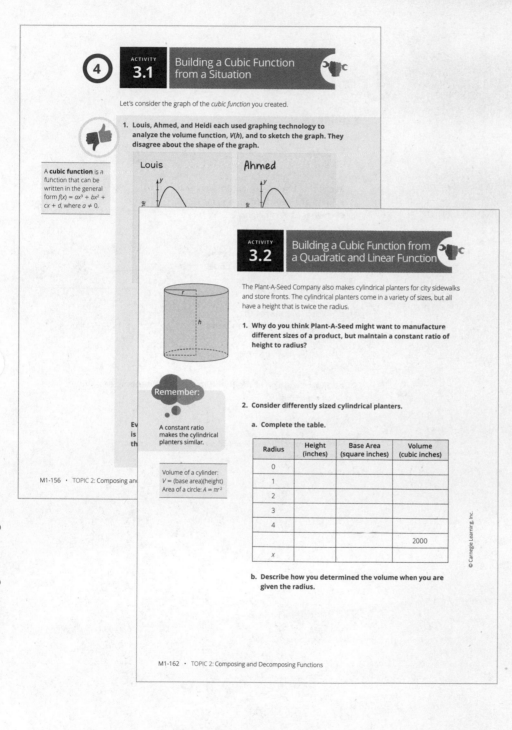

4. Activities

You are going to build a deep understanding of mathematics through a variety of activities in an environment where collaboration and conversations are important and expected.

You will learn how to solve new problems, but you will also learn why those strategies work and how they are connected to other strategies you already know.

Remember:

- It's not just about answer-getting. The process is important.

- Making mistakes is a critical part of learning, so take risks.

- There is often more than one way to solve a problem.

Activities may include real-world problems, sorting activities, worked examples, or analyzing sample student work.

Be prepared to share your solutions and methods with your classmates.

The content within the overlapping activity pages:

ACTIVITY 3.1 — Building a Cubic Function from a Situation

Let's consider the graph of the *cubic function* you created.

1. Louis, Ahmed, and Heidi each used graphing technology to analyze the volume function, $V(h)$, and to sketch the graph. They disagree about the shape of the graph.

Louis   Ahmed

A **cubic function** is a function that can be written in the general form $f(x) = ax^3 + bx^2 + cx + d$, where $a \neq 0$.

M1-156 • TOPIC 2: Composing and

ACTIVITY 3.2 — Building a Cubic Function from a Quadratic and Linear Function

The Plant-A-Seed Company also makes cylindrical planters for city sidewalks and store fronts. The cylindrical planters come in a variety of sizes, but all have a height that is twice the radius.

1. Why do you think Plant-A-Seed might want to manufacture different sizes of a product, but maintain a constant ratio of height to radius?

Remember:

A constant ratio makes the cylindrical planters similar.

Volume of a cylinder:
$V = (\text{base area})(\text{height})$
Area of a circle: $A = \pi r^2$

2. Consider differently sized cylindrical planters.

a. Complete the table.

Radius	Height (inches)	Base Area (square inches)	Volume (cubic inches)
0			
1			
2			
3			
4			
			2000
x			

b. Describe how you determined the volume when you are given the radius.

M1-162 • TOPIC 2: Composing and Decomposing Functions

5. Talk the Talk

Talk the Talk gives you an opportunity to reflect on the main ideas of the lesson.

- Be honest with yourself.

- Ask questions to clarify anything you don't understand.

- Show what you know!

Don't forget to revisit the question posed on the lesson opening page to gauge your understanding.

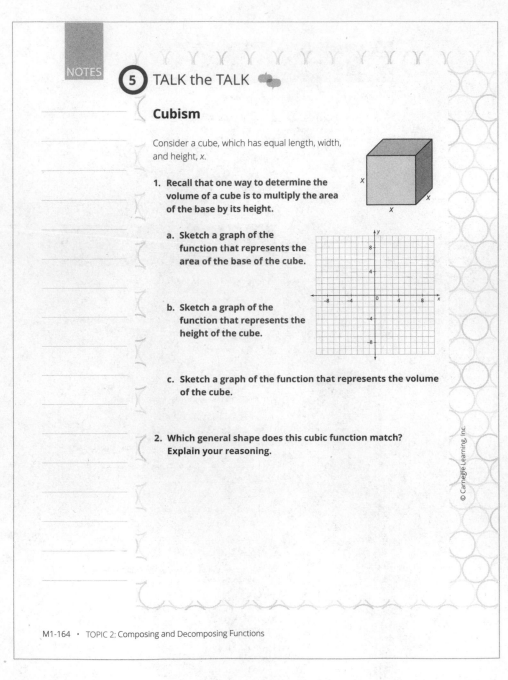

NOTES

5 TALK the TALK

Cubism

Consider a cube, which has equal length, width, and height, x.

1. Recall that one way to determine the volume of a cube is to multiply the area of the base by its height.

   a. Sketch a graph of the function that represents the area of the base of the cube.

   b. Sketch a graph of the function that represents the height of the cube.

   c. Sketch a graph of the function that represents the volume of the cube.

2. Which general shape does this cubic function match? Explain your reasoning.

ASSIGNMENT

Assignment

6 **Write**
Provide an example of each key term.
1. relative minimum
2. relative maximum
3. cubic function

7 **Remember**
A cubic function is a polynomial function of degree 3 that can be written in the form $f(x) = ax^3 + bx^2 + cx + d$, where $a \neq 0$. The graph has 2 general shapes.

8 **Practice**
1. Cynthia is an engineer at a manufacturing plant. Her boss asks her to use rectangular metal sheets to build storage bins with the greatest possible volume. Each rectangular sheet is 8 feet by 10 feet. Cynthia's sketch shows the squares to be removed from the corners of each sheet. The dashed lines indicate where the metal sheets will be folded before they are welded to form
   a. Write a function $V(x)$ t
      side length, x, of the r
   b. Represent the functio
      Determine the domai
      Explain your reasonin
   c. Determine the maximu
   d. Determine any relativ
      over which the functio
   e. Determine the x- and y
   f. Cynthia's boss asks h
      bin dimensions that w

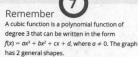

9 **Stretch**
1. Nikki is an engineer at a
   boss asks her to use rec
   build storage bins with t
   Each rectangular sheet i
   sketch shows the square
   sheet. The dashed lines
   sheets will be folded bet
   a. Write a function $V(x)$ t
      squares. Explain your
   b. Represent the functio
      Determine the domai
      your reasoning.

c. Determine the maximum volume of a bin. What are the dimensions of a bin with the maximum volume?

d. Determine any relative maximums or relative minimums of $V(x)$. Then, determine the intervals over which the function is increasing and decreasing.

e. Determine the x- and y-intercepts of the graph of $V(x)$. What do they represent in this problem situation?

f. Nikki's boss asks her to make several bins with volumes of exactly 40 cubic feet. Determine the bin dimensions that will work.

10 **Review**

1. Dilate each function by the given factor to create a new function of higher degree. Sketch the graph and then identify the zeros of the new function.

   a. $f(x) = \left(\frac{1}{2}x + 1\right)(x - 3)$
      Sketch $(x + 1) \cdot f(x)$.

   b. $g(x) = (3x + 4)\left(\frac{1}{4}x + 2\right)$
      Sketch $(x - 1) \cdot f(x)$.

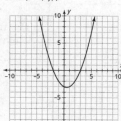 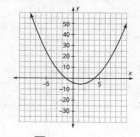

2. The figures shown represent a visual pattern of tiles.
   a. Create a table to display the number of squares used in each of the first 6 figures.
   b. Create a graph of the data points in your table on the coordinate plane shown. Draw a smooth curve to connect the points.
   c. Describe the pattern as linear, exponential, quadratic, or none of these. Explain your reasoning.

3. Solve the equation $x^2 - 6x + 35 = 10$.

6. Write
Reflect on your work and clarify your thinking.

7. Remember
Take note of the key concepts from the lesson.

8. Practice
Use the concepts learned in the lesson to solve problems.

9. Stretch
Ready for a challenge?

10. Review
Remember what you've learned by practicing concepts from previous lessons and topics.

Worked Example

When you see a Worked Example:
- Take your time to read through it.
- Question your own understanding.
- Think about the connections between steps.

Ask Yourself:
- What is the main idea?
- How would this work if I changed the numbers?
- Have I used these strategies before?

Worked Example

You can determine the average rate of change of Zorzansa's profit for the time interval (3.25, 4.25).

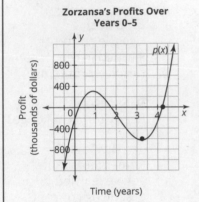

Zorzansa's Profits Over Years 0–5

Substitute the input and output values into the average rate of change formula.

Evaluate the expression.

$$\frac{f(b) - f(a)}{b - a} = \frac{f(4.25) - f(3.25)}{4.25 - 3.25}$$

$$= \frac{0 - (-600)}{1}$$

$$= \frac{600}{1} = 600$$

The average rate of change for the time interval (3.25, 4.25) is approximately $600,000 per year.

Who's Correct

When you see a Who's Correct icon:
- Take your time to read through the situation.
- Question the strategy or reason given.
- Determine correct or not correct.

Ask Yourself:
- Does the reasoning make sense?
- If the reasoning makes sense, what is the justification?
- If the reasoning does not make sense, what error was made?

---

4. **Novena created this graph of a fourth degree polynomial. Armondo said that she is incorrect, that it is a fifth degree polynomial. Who is correct? For the student who is incorrect, explain the error in their thinking.**

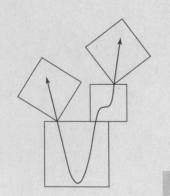

Novena

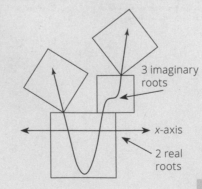

Armondo

3 imaginary roots

x-axis

2 real roots

Thumbs Up

When you see a Thumbs Up icon:

- Take your time to read through the correct solution.
- Think about the connections between steps.

Ask Yourself:

- Why is this method correct?
- Have I used this method before?

Augie

The cubic function $f(x) = (x - 3)(x - 1)(x + 4)$ has the three zeros given. I can verify this by solving the equations $x - 3 = 0$, $x - 1 = 0$, and $x + 4 = 0$.

Thumbs Down

When you see a Thumbs Down icon:

- Take your time to read through the incorrect solution.
- Think about what error was made.

Ask Yourself:

- Where is the error?
- Why is it an error?
- How can I correct it?

Emily

A cubic function must have three zeros. I know this from the Fundamental Theorem of Algebra. However, the number of real and imaginary zeros can vary. The function may have 0, 1, 2, or 3 imaginary zeros.

HABITS OF MIND

The types of activities within this book require you to make sense of mathematics and to demonstrate your reasoning through problem solving, writing, discussing, and presenting. Effective communication and collaboration are essential skills of a successful learner.

Each activity is denoted with an icon that represents a practice or pair of practices intentionally being developed. To help develop these habits of mind ask yourself the types of questions listed as you work.

With practice, you can develop the habits of mind of a productive mathematical thinker.

▶ Make sense of problems and persevere in solving them.

This practice is evident every day in every lesson. No icon used.

Questions to ask:

- What is this problem asking and what is my plan for answering it?
- What tools do I need to solve this problem?
- Does my answer make sense?

▶ Reason abstractly and quantitatively.
▶ Construct viable arguments and critique the reasoning of others.

Questions to ask:

- What representation can I use to solve this problem?
- How can this problem be represented with symbols and numbers?
- How can I explain my thinking?
- How does my strategy compare to my partner's?

"In this class, you won't experiment with beakers full of unearthly liquids, but you'll still be thinking and working like a scientist. So, you will notice patterns, predict how they will behave, test out the predictions, and then unscramble the results. Patterns are everywhere throughout this book, so be **constantly** on the lookout—ready to spot them. There may even be a pleasing pattern buried somewhere in this quotation."

Josh Fisher, Instructional Designer

▶ Model with mathematics.
▶ Use appropriate tools strategically.

Questions to ask:

- What expression or equation could represent this situation?
- What tools would help me solve this problem?
- What representations best show my thinking?
- How does this answer make sense in the context of the original problem?

▶ Attend to precision.

Questions to ask:

- Is my answer accurate?
- Did I use the correct units or labels?
- Is there a more efficient way to solve this problem?
- Is there more sophisticated vocabulary that I could use in my explanation?

▶ Look for and make use of structure.
▶ Look for and express regularity in repeated reasoning.

Questions to ask:

- What characteristics of this expression or equation are made clear through this representation?
- How can I use what I know to explain why this works?
- Can I develop a more efficient method?
- How could this problem help me to solve another problem?

> "It's okay to make mistakes. There is great value in taking risks, making mistakes, and communicating about your mathematical thinking. Only when you reveal your misconceptions, can they be addressed and clarified. You will be amazed at the power you have when you can reason to make sense of the math!"
>
> Janet Sinopoli, Instructional Designer

ACADEMIC GLOSSARY

There are important terms you will encounter throughout this book. It is important that you have an understanding of these words as you get started on your journey through the mathematical concepts. Knowing what is meant by these terms and using these terms will help you think, reason, and communicate your ideas.

ANALYZE

Related Phrases

- Examine
- Evaluate
- Determine
- Observe
- Consider
- Investigate
- What do you notice?
- What do you think?
- Sort and match

Definition

To study or look closely for patterns. Analyzing can involve examining or breaking a concept down into smaller parts to gain a better understanding of it.

Ask Yourself

- Do I see any patterns?
- Have I seen something like this before?
- What happens if the shape, representation, or numbers change?

EXPLAIN YOUR REASONING

Related Phrases

- Show your work
- Explain your calculation
- Justify
- Why or why not?

Definition

To give details or describe how to determine an answer or solution. Explaining your reasoning helps justify conclusions.

Ask Yourself

- How should I organize my thoughts?
- Is my explanation logical?
- Does my reasoning make sense?
- How can I justify my answer to others?

REPRESENT

Definition

To display information in various ways. Representing mathematics can be done using words, tables, graphs, or symbols.

Ask Yourself

- How should I organize my thoughts?
- How do I use this model to show a concept or idea?
- What does this representation tell me?
- Is my representation accurate?

Related Phrases

- Show
- Sketch
- Draw
- Construct
- Create
- Plot
- Graph
- Write an equation
- Complete the table

DESCRIBE

Definition

To represent or give an account of in words. Describing communicates mathematical ideas to others.

Ask Yourself

- How should I organize my thoughts?
- Is my explanation logical?
- Did I consider the context of the situation?
- Does my reasoning make sense?

Related Phrases

- Demonstrate
- Label
- Display
- Compare
- Determine
- Define
- What are the advantages?
- What are the disadvantages?
- What is similar?
- What is different?

PREDICT

Definition

To declare or tell in advance based on the analysis of given data. Predicting first helps inform reasoning.

Ask Yourself

- What do I know about this problem situation?
- What predictions can I make from this problem situation?
- Does my reasoning make sense?
- Is my solution close to my estimation?

Related Phrases

- Estimate
- Approximate
- Expect
- About how much?

> Imagine a room full of art tools. You and your peers must each use the tools to represent a frog. Some may choose to paint the frog. Others may sculpt or write a poem about it. As a mathematician, you are an artist representing your world with your choice of tools—numbers, equations, graphs, tables, or even words. We can express ourselves in different ways even if we are representing the same idea.

Victoria Fisher, Instructional Designer

© Carnegie Learning, Inc.

Thought Bubbles

Look for these icons as you journey through the textbook. Sometimes they will remind you about things you already learned. Sometimes they will ask you questions to help you think about different strategies. Sometimes they will share fun facts. They are here to help and guide your learning.

Side notes are included to provide helpful insights as you work.

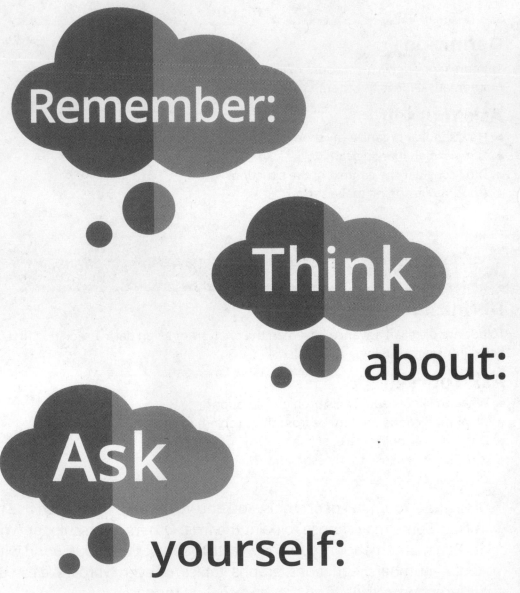

MODULE 1

ANALYZING
= Stru^c–(ture)

The lessons in this module build on what you already know about the properties of linear and quadratic functions. You will strengthen your skills in representing quadratic functions in a variety of forms and verifying the equivalence of representations. You will learn to compose higher-order polynomial functions using linear and quadratic functions as factors. You will relate the characteristics of the factors to the key characteristics of the polynomial functions. For any higher-order polynomial, you will be able to identify the number and types of zeros, intervals of increase or decrease, end behavior, and extrema.

Exploring and Analyzing Patterns

Knitting stitch patterns use repetitive sequences. The one above is called a Triple Seed Stitch: [knit one, purl one] across the row for three rows, then [purl one, knit one] for the next three. This pattern repeats for the desired length. Do you have a hand-knitted sweater? What patterns do you see?

Module 1: Analyzing Structure

TOPIC 1: EXPLORING AND ANALYZING PATTERNS

This topic gives students opportunities to analyze and describe various patterns. Students are asked to represent algebraic expressions in different forms and use algebra and graphs to determine whether they are equivalent. Lessons provide opportunities for students to review linear, exponential, and quadratic functions using multiple representations. Students also learn to write quadratic equations given any three points. They are introduced to the complex number system and solve quadratic equations with imaginary roots.

Where have we been?

In previous courses, students gained extensive experience with multiple representations of linear, exponential, and quadratic functions. This topic serves as an opportunity for students to recall what they already know and prepare for how they will use this knowledge throughout the rest of the course.

Where are we going?

Throughout the rest of this course, students will be exploring more complex functions: polynomials, rational functions, radical functions, and trigonometric functions. This topic is critical for preparing students for this work, which includes identifying key characteristics, connecting representations, writing expressions, using expressions and equations to solve for unknown values, analyzing graphical representations, and making connections to the real world.

The Complex Number System

The set of complex numbers is the set of all numbers written in the form $a + bi$, where a and b are real numbers. The term a is the real part of a complex number, and the term bi is the imaginary part of a complex number. The set of complex numbers is represented by the notation $\mathbb{C}$.

The set of imaginary numbers is represented by the notation $\mathbb{I}$. A pure imaginary number is a number of the form $a + bi$, where a is equal to 0 and b is not equal to 0.

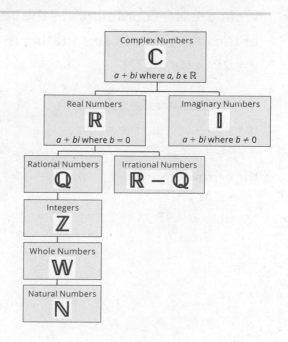

Droning On and On

You can find patterns everywhere! And sometimes a pattern's beauty isn't evident until you describe it using mathematics. Consider a pattern found in nature—the family tree of a male drone bee. Female bees have two parents, a male and a female, whereas male bees have just one parent, a female. In this family tree the parents appear below the original male drone bee.

The total number of bees in each generation follows the pattern 1, 1, 2, 3, 5, 8, . . .

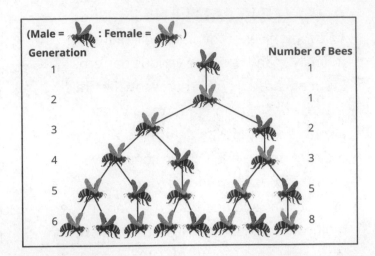

What makes this particular pattern fascinating is that it seems to appear everywhere! This pattern is called the Fibonacci sequence and you can find it in flowers, seashells, pineapples, art, architecture, and even in your DNA! Do you see the pattern? If so, name the next three terms.

Talking Points

Quadratic functions can be an important topic to know about for college admissions tests.

Here is an example of a sample question:

What are the coordinates of the vertex of the parabola whose equation is $y = 2x^2 + 4x - 5$?

If you represent the quadratic equation as $ax^2 + bx + c$, then the x-coordinate of the vertex is $\frac{-b}{2a} = \frac{-4}{2(2)} = -1$. The y-coordinate of the vertex is then $2(-1)^2 + 4(-1) - 5 = -7$.

So, the vertex is at $(-1, -7)$.

Key Terms

relation

A relation is a mapping between a set of input values and a set of output values.

function

A function is a relation such that for each element of the domain there exists exactly one element in the range.

factored form of a quadratic equation

An equation of the form $f(x) = a(x - r_1)(x - r_2)$, where a does not equal 0.

vertex form of a quadratic equation

An equation of the form $f(x) = a(x - h)^2 + k$, where a does not equal 0.

Patterns: They're Grrrrrowing!

Observing Patterns

Warm Up

Consider the block designs.

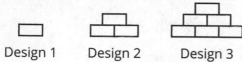

Design 1   Design 2   Design 3

1. Describe Design 4, and draw the design.

2. Describe the observable pattern.

Learning Goals

- Identify multiple patterns within a sequence.
- Use patterns to solve problems.

You have used patterns to make mathematical connections since you started school. How can you continue to build on patterns to understand more complex mathematics?

Covered in Bees!

You can find patterns everywhere! Sometimes you can describe them in terms of color, shape, size, or texture. Other times, a pattern's beauty isn't evident until you describe it mathematically.

Let's consider a pattern found in nature—the family tree of a male bee. Female bees have two parents, a male and a female, whereas male bees have just one parent, a female. In this family tree, the parents appear below the original male bee.

In every bee hive, there is one female queen bee who lays all the eggs. If an egg is not fertilized, it will eventually hatch into a male bee, called a drone.

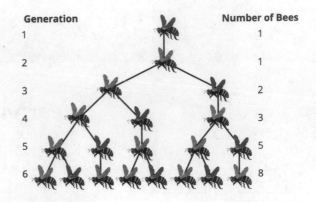

1. **The total number of bees in each generation follows a pattern.**

   a. **Describe the pattern for the number of bees in each generation.**

   b. **Determine the number of bees in the next three generations.**

   c. **What is the mathematical rule that describes the pattern of bees in each generation? Explain your thinking.**

Recognizing and Extending Patterns

Miriam owns a flooring company. Her latest job involves tiling a square room. Miriam's customer, Mr. Rivera, requests a tile pattern of alternating black, white, and gray tiles as shown. Each tile is one square foot.

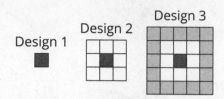

Design 1   Design 2   Design 3

1. Analyze Miriam's design of a tile pattern for a square floor. Describe as many patterns as you can.

© Carnegie Learning, Inc.

2. Sketch the design for a square floor that is 9 feet by 9 feet.

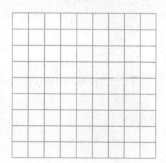

> **Think**
> **about:**
>
> What tools can help you analyze the situation?
>
> You can . . .
>
> - Draw a picture.
> - Sketch a graph.
> - Create a table.
> - Write an equation.

Each tile is one square foot.

Think

about:

How can you work backwards to get to this answer efficiently?

3. A hotel manager wants Miriam to tile their lobby using the same design she created for Mr. Rivera. The lobby measures 45 feet by 45 feet. He wants the outer edge to be the same color as the center tile. Will this occur? Justify your answer.

Ask

yourself:

How can you predict what will happen without doing all of the calculations?

4. Very picky Paula Perkins requests a tile floor from Miriam. She also wants the alternating black, white, and gray tile pattern; however, she wants the outer edge of the tile to match her wall color. The room is 101 feet by 101 feet and the wall color is white. What color must the center tile be to ensure the outer edge is white? Show or explain your work.

The class president, vice president, and treasurer of a high school count the ballots for the homecoming king election. The election result is generally kept a secret until the pep rally, when the winner is announced in front of the entire senior class.

Unfortunately, this year's ballot counters are not very good at keeping a secret. The very next day after counting the ballots, each ballot counter tells two of their friends in the senior class the election result, but makes each friend vow not to spread the result.

However, each of the ballot counter's friends cannot keep a secret either. The following day, each friend of each ballot counter shares the election result with two of their friends in the senior class. This pattern continues for the entire week leading up to the pep rally.

> Assume that no student is told the result of the election twice.

1. **Create a visual model to represent this problem situation. Describe the patterns you observe.**

2. How many new seniors will know the winner of the homecoming king election on the fourth day? Explain your reasoning.

3. The total number of students in the senior class is 250. If the ballot counters knew the election result on Monday, will every senior already know the winner of the election when the result is announced at the pep rally 6 days later? Explain your reasoning.

Maximizing with Patterns

Maureen and Matthew are designing their backyard patio. There will be an entrance and exit off the front and back of the patio. The sequence shown represents different designs depending on the size of the patio.

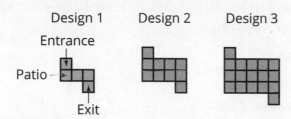

Design 1 Design 2 Design 3

Entrance

Patio

Exit

> Each square represents 1 square foot.

1. **Analyze each design in the sequence. Describe as many patterns as you can.**

2. **Sketch Design 6 of the sequence.**

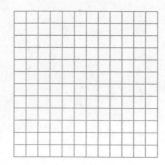

3. **Matthew has 170 tiles he can use for this project. Identify the largest patio design that he can make. Show or explain your reasoning.**

© Carnegie Learning, Inc.

TALK the TALK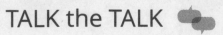

Think Back

Consider the three scenarios from this lesson.

1. **Explain how the relationship described in each scenario represents a function.**

Assignment

© Carnegie Learning, Inc.

Write

Explain what it means for a pattern to be a function.

Remember

Sequences can be used to show observable patterns. Patterns can be used to solve problems.

Practice

1. A jewelry box company offers simple jewelry boxes with decorative tiles. The top and bottom of each box are adorned with heart tiles while the sides consist of diamond tiles. Pictures of the first 3 jewelry box designs and their corresponding tile layouts are shown.

Design 1

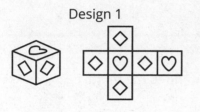

Design 2

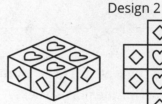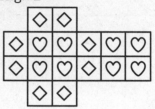

Design 3

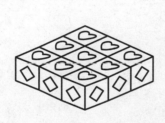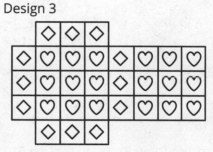

a. Sketch the tile layout for Design 4.

b. Analyze the jewelry box designs. Describe as many patterns as you can.

c. Determine a method you can use to calculate the number of diamond tiles, the number of heart tiles, and the total number of tiles used for any design.

d. The company has 4 times as many heart tiles as they have diamond tiles in their inventory. The owner decides to advertise a sale on the box design, which uses 4 times as many heart tiles as diamond tiles. Determine which design the owner will place on sale.

2. Susan starts her own telemarketing company by recruiting 3 employees into what she calls Recruiting Group 1. She requires each employee in Recruiting Group 1 to recruit 3 additional employees for Recruiting Group 2. The employees in each successive recruiting group must meet the same requirement of recruiting 3 additional employees.

   a. Create a visual model to represent the number of employees in the company. Only include the first 3 recruiting groups in your model. Do not include Susan as an employee.

   b. Determine a method to calculate the number of employees in any given recruiting group. Use that method to calculate the number of employees hired in each of the first 6 recruiting groups.

   c. Susan can only afford to hire a total of 800 employees. She tells the employees to halt all recruiting as soon as the 800th employee is hired. Which recruiting group will be partially completed at that time? Explain your reasoning.

Stretch

Students in an art class are constructing a tile mural. The students add to the mural each week. The design of the mural is shown for the first 3 weeks.

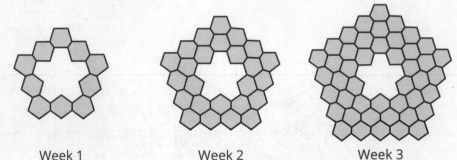

Week 1   Week 2   Week 3

Define a function to represent the number of tiles on the mural in any week.

Review

Solve each equation for the unknown.

1. $3(5x - 4) - 2 = 10 - 3x$ 2. $-6a - 4(a - 3) = -6a + 15$

The Cat's Out of the Bag!

Generating Algebraic Expressions

Warm Up

Consider the block designs.

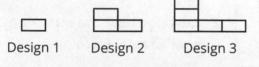

Design 1 Design 2 Design 3

1. Describe and then draw Design 4.

2. Describe the observable pattern.

Learning Goals

- Generate algebraic expressions using geometric patterns.
- Represent algebraic expressions in different forms.
- Determine whether expressions are equivalent.
- Identify patterns as linear, exponential, or quadratic using a visual model, a table of values, or a graph.

You have described geometric patterns using words. How can you write an algebraic expression to represent a pattern? And how do you know whether two expressions are equivalent?

Blast from the Very Recent Past

Miriam owns a flooring company. Her latest job involves tiling a square room in a pattern of alternating black, white, and gray tiles as shown.

Design 1   Design 2   Design 3

Consider the scenarios from the previous lesson.

1. **Describe the growth pattern for each scenario.**

The class president, vice president, and treasurer of a high school count the ballots for the homecoming king election. The day after the ballot counting, each ballot counter tells two of their friends in the senior class the election result. The following day, each of the ballot counter's friends shares the election result with two of their friends in the senior class. This pattern continues for the entire week leading up to the pep rally.

Day 1	Day 2	Day 3	Day 4	Day 5	Day 6	Day 7
3	6	12	24	48	96	192

2. **Describe how the quantities change relative to one another.**

Maureen and Matthew are designing their backyard patio. There will be an entrance and exit off the front and back of the patio. The sequence shown represents different designs depending on the size of the patio.

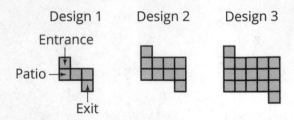

Design 1   Design 2   Design 3

Entrance

Patio →

Exit

Using Patterns to Build Expressions

Miriam's flooring business is booming! She decides to hire several employees to help lay out her tile designs. It will be necessary for Miriam to describe her tile designs in a clear manner so that all of the employees can create them correctly. Miriam's square floor design uses alternating black, white, and gray tiles.

Design 1   Design 2   Design 3

1. **Describe the pattern of new tiles that are added to each design. Is the pattern linear, quadratic, or exponential? Explain your reasoning.**

Think about:

Describe the pattern in terms of the number of new tiles that must be added to each new square floor design.

2. **Write an expression to represent the number of new tiles that must be added to an $n \times n$ square floor design to build the next design. Let n represent the number of tiles along each edge of the square.**

3. **Describe which values for n make sense in this problem situation.**

4. **Ramone determined an expression to represent this pattern. His expression and explanation are shown. Explain why Ramone's expression is incorrect.**

Ramone

Design	1	2	3
New Tiles	0	8	16

The expression 8(n − 1) represents Miriam's square floor pattern. I noticed that the number of new tiles is increasing by 8 in each new design.

Miriam asks her employees to determine the number of new tiles added to Design 2 to create Design 3. Each employee describes a unique method to determine the number of additional tiles needed to create Design 3.

5. **Represent each of her employee's explanations with an algebraic expression that describes how many new tiles must be added to an *n* × *n* square to build the next design.**

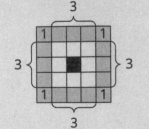

Wilma

I must add 3 tiles to each of the four sides of the white square, which is 4 · 3 tiles. Then I must add 1 tile at each corner. So the number of additional tiles added to the Design 2 square floor design is 4 · 3 + 4.

Expression: _____

Howard

I must add 5 tiles to two of the sides and 3 tiles to the other two sides. The number of additional tiles added to the Design 2 square floor design is $2(3 + 2) + 2 \cdot 3$.

Expression: _____

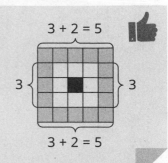

Tyler

I need to add 3 tiles four times and then add the four corner tiles. The number of additional tiles added to the Design 2 square floor design is $3 + 3 + 3 + 3 + 4$.

Expression: _____

Tamara

The way I look at it, I really have two squares. The original square for Design 2 has $3 \cdot 3$ tiles. The newly formed Design 3 square has $5 \cdot 5$ tiles. So, the number of additional tiles added to the Design 2 square floor design is $5 \cdot 5 - 3 \cdot 3$.

Expression: _____

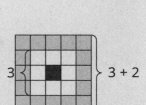

6. Which expression do you think Miriam should use? Explain your reasoning.

Think about:

Does the expression you determined match one of the expressions Miriam's employees determined?

7. Michael and Louise analyze the expressions they wrote for each student. They both determined that the expression to represent Tamara's method is $(n + 2)^2 - n^2$. Michael claims that this expression is quadratic because of the n^2 term. Louise disagrees and says the expression is linear because the pattern grows by a constant amount. Who is correct? Explain your reasoning.

8. Use each expression you determined in Question 5 to calculate the number of tiles that must be added to squares with side lengths of 135 tiles to create the next design.

Wilma's expression: Howard's expression:

Tyler's expression: Tamara's expression:

9. Wilma tells Miriam that since all of the expressions resulted in the same solution, any of the expressions can be used to determine the number of additional tiles needed to make more $n \times n$ designs. Miriam thinks that the employees need to use more values in the expressions than just one to make this conclusion. Who is correct? Explain your reasoning.

Recall that two or more algebraic expressions are equivalent if they produce the same output for all input values. You can verify that two expressions are equivalent by using properties to rewrite the two expressions as the same expression.

10. Use algebraic properties to show that Wilma, Howard, Tyler, and Tamara's expressions are equivalent. Justify your reasoning.

Patterns of Growth

The visual model shown represents the number of new seniors who learn about the homecoming election result each day that passes.

Day 1

Day 2

Day 3

1. Analyze the pattern.

Number of Days That Pass	Number of Seniors Who Hear the Results That Day
1	
2	
3	
4	
5	
6	
n	

a. Complete the table to summarize the number of seniors who learn about the election result each day. Then write an expression to represent the number of seniors who learn about the election result on the nth day. Finally, describe how each part of your expression relates to the visual model.

b. Create a graph of the data from your table on the coordinate plane shown. Then draw a smooth curve to model the relationship between the number of days that pass and the number of seniors who hear the senior election results that day.

2. Do all the points on the smooth curve make sense in terms of this problem situation? Why or why not?

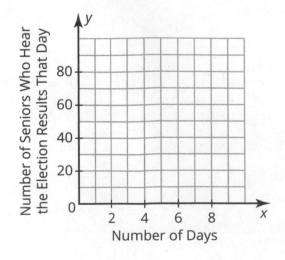

3. Describe this pattern as linear, exponential, or quadratic. Then write the corresponding equation. How does each representation support your answer?

When you model a relationship on a coordinate plane with a smooth curve, it is up to you to consider the situation and interpret the meaning of the data values shown.

4. Describe the key characteristics of your graph. Explain each characteristic algebraically and in terms of this problem situation.

5. After how many days will 500 new seniors learn about the election results?

6. Determine the number of seniors who hear the election results on the twelfth day. Does your answer make sense in the context of this problem? Explain your reasoning.

The model shown represents the first three designs Maureen and
Matthew could use. Each square represents 1 square foot.

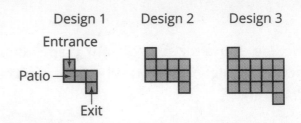

Design 1

Entrance

Patio

Exit

Design 2

Design 3

1. **Describe the pattern as linear, exponential, or quadratic.
   Explain your reasoning.**

Maureen and Matthew each write different expressions to represent the
patio designs.

2. **Describe how each term in Maureen's expression represents
   the visual model.**

© Carnegie Learning, Inc.

Think

about:

How can Maureen
use subtraction
when the number of
tiles in each term is
increasing?

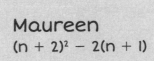

Maureen

$(n + 2)^2 - 2(n + 1)$

3. Consider Matthew's expression.

Matthew
$n^2 + 2n + 2$

   a. Use technology to verify graphically the equivalence of the two expressions.

   b. Identify the parts of the graph that represent this problem situation.

   c. Verify the equivalence of the two expressions algebraically.

4. To accommodate outdoor furniture, a grill, and a shed, the patio must have an area of at least 125 square feet (not including the walkways). What is the smallest design Matthew can build and still have enough space for these items?

Ask yourself:

How is the number of tiles in each design related to the one that came before it?

TALK the TALK

You Know the Type

In this activity, you examined three different patterns and wrote a function to describe each.

1. **Describe the similarities and differences among linear, exponential, and quadratic functions.**

Assignment

Write

Write three functions: one linear, one exponential, and one quadratic. Describe the differences between the functions.

Remember

A visual model, a table of values, and a graph are used to identify patterns as linear, exponential, or quadratic. Two or more algebraic expressions are equivalent if they produce the same output for all input values.

Practice

1. Hyatt Home Improvement uses H-shaped tile designs on their buildings, advertisements, and vehicles. The designs they use follow a specific pattern. The first three designs are shown.

   Design 1   Design 2   Design 3

   a. Describe the pattern in the designs.
   b. Write two different expressions to represent the number of tiles used in Design n. Use algebraic properties to prove the two expressions are equivalent.
   c. Explain how you could use technology to prove the two expressions in part (b) are equivalent.
   d. Create a table that displays the number of tiles used in each of the first 6 designs.
   e. Create a graph of the data points in your table on the coordinate plane shown. Draw a smooth curve to connect the points.
   f. Do all of the points on the smooth curve make sense in terms of the problem situation? Explain your reasoning.
   g. Describe the pattern as linear, exponential, quadratic, or none of these. Explain your reasoning.
   h. The owner of Hyatt Home Improvement wants to put one of their designs on an empty rectangular sign in front of their headquarters. The empty sign is 10 feet tall and 12 feet wide. If he uses square tiles measuring 1 foot by 1 foot, what is the number of the largest design that will fit on the sign? How many tiles will that design require?

Stretch

The figures shown represent a visual pattern of tiles.

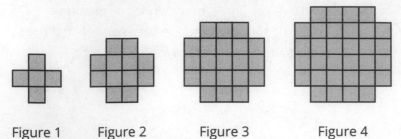

Figure 1   Figure 2   Figure 3   Figure 4

1. Write two different expressions to represent the number of tiles used in Figure *n*.
2. Use algebraic properties to prove the two expressions are equivalent.

Review

1. Taye recruits two people to be election campaign volunteers. The next week he ask each of those volunteers to recruit two more campaign volunteers. He wants all new volunteers each week to recruit two more volunteers.

   a. Determine a method to calculate the number of volunteers in any given week. Use that method to calculate the number of volunteers recruited for each of the first 5 weeks.

   b. Taye wants to recruit 150 volunteers by election day. During which week can some of the volunteers stop recruiting new volunteers? Explain your reasoning.

2. Solve each equation for the unknown value.

   a. $2^{x+2} = 32$

   b. $27 = \left(\frac{1}{3}\right)^{x}$

Samesies

Comparing Multiple Representations of Functions

Warm Up

Rewrite each expression as a different equivalent expression.

1. $7n(3n + 1)$

2. $x^2 - 25$

3. $(4w + 2)^2$

Learning Goals

- Identify equivalent forms of functions in various representations.
- Model situations using tables, graphs, and equations.
- Use functions to make predictions.
- Determine whether two forms of a function are equivalent.

Key Terms

- relation
- function
- function notation

You have explored different representations of linear, exponential, and quadratic functions, either as a table, graph, equation, or scenario. How can you determine when different representations describe the same function?

Odd One Out

Consider the relationships shown by each of the given representations.

Relationship A	Relationship B
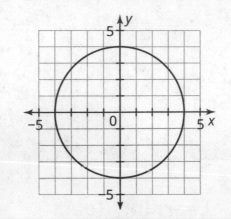	

Relationship B

x	y
−6	5
−4	−3
−2	−3
0	5
2	21

Relationship C

$$y = -\frac{3}{4}x + 8$$

Relationship D

Zeke has one app on his phone when he buys it. He downloads a different number of apps each week. The total number of apps on his phone doubles each week until he has no more storage space.

1. **Choose the relationship that does not belong with the others and justify your choice.**

Equivalent Representations

Understanding patterns not only gives insight into the world around you, it provides you with a powerful tool for predicting the future. Pictures, words, graphs, tables, and equations can describe the exact same pattern, but in different ways.

In the previous lesson, you used a visual model, graph, table, and context to describe the *relation* between the number of days that had passed and the total number of seniors that learned the results of the homecoming king election. In relations such as this one, there is only one output for each input. This type of relation is called a *function*. Functions can be represented algebraically using *function notation*.

> A **relation** is a mapping between a set of input values and a set of output values. A **function** is a relation such that for each element of the domain there exists exactly one element in the range. In **function notation**, the function $f(x)$ is read as "f of x" and indicates that x is the input and $f(x)$ is the output.

1. **Cut out the relations provided at the end of the lesson. Analyze each relation and then create groups of equivalent relations. All relations have at least one match.**

   Provide a brief rationale for how you grouped each set of relations.

2. What strategies did you use to sort the representations into groups?

3. How do you know which relations are functions and which are not functions? Explain your reasoning in terms of the graph, table, and equation.

4. Identify the function family associated with each grouping. How can you determine the function family from the graph, table, context, and the equation?

© Carnegie Learning, Inc.

ACTIVITY

3.2 Equivalent Functions

A ceramic tile company creates a new line of decorative kitchen and bathroom tiles. The company sells designs that are created from combinations of small gray and white square tiles. The designs follow the pattern shown.

Design 1 Design 2 Design 3

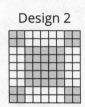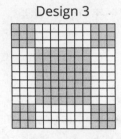

1. **Analyze the tile designs. Describe all of the various patterns that you notice.**

2. **Numerically organize the pattern.**

Design Number	1	2	3	4	7	10	
Number of White Tiles, $w(n)$							
Number of Gray Tiles, $g(n)$							
Total Number of Tiles, $t(n)$							

Don't worry about the last column for now. You will determine an expression for each type of tile later.

3. **What new patterns do you notice?**

© Carnegie Learning, Inc.

4. How many total tiles are in Design 7? How many of the tiles are white? How many are gray? Explain your reasoning.

5. A hotel would like to order the largest design possible. They have enough money in their budget to order a design made up of 1700 total gray and white tiles. Which design can they afford? How many tiles in the design will be white? How many will be gray? Explain your reasoning.

6. Complete the last column of the table in Question 2 by writing an expression to describe the number of white tiles, gray tiles, and total tiles for Design n.

7. Tonya and Alex came up with different expressions to represent the number of gray tiles in each pattern. Their expressions are shown.

Tonya	Alex
$4n^2 + (2n + 1)(2n + 1)$	$(4n + 1)^2 - 4n(2n + 1)$

Tonya claims that they are the same expression written different ways. Alex says, "One expression has addition and the other has subtraction. There is no way they are equivalent!"

Who is correct? Justify your reasoning using algebraic and graphical representations.

You may have noticed several patterns in this sequence. An obvious pattern is that the sum of the white tiles and gray tiles is equal to the total number of tiles. This pattern is clear when analyzing the values in the table. However, adding $w(n)$ and $g(n)$ creates a brand new function that looks very different from the function $t(n)$.

Worked Example

To prove that the sum of the white tiles and gray tiles is equal to the total number of tiles, you must show that the expressions are equivalent.

$w(n) + g(n)$	$t(n)$
$4n(2n + 1) + (2n + 1)^2 + 4n^2$	$(4n + 1)^2$
$(8n^2 + 4n) + (4n^2 + 4n + 1) + 4n^2$	$(4n + 1)(4n + 1)$
$16n^2 + 8n + 1$	$16n^2 + 8n + 1$

8. **Analyze the context, table, and expressions in this problem.**

   a. **Identify the function family that describes the pattern for the number of white tiles. Explain your reasoning.**

   b. **Identify the function family that describes the pattern for the number of gray tiles. Explain your reasoning.**

   c. **When you add the functions that represent the number of white tiles and gray tiles, does the new function belong to the same function family? Explain your reasoning.**

© Carnegie Learning, Inc.

There are many ways to prove something. Mathematical proofs consist of equations, written arguments, pictures, and flow charts. You should always use precise terminology to describe mathematically why you know something is true.

9. **Describe the relationship between the number of white tiles and gray tiles in each design. Prove that this relationship exists.**

10. **Analyze the tile patterns.**

   a. **Prove that the number of white tiles is always an even number.**

   b. **Prove that the total number of tiles is always an odd number.**

TALK the TALK

Equal to the Task

1. Use *always*, *sometimes*, or *never* to complete each statement. Explain your reasoning.

   a. Two functions are _____ equivalent if their algebraic representations are the same.

   b. Two functions are _____ equivalent if they produce the same output for a specific input value.

   c. Two functions are _____ equivalent if their graphical representations are the same.

2. **Determine whether each table of values is a function. If so, identify its function family.**

a.

x	y
−5	−13
−4	−12
0	−8
1	−7
5	−3

b.

x	y
−2	−2
0	0
1	4
3	18
5	40

c.

x	y
4	1
4	2
4	3
4	4
4	5

3. **Determine whether the functions in each pair are equivalent.**

a. $f(x) = (x + 4)^2 + 6$
   $f(x) = x^2 + 8x + 22$

b. $f(x) = (x + 1)^2 + 2x^2$
   $f(x) = (2x + 1)^2 − 2x(x + 1)$

© Carnegie Learning, Inc.

Graph Cutouts

D. $f(x) = x^2 + 6x + 5$

H. $f(x) = (x + 5)(x + 1)$

C.

x	y
1	2
2	4
3	6
4	8
5	10

G. $f(x) = 2x$

B. $f(x) = x^2 + 2x + 5$

F. $f(x) = -(x^2 + 6x + 9)$

A.

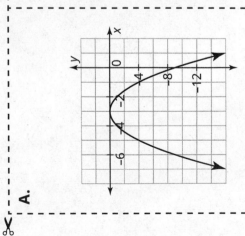

E.

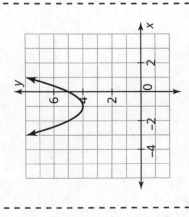

I.

$f(x) = -(x + 3)(x + 3)$

J.

A parabola with a line of symmetry at $x = -3$, a vertex that is a maximum value, and a graph that opens down.

K.

Louise heard a rumor. She tells the rumor to two people the next day. The two people that she told then tell two more people the following day, who each then go on to tell two more new people the rumor the following day.

L.

x	y
−3	8
−2	5
−1	4
0	5
1	8

M.

x	y
−4	−1
−3	0
−2	−1
−1	−4
0	−9

N.

$y = 2^x$

O.

P.

$y = (x + 3)^2 - 4$

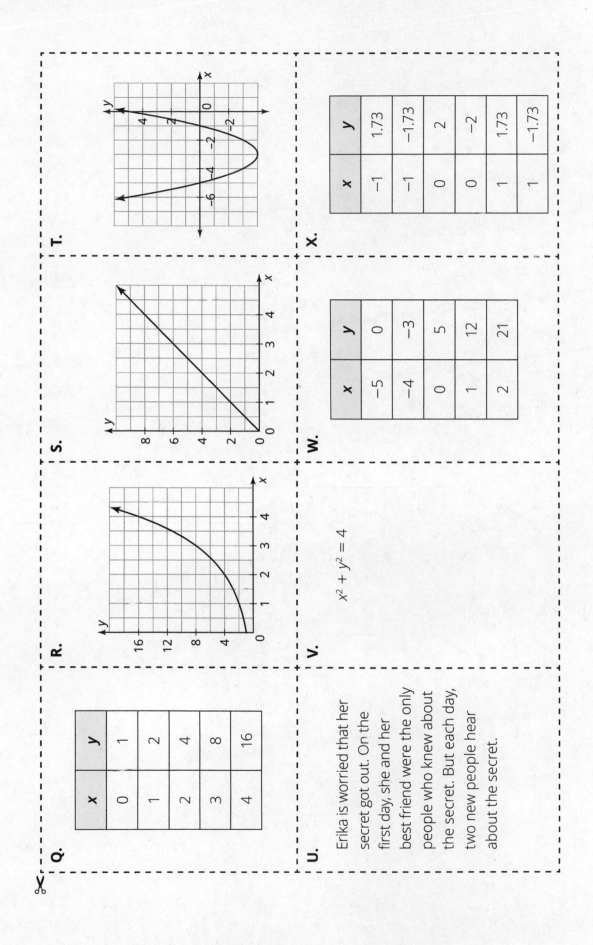

T.

S.

R.

X.

x	y
−1	1.73
−1	−1.73
0	2
0	−2
1	1.73
1	−1.73

W.

x	y
−5	0
−4	−3
0	5
1	12
2	21

V.

$x^2 + y^2 = 4$

Q.

x	y
0	1
1	2
2	4
3	8
4	16

U.

Erika is worried that her secret got out. On the first day, she and her best friend were the only people who knew about the secret. But each day, two new people hear about the secret.

Assignment

Write

Define each term in your own words.

1. relation
2. function
3. function notation

Remember

Relationships between quantities can be represented in graphs, tables, equations, and contexts. Two functions are equivalent if their algebraic or graphical representations are the same.

Practice

1. Consider the three scenarios given. Match each with the corresponding function, graph, and table.

   a. Juanita is driving home from her vacation spot at a constant rate. Which function, graph, and table represent her distance from home as a function of the number of hours she has traveled? Explain your reasoning.

   b. A mechanic drops a wrench from a flying helicopter. Which function, graph, and table represent the height of the wrench above the ground as a function of the time since it was dropped? Explain your reasoning.

   c. Scientists watch as a single cell divides into 4 cells over the course of an hour. During the next hour, each of the 4 new cells divides into 4 cells and the process continues. Which function, graph, and table represent the total number of cells as a function of time? Explain your reasoning.

$$f(x) = -16x^2 + 1900 \qquad g(x) = 4^x \qquad h(x) = -50x + 450$$

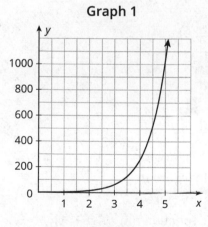

Graph 1

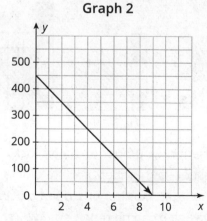

Graph 2

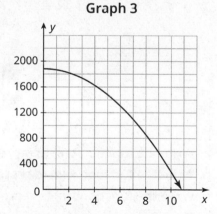

Graph 3

Table 1

x	y
0	1
1	4
2	16
3	64
4	256

Table 2

x	y
0	1900
2	1836
4	1644
6	1324
8	876

Table 3

x	y
0	450
2	350
4	250
6	150
8	50

© Carnegie Learning, Inc.

2. Ingrid makes quilts in designs that follow a specific pattern. The first three designs are shown. In the designs, the white blocks represent blocks containing pictures while the gray blocks represent border blocks of a single color.

Design 1   Design 2   Design 3

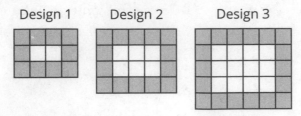

a. Analyze the quilt designs. Describe as many patterns as you can.

b. Write the function $p(n)$ to represent the number of picture blocks in Design n.

c. Write the function $b(n)$ to represent the number of border blocks in Design n.

d. The total number of blocks in Design n can be represented by the function $t(n) = (n + 2)(n + 3)$. Use the functions you wrote to show that $t(n) = p(n) + b(n)$.

e. An art museum hires Ingrid to make one of her quilt designs to display pictures of each of their 90 paintings in 90 individual picture blocks. Which design does the art museum choose? How many total blocks are in the design?

Stretch

1. The figures shown represent a visual pattern of tiles.

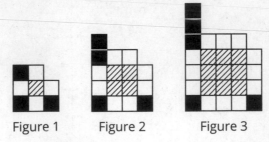

Figure 1   Figure 2   Figure 3

a. Write the function $b(n)$ to represent the number of black blocks in Figure n.

b. Write the function $w(n)$ to represent the number of white blocks in Figure n.

c. Write the function $s(n)$ to represent the number of striped blocks in Figure n.

d. The total number of blocks in Design n can be represented by the function $t(n) = \left(n + \frac{5}{2}\right)^2 - \frac{17}{4}$. Use the functions you wrote to show that $t(n) = b(n) + w(n) + s(n)$.

Review

1. A video game consists of a figure made of squares that resembles a snake. The figure gets longer in each minute of the game. The first three figures are shown.

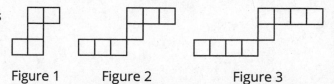

Figure 1   Figure 2   Figure 3

   a. Create a table to display the number of squares in each of the first 6 figures.

   b. Describe the pattern as linear, exponential, quadratic, or none of these. Explain your reasoning.

2. The figures shown represent a visual pattern of tiles.

   a. Create a table to display the number of squares in each of the first 6 figures.

   b. Create a graph of the data points in your table on the coordinate plane shown. Draw a smooth curve to connect the points.

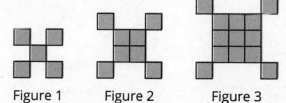

Figure 1   Figure 2   Figure 3

   c. Describe the pattern as linear, exponential, quadratic, or none of these. Explain your reasoning.

3. Solve the equation $-5\frac{1}{2} + 12y = \frac{1}{2}(7 - 8y)$.

4

True to Form

Forms of Quadratic Functions

Warm Up

Identify the axis of symmetry of each quadratic function.

1. $f(x) = -4(x - 3)^2 + 2$

2. $g(x) = 2(x + 5)(x - 7)$

3. $h(x) = 4x^2 + 6x + 1$

Learning Goals

- Determine how many points are necessary to create a unique quadratic equation.
- Match a quadratic function with its corresponding graph.
- Identify key characteristics of quadratic functions based on the form of the function.
- Analyze the different forms of quadratic functions.
- Use key characteristics of specific forms of quadratic functions to write equations.
- Derive a quadratic equation given three points using a system of equations.
- Write quadratic functions to represent problem situations.

Key Terms

- standard form of a quadratic function
- factored form of a quadratic function
- vertex form of a quadratic function
- concavity of a parabola

You have explored the key characteristics of different forms of quadratic functions. How can you use these characteristics to write a quadratic equation to model the graph of a parabola, even if you only know certain points on the graph?

Be My One and Only

Consider the family of linear functions.

1. Use the given point(s) to sketch possible solutions.

   a. How many lines can you draw through point *A*?

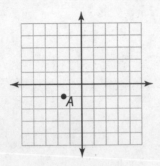

   b. How many lines can you draw through both points *A* and *B*?

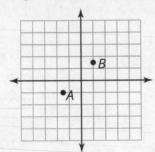

   c. How many lines can you draw through all points *A*, *B*, and *C*?

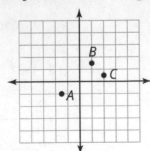

2. What is the minimum number of points you need to draw a unique line?

Consider the family of quadratic functions.

3. Use the given point(s) to sketch possible solutions.

    a. How many parabolas can you draw through point *A*?

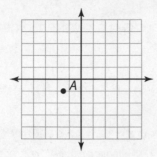

    b. How many parabolas can you draw through both points *A* and *B*?

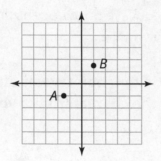

    c. How many parabolas can you draw through all points *A*, *B*, and *C*?

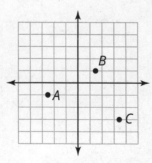

ACTIVITY 4.1 — Forms of Quadratic Functions

Recall that quadratic functions can be written in different forms.

Standard form: $f(x) = ax^2 + bx + c$, where a does not equal 0

Factored form: $f(x) = a(x - r_1)(x - r_2)$, where a does not equal 0

Vertex form: $f(x) = a(x - h)^2 + k$, where a does not equal 0

The graphs of quadratic functions can be described using key characteristics: x-intercept(s), y-intercept, vertex, axis of symmetry, and concavity.

Concavity of a parabola describes whether a parabola opens up or opens down. A parabola is concave up if it opens upward; a parabola is concave down if it opens downward.

1. **The form of a quadratic function reveals different key characteristics. State the characteristics you can determine from each form.**

   a. **Standard form**

   b. **Factored form**

   C. **Vertex form**

2. **Christine and Kate were asked to determine the vertex of two different quadratic functions, each written in a different form. Analyze their calculations.**

Christine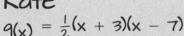

$f(x) = 2x^2 + 12x + 10$

The quadratic function is in standard form. So I know the axis of symmetry is $x = \frac{-b}{2a}$.

$$x = \frac{-12}{2(2)}$$
$$= -3$$

Now that I know the axis of symmetry, I can substitute that value into the function to determine the y-coordinate of the vertex.

$f(-3) = 2(-3)^2 + 12(-3) + 10$

$\quad = 2(9) - 36 + 10$

$\quad = 18 - 36 + 10$

$\quad = -8$

Therefore, the vertex is $(-3, -8)$.

Kate 👍

$g(x) = \frac{1}{2}(x + 3)(x - 7)$

The form of the function tells me the x-intercepts are -3 and 7. I also know the x-coordinate of the vertex is directly in the middle of the x-intercepts. So, all I have to do is calculate their average.

$$x = \frac{-3 + 7}{2}$$
$$= \frac{4}{2} = 2$$

Now that I know the x-coordinate of the vertex, I can substitute that value into the function to determine the y-coordinate.

$g(2) = \frac{1}{2}(2 + 3)(2 - 7)$

$\quad = \frac{1}{2}(5)(-5)$

$\quad = -12.5$

Therefore, the vertex is $(2, -12.5)$.

a. **How are these methods similar? How are they different?**

b. **What must Kate do to use Christine's method?**

c. **What must Christine do to use Kate's method?**

3. Cut out each quadratic equation and graph located at the end of the lesson.

   a. Tape each quadratic equation to its corresponding graph.

   b. Explain the method(s) you used to match each equation with its graph.

4. Analyze the three tables located at the end of the lesson. Tape each function and its corresponding graph from Question 3 in the "Graphs and Their Functions" section of the appropriate table. Then, explain how you can determine each key characteristic based on the form of the given function.

© Carnegie Learning, Inc.

1. **Analyze each graph. Then, circle the function(s) which could model the graph. Describe the reasoning you used to either eliminate or choose each function.**

a.

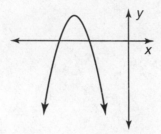

$f_1(x) = -2(x + 1)(x + 4)$ $f_2(x) = -\frac{1}{3}x^2 - 3x - 6$ $f_3(x) = 2(x + 1)(x+4)$

$f_4(x) = 2x^2 - 8.9$ $f_5(x) = 2(x - 1)(x - 4)$ $f_6(x) = -(x - 6)^2 + 3$

$f_7(x) = -3(x + 2)(x - 3)$ $f_8(x) = -(x + 6)^2 + 3$

b.

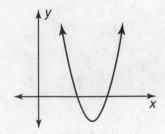

$f_1(x) = 2(x - 75)^2 - 92$ $f_2(x) = (x - 8)(x + 2)$ $f_3(x) = 8x^2 - 88x + 240$

$f_4(x) = -3(x - 1)(x - 5)$ $f_5(x) = -2(x - 75)^2 - 92$ $f_6(x) = x^2 + 6x - 2$

$f_7(x) = 2(x + 4)^2 - 2$ $f_8(x) = (x + 1)(x + 3)$

c.

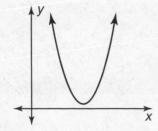

$$f_1(x) = 3(x + 1)(x - 5)$$ $$f_2(x) = 2(x + 6)^2 - 5$$ $$f_3(x) = 4x^2 - 400x + 10{,}010$$

$$f_4(x) = 3(x + 1)(x + 5)$$ $$f_5(x) = 2(x - 6)^2 + 5$$ $$f_6(x) = x^2 + 2x - 5$$

2. **Consider the two functions shown from Question 1. Identify the form of the function given, and then write the function in the other two forms, if possible. If it is not possible, explain why.**

a. $f_1(x) = -2(x + 1)(x + 4)$

b. $f_5(x) = 2(x - 6)^2 + 5$

ACTIVITY 4.3 Writing a Unique Quadratic Function

You have used properties of linear functions to write linear equations. In this activity, you will use properties of quadratic functions to write quadratic equations in various forms.

1. **George and Pat each wrote a quadratic equation with a vertex of (4, 8). Analyze each student's work. Describe the similarities and differences in their equations and determine who is correct.**

George	Pat
$y = a(x - h)^2 + k$	$y = a(x - h)^2 + k$
$y = a(x - 4)^2 + 8$	$y = a(x - 4)^2 + 8$
$y = -\frac{1}{2}(x - 4)^2 + 8$	$y = (x - 4)^2 + 8$

You can write a unique quadratic function given a vertex and a point on the parabola.

Worked Example

Write the quadratic function given the vertex (5, 2) and the point (4, 9).

Substitute the given values into the vertex form of the function.

$$f(x) = a(x - h)^2 + k$$
$$9 = a(4 - 5)^2 + 2$$

Then solve for a.

$$9 = a(-1)^2 + 2$$
$$9 = 1a + 2$$
$$7 = 1a$$
$$7 = a$$

Finally, substitute the a-value into the function.

$$f(x) = 7(x - 5)^2 + 2$$

© Carnegie Learning, Inc.

You can write a unique quadratic function given the roots and a point on the parabola.

Worked Example

Write a quadratic function given the roots $(-2, 0)$ and $(4, 0)$, and the point $(1, 6)$.

Substitute the given values into
the factored form of the function.

$$f(x) = a(x - r_1)(x - r_2)$$
$$6 = a(1 - (-2))(1 - 4)$$

Then solve for a.

$$6 = a(1 + 2)(1 - 4)$$
$$6 = a(3)(-3)$$
$$6 = -9a$$
$$-\frac{2}{3} = a$$

Finally, substitute the a-value
into the function.

$$f(x) = -\frac{2}{3}(x + 2)(x - 4)$$

2. **Determine which form of a quadratic function would be most efficient to write the function using the given information. Write *standard form, factored form, vertex form,* or *none* in the space provided.**

   a. **minimum point (6, −75)**
      y-intercept (0, 15)   _____

   b. **points (2, 0), (8, 0), and (4, 6)**   _____

   c. **points (100, 75), (450, 75),**   _____
      and (150, 95)

   d. **points (3, 3), (4, 3), and (5, 3)**   _____

   e. **x-intercepts (7.9, 0) and (−7.9, 0)**
      point (−4, −4)   _____

   f. **roots (3, 0) and (12, 0)**
      point (10, 2)   _____

   g. **Max hits a baseball off a tee that**
      is 3 feet high. The ball reaches a
      maximum height of 20 feet when
      it is 15 feet from the tee.   _____

3. Write a quadratic function that includes the given points. If it is not possible to write a function, state why not.

a. Given: vertex (−3, 4); point (−4, 1)

$f(x) =$ _____

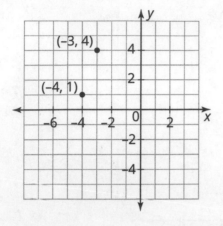

b. Given: vertex (3, −2); one of two x-intercepts (4, 0)

$f(x) =$ _____

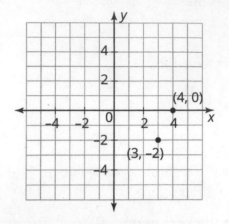

c. Given: points (2, 1), (−1, −2), (3, −10)

$f(x) =$ _____

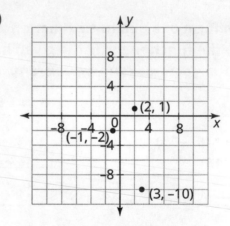

4. Wilhemina says that she can write a unique quadratic function given only two points. Is she correct? Explain your reasoning.

Using Algebra to Write a Quadratic Equation

In the previous activity, there were times when you could not determine a quadratic equation using known strategies. You know how to use technology to determine the equation, but what if you don't have technology?

You know that you need a minimum of 3 non-linear points to create a unique parabola. To create an equation to represent the parabola, you can use a system of equations.

Worked Example

Consider the three points given in Question 3 part (c) in the previous activity: A (2, 1), B (−1, −2), and C (3, −10).

To write an equation in standard form to represent a parabola that passes through three given points, begin by substituting the x- and y-values of each point into $y = ax^2 + bx + c$.

Point A: $1 = a(2)^2 + b(2) + c$
$\qquad\quad 1 = 4a + 2b + c$ Equation A: $1 = 4a + 2b + c$

Point B: $−2 = a(−1)^2 + b(−1) + c$
$\qquad\quad −2 = a − b + c$ Equation B: $−2 = a − b + c$

Point C: $−10 = a(3)^2 + b(3) + c$
$\qquad\quad −10 = 9a + 3b + c$ Equation C: $−10 = 9a + 3b + c$

Now, use linear combinations and substitution to solve for a, b, and c.

STEP 1: Subtract Equation B from A:

$$\begin{array}{r} 1 = 4a + 2b + c \\ −(−2 = a − b + c) \\ \hline 3 = 3a + 3b \end{array}$$

STEP 2: Subtract Equation B from C:

$$\begin{array}{r} −10 = 9a + 3b + c \\ −(−2 = a − b + c) \\ \hline −8 = 8a + 4b \end{array}$$

STEP 3: Solve the equation from Step 1 in terms of a.

$$\begin{array}{r} 3 = 3a + 3b \\ 3 − 3b = 3a \\ 1 − b = a \end{array}$$

STEP 4: Substitute the value for a into the equation from Step 2.

$-8 - 8(1 - h) + 4b$

$-8 = 8 - 4b$

$16 = 4b$

$4 = b$

STEP 5: Substitute the value for b into the equation from Step 3.

$a = 1 - (4)$

$a = -3$

STEP 6: Substitute the values for a and b into Equation A.

$1 = 4a + 2b + c$

$1 = 4(-3) + 2(4) + c$

$1 = -12 + 8 + c$

$1 = -4 + c$

$5 = c$

STEP 7: Substitute the values for a, b, and c into the standard form of a quadratic.

$y = -3x^2 + 4x + 5$

1. **Use the worked example to write a quadratic equation that passes through the points $(-1, 5)$, $(0, 3)$, and $(3, 9)$.**

Happy Homes Development Company has hired Splish Splash Pools to create the community pool for their new development of homes. The rectangular pool is to have one section with a 4-foot depth, and another section with a 9-foot depth. The pool will also have a diving board. By law, the regulation depth of water necessary to have a diving board is 9 feet. Happy Homes would like to have the majority of the pool be a 4-feet depth in order to accommodate a large number of young children.

The diving board will be 3 feet above the edge of the pool's surface and extend 5 feet into the pool. After doing some research, Splish Splash Pools determined that the average diver would be 5 feet in the air when he is 8 feet from the edge of the pool, and 6 feet in the air when he is 10 feet from the edge of the pool.

2. **Use the dive model shown to write an equation, and then determine the minimum length of the 9-foot depth section of the pool. Explain your reasoning.**

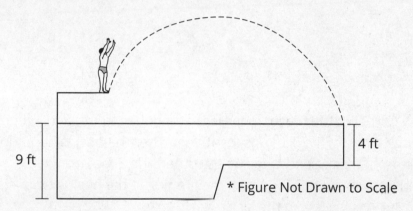

9 ft

4 ft

* Figure Not Drawn to Scale

NOTES

Remember:

The general equation to represent height over time is
$h(t) = -16t^2 + v_0t + h_0$
where v_0 is the initial velocity in feet per second and h_0 is the initial height in feet.

TALK the TALK

Fantastic Feats of Function

The Amazing Larry is a human cannonball. He would like to reach a maximum height of 30 feet during his next launch. Based on Amazing Larry's previous launches, his assistant DaJuan has estimated that this will occur when Larry is 40 feet from the cannon. When Amazing Larry is shot from the cannon, he is 10 feet above the ground.

1. **Write a quadratic equation to represent Amazing Larry's height in terms of his distance.**

Crazy Cornelius is a fire jumper. He is attempting to run and jump through a ring of fire. He runs for 10 feet. Then, he begins his jump just 4 feet from the fire and lands on the other side 3 feet from the fire ring. When Cornelius was 1 foot from the fire ring at the beginning of his jump, he was 3.5 feet in the air.

2. **Write a quadratic equation to represent Crazy Cornelius' height in terms of his distance. Round to the nearest hundredth.**

© Carnegie Learning, Inc.

Harsh Knarsh is attempting to jump across an alligator filled swamp. She takes off from a ramp 30 feet high with a speed of 95 feet per second.

3. **Write a quadratic equation to represent Harsh Knarsh's height in terms of time.**

Van McSlugger needs one more home run to advance to the next round of the home run derby. On the last pitch, he takes a swing and makes contact. Initially, he hits the ball at 5 feet above the ground. At 32 feet from home plate, his ball was 23.7 feet in the air, and at 220 feet from home plate, his ball was 70 feet in the air.

4. **Consider the function that represents the relationship between the height of the ball and its distance from home plate.**

   a. **If Van's ball needs to travel a distance of 399 feet in order to get the home run, did he succeed? Explain why or why not.**

   b. **What was the maximum height of Van's baseball?**

Quadratic Equations Cutouts

a. $f(x) = 2(x + 1)(x + 5)$

b. $f(x) = \frac{1}{3}x^2 + \pi x + 6.4$

c. $f(x) = -2.5(x - 3)(x - 3)$

d. $f(x) = (x - 1)^2$

e. $f(x) = 2(x - 1)(x - 5)$

f. $f(x) = x^2 + 12x - 1$

g. $f(x) = -(x + 4)^2 - 2$

h. $f(x) = -5x^2 - x + 21$

i. $f(x) = -(x + 2)^2 - 4$

Graph Cutouts

A.
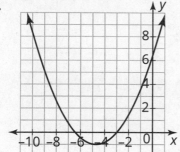

B.
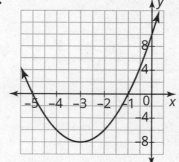

C.
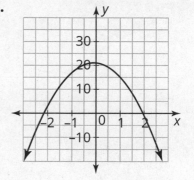

D.
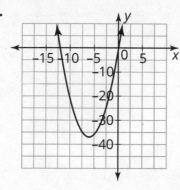

E.
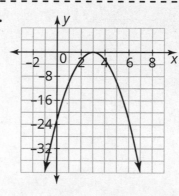

F.
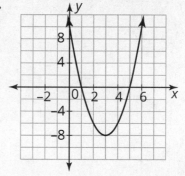

G.
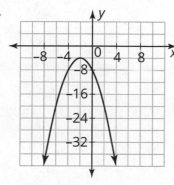

H.
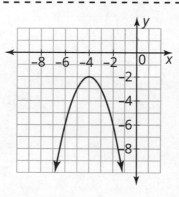

I.
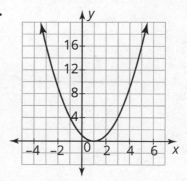

Standard Form
$f(x) = ax^2 + bx + c$, where $a \neq 0$

Graphs and Their Functions

Methods to Determine Key Characteristics

Axis of Symmetry

x-intercept(s)

Concavity

Vertex

y-intercept

Factored Form
$$f(x) = a(x - r_1)(x - r_2), \text{ where } a \neq 0$$

Graphs and Their Functions

Methods to Determine Key Characteristics

Axis of Symmetry	x-intercept(s)	Concavity

Vertex	y-intercept

Vertex Form $f(x) = a(x - h)^2 + k$, where $a \neq 0$
Graphs and Their Functions

Methods to Determine Key Characteristics

Axis of Symmetry	**x-intercept(s)**	**Concavity**

Vertex	**y-intercept**

Write

1. Write a quadratic function for each form and state whether the form helps determine the x-intercepts, the y-intercept, or the vertex of the graph.

    a. Standard form

    b. Factored form

    c. Vertex form

2. Describe how to determine the concavity of a parabola.

Remember

The form of a quadratic function—standard, factored, or vertex—reveals different key characteristics, such as the x-intercept(s), y-intercept, vertex, axis of symmetry, and concavity up or down.

Given three points, you can determine a unique quadratic function algebraically by writing and solving a system of equations.

Practice

1. Write a quadratic equation for the parabola that passes through the point (2, −3) with roots (−6, 0) and (4, 0).

2. Mitzu shoots an arrow from an initial height of 2 meters. The arrow reaches its maximum height of 20 meters after it has flown a distance of 60 meters.

    a. Write a quadratic function to represent the height of the arrow as a function of its distance.

    b. Determine the height of the arrow after it has flown a distance of 100 meters.

3. Use your knowledge of reference points to write an equation for the quadratic function that has a vertex at (4, −3) and passes through (6, −1) .

4. Write a quadratic equation that passes through the points (−2, 8), (1, 14), and (0, 10) .

Stretch

Use algebra to write a quadratic equation that passes through the points $\left(\frac{1}{2}, \frac{9}{16}\right)$, $\left(1, \frac{9}{2}\right)$, and $\left(-1, \frac{11}{2}\right)$.

Review

1. Anita is on a competitive rowing team. After 2 minutes, the team rows at a constant speed of 4 meters per second. Which function represents the distance the boat travels as a function of the number of seconds they have rowed after the first 2 minutes? Explain your reasoning.

$f_1(x) = 4x^2 + 2$ $\qquad\qquad$ $f_2(x) = 4x$ $\qquad\qquad$ $f_3(x) = 4^x$

2. The figures shown represent a visual pattern of tiles.

   a. Write the function $w(n)$ to represent the number of white blocks in Figure n.

   b. Write the function $b(n)$ to represent the number of black blocks in Figure n.

   c. The total number of blocks in Figure n can be represented by the function $t(n) = (n + 2)(n + 2)$.
   Use the functions you wrote to show that $t(n) = w(n) + b(n)$.

Figure 1 $\qquad$ Figure 2 $\qquad$ Figure 3

3. Determine the volume of each figure. Round your answer to the nearest hundredth.

   a. Cylinder $\qquad\qquad\qquad\qquad\qquad\qquad$ b. Cone

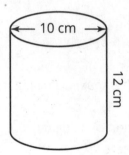

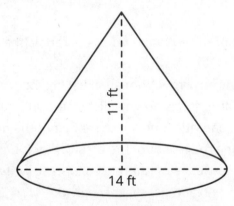

The Root of the Problem

Solving Quadratic Equations

5

Warm Up

Use the Distributive Property to determine each product.

1. $(x + 1)(x + 2)$

2. $(x + 4)(x - 5)$

3. $(2x - 3)(x - 4)$

4. $(x + 2)^2$

Learning Goals

- Factor quadratic trinomials to determine the roots of quadratic equations and to rewrite quadratic functions in forms that reveal different key characteristics.
- Complete the square to determine the roots of quadratic equations of the form $ax^2 + bx + c$.
- Use the Quadratic Formula to determine roots and zeros.
- Solve systems of two quadratic equations.

Key Term

- Quadratic Formula

You have analyzed the different structures of quadratic equations. How can the structure of a quadratic equation help you determine a solution strategy? Is there a single strategy that works to solve any quadratic equation?

Grassroots

You know how to use the Properties of Equality to solve equations in the forms shown.

$$y = x^2 + d$$
$$y = (x - c)^2$$
$$y = a(x - c)^2$$
$$y = a(x - c)^2 + d$$

1. **Use Properties of Equality to solve each equation. State the property used in each step of your solution.**

   a. $27 = x^2 - 9$

   b. $(x + 3)^2 = 121$

   c. $48 = 3(x - 1)^2$

   d. $\frac{1}{2}(x + 5)^2 - 18 = 0$

2. **Describe the strategy Oscar used to solve part (a) in Question 1.**

Oscar

$$27 = x^2 - 9$$
$$27 - 27 = x^2 - 9 - 27$$
$$0 = x^2 - 36$$
$$0 = (x - 6)(x + 6)$$

$(x - 6) = 0$ and $(x + 6) = 0$
     $x = 6$ and $x = -6$

ACTIVITY 5.1 Solving Quadratic Equations by Factoring

Let's consider strategies to solve quadratics in the form $y = ax^2 + bx + c$ using the factoring strategies you have learned.

Worked Example

You can use factoring to calculate the roots for the quadratic equation $x^2 - 4x = -3$.

$$x^2 - 4x = -3$$
$$x^2 - 4x + 3 = -3 + 3$$
$$x^2 - 4x + 3 = 0$$
$$(x - 3)(x - 1) = 0$$

$(x - 3) = 0$	and	$(x - 1) = 0$
$x - 3 + 3 = 0 + 3$	and	$x - 1 + 1 = 0 + 1$
$x = 3$	and	$x = 1$

Remember:

The Zero Product Property states that if the product of two or more factors is equal to zero, then at least one factor must be equal to zero.

1. **Why is 3 added to both sides in the first step of the worked example?**

Think  **about:**

What is the connection between the worked example and determining the roots from factored form, $y = a(x - r_1)(x - r_2)$?

2. **Determine each student's error and then solve each equation correctly.**

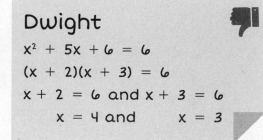

Angela 👎
$x^2 + 6x = 7$
$x(x + 6) = 7$
$x = 7$ and $x + 6 = 7$
$x = 1$

Dwight 👎
$x^2 + 5x + 6 = 6$
$(x + 2)(x + 3) = 6$
$x + 2 = 6$ and $x + 3 = 6$
$x = 4$ and $x = 3$

3. Use factoring to solve each quadratic equation, if possible.

   a. $x^2 - 8x + 12 = 0$

   b. $x^2 + 8x = -7$

Think about:

What efficiency strategies did you use to solve linear equations with fractional coefficients?

   c. $\frac{2}{3}x^2 - \frac{5}{6}x = 0$

   d. $f(x) = x^2 + 10x + 12$

4. Describe the different strategies and reasoning that Jim and Pam used to solve $4x^2 - 25 = 0$.

Jim 👍

$$4x^2 - 25 = 0$$
$$4x^2 = 25$$
$$x^2 = \frac{25}{4}$$
$$x = \pm\sqrt{\frac{25}{4}}$$
$$x = \pm\frac{5}{2}$$

Pam 👍

$$4x^2 - 25 = 0$$
$$(2x - 5)(2x + 5) = 0$$
$$2x - 5 = 0 \text{ and } 2x + 5 = 0$$
$$2x = 5 \qquad 2x = -5$$
$$x = \frac{5}{2} \text{ and } \quad x = -\frac{5}{2}$$

You can use the completing the square method to determine the roots of a quadratic equation that cannot be factored.

Worked Example

Complete the square to determine the roots of the equation
$x^2 + 10x + 12 = 0$.

Isolate $x^2 + 10x$.

$$x^2 + 10x + 12 - 12 = 0 - 12$$
$$x^2 + 10x = -12$$

Determine the constant term that would complete the square. Add this term to both sides of the equation.

$$x^2 + 10x + \underline{} = -12 + \underline{}$$
$$x^2 + 10x + 25 = -12 + 25$$
$$x^2 + 10x + 25 = 13$$

Rewrite the left side as a perfect square.

$$(x + 5)^2 = 13$$

Take the square root of each side of the equation.

$$\sqrt{(x + 5)^2} = \pm\sqrt{13}$$
$$x + 5 = \pm\sqrt{13}$$

Set the factor of the perfect square trinomial equal to each square root of the constant. Then solve for x.

$$x + 5 = \sqrt{13} \quad \text{and } x + 5 = -\sqrt{13}$$
$$x = -5 + \sqrt{13} \text{ and } x = -5 - \sqrt{13}$$
$$x \approx -1.39 \quad \text{and } x \approx -8.61$$

The roots are approximately -1.39 and -8.61.

Ask
yourself:

How was equality of the equation maintained through the completing the square process?

1. **Complete the square to determine the roots of each equation.**

   a. $x^2 - 6x + 4 = 0$

   b. $x^2 - 12x + 6 = 0$

2. **A ball is thrown straight up from 4 feet above the ground with a velocity of 32 feet per second. The height of the ball over time can be modeled with the function $h(t) = -16t^2 + 32t + 4$. What is the maximum height of the ball?**

3. **Jessie is fencing in a rectangular plot outside of her back door so that she can let her dogs out to play. She has 60 feet of fencing and only needs to place it on three sides of the rectangular plot because the fourth side will be bound by her house. What dimensions should Jesse use for the plot so that the maximum area is enclosed? What is the maximum area? Draw a diagram to support your work.**

The **Quadratic Formula**, $x = \dfrac{-b \pm \sqrt{b^2 - 4ac}}{2a}$, can be used to calculate the solutions to any quadratic equation of the form $ax^2 + bx + c = 0$, where a, b, and c represent real numbers and $a \neq 0$.

Worked Example

You can use the Quadratic Formula to determine the zeros of the function $f(x) = -4x^2 - 40x - 99$.

Rewrite the function as an equation to be solved for x when $y = 0$.

$$-4x^2 - 40x - 99 = 0$$

Determine the values of a, b, and c.

$$a = -4, b = -40, c = -99$$

Substitute the values into the Quadratic Formula.

$$x = \frac{-(-40) \pm \sqrt{(-40)^2 - 4(-4)(-99)}}{2(-4)}$$

Perform operations to rewrite the expression.

$$x = \frac{40 \pm \sqrt{1600 - 1584}}{-8}$$

$$x = \frac{40 \pm \sqrt{16}}{-8}$$

$$x = \frac{40 \pm 4}{-8}$$

$$x = \frac{40 + 4}{-8} \quad \text{and} \quad x = \frac{40 - 4}{-8}$$

$$x = \frac{44}{-8} \quad \text{and} \quad x = \frac{36}{-8}$$

$$x = -5.5 \quad \text{and} \quad x = -4.5$$

The zeros of the function $f(x) = -4x^2 - 40x - 99$ are $x = -5.5$ and $x = -4.5$.

The Seaside Serpents baseball team has a new promotional activity to encourage fans to attend games: launching free T-shirts! They can launch a T-shirt in the air with an initial velocity of 91 feet per second from $5\frac{1}{2}$ feet off the ground (the height of the team mascot).

A T-shirt's height can be modeled with the quadratic function $h(t) = -16t^2 + 91t + 5.5$, where t is the time in seconds and $h(t)$ is the height of the launched T-shirt in feet. They want to know how long it will take for a T-shirt to land back on the ground after being launched (if no fans grab it before then!).

Ask

yourself:

What would a sketch showing the height of the T-shirt over time look like?

1. Why does it make sense to use the Quadratic Formula to solve this problem?

Ask yourself:

Do you think an exact solution or approximate solution is more appropriate for this context?

2. Use the Quadratic Formula to determine how long it will take for a T-shirt to land back on the ground after being launched.

3. Meredith is solving the quadratic equation $x^2 - 7x - 8 = 3$. Her work is shown.

   a. Identify Meredith's error.

   b. Determine the solution to Meredith's quadratic equation.

Meredith

$x^2 - 7x - 8 = 3$

$a = 1, b = -7, c = -8$

$x = \dfrac{-(-7) \pm \sqrt{(-7)^2 - 4(1)(-8)}}{2(1)}$

$x = \dfrac{7 \pm \sqrt{49 + 32}}{2}$

$x = \dfrac{7 \pm \sqrt{81}}{2}$

$x = \dfrac{7 \pm 9}{2}$

$x = \dfrac{7 + 9}{2}$ or $x = \dfrac{7 - 9}{2}$

$x = \dfrac{16}{2}$ or $x = \dfrac{-2}{2} = -1$

The roots are 8 and −1.

4. Use the Quadratic Formula to determine the zeros for each function. Round the solutions to the nearest hundredth.

   a. $f(x) = 2x^2 + 10x - 1.02$

   b. $h(x) = 3x^2 + 11x - 2$

Solving Systems of Quadratic Equations

You previously solved a system of a linear equation and a quadratic equation using methods similar to solving a system of linear equations. You can use these same methods to solve a system of two quadratic equations.

1. **Consider the system of two quadratic equations.**

$$\begin{cases} y = x^2 + 3x - 5 \\ y = -x^2 + 10x - 1 \end{cases}$$

   a. **Set the expressions equal to each other.**

   b. **Solve the resulting equation for _x_.**

   c. **Calculate the corresponding values for _y_.**

   d. **What is the solution to the system of equations?**

e. **Graph each equation of the system and calculate the points of intersection.**

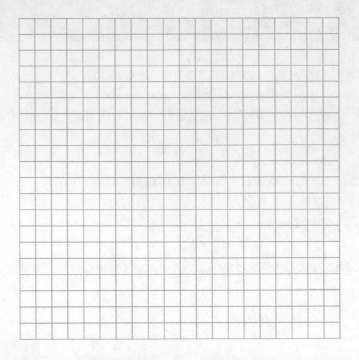

f. **What do you notice about the solutions you calculated algebraically and graphically?**

2. **Think about the graphs of two quadratic equations. Describe the different ways in which the two graphs can intersect and provide a sketch of each case.**

3. **Solve each system of equations algebraically over the set of real numbers. Then verify the solution graphically.**

a. $\begin{cases} y = x^2 + 2x + 1 \\ y = 2x^2 - x - 3 \end{cases}$

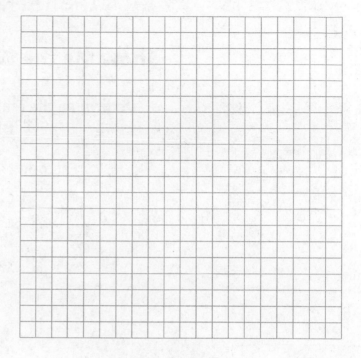

b. $\begin{cases} y = 2x^2 - 7x + 6 \\ y = -2x^2 + 5x - 3 \end{cases}$

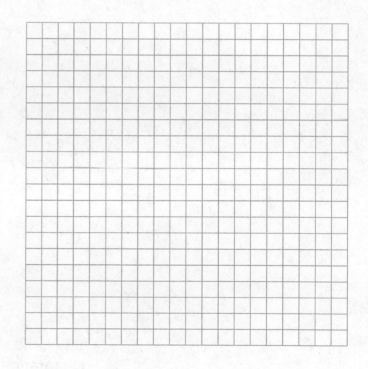

TALK the TALK

Show Me the Ways

1. Determine the real roots of the quadratic equation
$y = 2x^2 + 4x - 6$ using each method.

Factoring

Completing
the Square

$y = 2x^2 + 4x - 6$

Using the
Quadratic
Formula

Graphing

Assignment

Write

Describe the solution to a system of equations.

Remember

You can solve quadratic equations using factoring, completing the square, the Quadratic Formula, and graphing.

Practice

1. Solve each equation.

   a. $0 = x^2 - 7x - 18$

   b. $x^2 + 10x = 39$

   c. $0 = x^2 - 10x + 12$

   d. $2x^2 + 4x = 0$

   e. $3x^2 - 22x + 7 = 0$

2. Determine the roots of each equation. Check your solutions.

   a. $y = x^2 + 9x + 3$

   b. $y = 3x^2 + 24x - 6$

3. Kian is driving 48 miles per hour and is speeding up to merge onto the highway. He gradually accelerates at a rate of 7 miles per hour for several seconds. The formula $s = ut + \frac{1}{2}at^2$ can be used to calculate the distance, s, an object travels in t seconds. In this formula, u represents the initial velocity, and a represents a constant acceleration.

   a. Substitute the initial velocity and constant acceleration into the formula to write an equation to represent the distance Kian travels.

   b. Use the Quadratic Formula to determine the roots of the equation. What do the roots represent in the context of the problem situation? Explain your reasoning.

4. Determine the solution to each system of equations

   a. $\begin{cases} y = x^2 - 4x - 8 \\ y = -x^2 - 10x + 12 \end{cases}$

   b. $\begin{cases} y = 2x^2 + 3x - 2 \\ y = -2x^2 + 7x - 3 \end{cases}$

Stretch

The function g is defined by $g(x) = x^2 - 3x - 10$. If $g(x + 3) = x^2 + bx - c$, what are the values of b and c? Show your work and justify your answer.

Review

1. Consider the function $f(x) = (x + \frac{1}{2})(x - \frac{3}{4})$.

   a. Identify the form of the function as factored, general, or vertex.

   b. Identify the zeros and axis of symmetry of the function.

2. Write a quadratic equation for the parabola that passes through the point $(-2, 12)$ with roots $(-5, 0)$ and $(-3, 0)$.

3. Solve each equation for the unknown value.

   a. $|2x + 3| = 25$
   b. $9 = |-3x - 1| - 7$

i Want to Believe

Imaginary and Complex Numbers

6

Warm Up

Determine the zeros of each function.

1. $f(x) = x^2 - 4x + 4$

2. $g(x) = x^2 - 25$

3. $h(x) = (x - 1)^2 - 9$

4. $j(x) = 2x^2 + 8x + 5$

Learning Goals

- Rewrite expressions involving negative roots using *i*.
- Rewrite expressions involving imaginary numbers.
- Understand properties of the set of complex numbers.
- Determine the sets to which numbers belong.
- Calculate complex roots of quadratic equations and complex zeros of quadratic functions.
- Interpret complex roots of quadratic equations and complex zeros of quadratic functions.
- Determine whether a function has complex solutions from a graph and from an equation in radical form.
- Determine the number of roots of a quadratic equation from a graph and from an equation in radical form.

Key Terms

- the number *i*
- imaginary zeros
- imaginary roots
- complex numbers
- real part of a complex number
- imaginary part of a complex number
- imaginary numbers
- pure imaginary number
- Fundamental Theorem of Algebra

You have solved quadratic equations with real number solutions. How can you solve a quadratic equation that has a solution that is not real?

Did I Cross the Line?

1. **Consider the quadratic functions and their graphs shown.**

$f(x) = x^2 - 10x + 25$

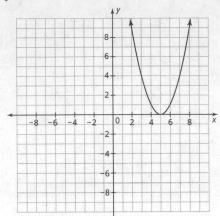

$c(x) = -x^2 + 6x$

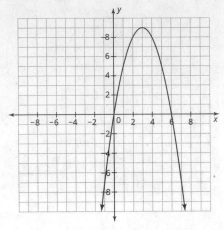

$p(x) = x^2 + 1$

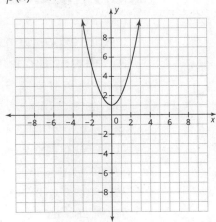

a. **List all the key characteristics you know about each function. Be sure to include the number of zeros, the x-intercept(s), the y-intercept, the axis of symmetry, and the vertex.**

b. **Compare the three functions. What do they have in common? What is different about the functions?**

Consider the function $p(x) = x^2 + 1$ and its graph from the Getting Started.

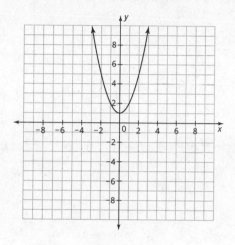

Elena and Mark determined the zeros of the function.

Elena

$x^2 + 1 = 0$

$x^2 = -1$

$x = \pm\sqrt{-1}$

Mark

$x^2 + 1 = 0$

$x^2 = -1$

$x = \pm 1$

1. **What did Mark do wrong? Use the graph to justify your answer.**

2. **Consider Elena's solution. Does the solution fall within the real number system? Explain your reasoning.**

In order to calculate the square of any real number, there must be some way to calculate the square root of a negative number. That is, there must be a number such that when it is squared, it is equal to a negative number. For this reason, mathematicians defined what is called *the number i*.

The number *i* is a number such that $i^2 = -1$. The number *i* is also called the imaginary identity.

The number *i* is similar to the number π: even though they are both numbers, each is special enough that it gets its very own symbol.

3. **If $i^2 = -1$, then what is the value of i?**

4. **Recall the function $p(x) = x^2 + 1$. Write the zeros of the function in terms of *i*.**

Functions and equations that have solutions requiring *i* have **imaginary zeros** or **imaginary roots**.

5. **How can you tell from the graph of a quadratic equation whether or not it has real solutions or imaginary solutions?**

6. **Do you think you can determine the imaginary solutions by examining the graph? Explain your reasoning.**

The Complex Number System

The set of **complex numbers** is the set of all numbers written in the form $a + bi$, where a and b are real numbers. The term a is called the **real part of a complex number**, and the term bi is called the **imaginary part of a complex number**. The set of complex numbers is represented by the notation $\mathbb{C}$.

The set of **imaginary numbers** is the set of all numbers written in the form $a + bi$, where a and b are real numbers and b is not equal to 0. The set of imaginary numbers is represented by the notation $\mathbb{I}$. A **pure imaginary number** is a number of the form $a + bi$, where a is equal to 0 and b is not equal to 0.

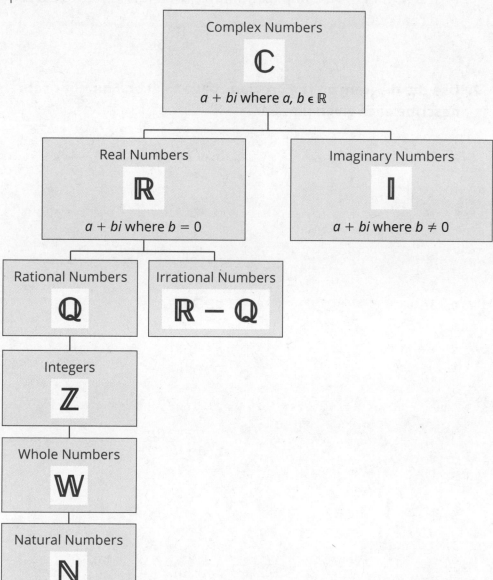

The ∈ symbol means "an element of". Therefore, "$a, b \in \mathbb{R}$" means that the values for a and b are elements of the set of real numbers.

1. **Complete each statement with *always*, *sometimes*, or *never*.**

   a. If a number is an imaginary number, then it is _____ a complex number.

   b. If a number is a complex number, then it is _____ an imaginary number.

   c. If a number is a real number, then it is _____ a complex number.

   d. If a number is a real number, then it is _____ an imaginary number.

   e. If a number is a complex number, then it is _____ a real number.

2. **Use the diagram on the previous page to list *all* number sets that describe each given number.**

   a. 3

   b. $\sqrt{7}$

   c. 3*i*

   d. $5.\overline{45}$

   e. $\frac{7}{8}$

   f. 6 − *i*

You can rewrite expressions involving negative roots by using *i*.

Worked Example

You can use the number *i* to rewrite $\sqrt{-25}$.

Factor out -1. $\qquad\qquad\qquad\qquad\qquad \sqrt{-25} = \sqrt{(-1)(25)}$

Rewrite the radical expression. $\qquad\qquad = \sqrt{-1} \cdot \sqrt{25}$

Apply the square root on $\sqrt{25}$. $\qquad\qquad = 5\sqrt{-1}$

Rewrite $\sqrt{-1}$ as *i*. $\qquad\qquad\qquad\quad = 5i$

So, $\sqrt{-25}$ can be rewritten as $5i$.

---

3. **Rewrite each expression using *i*.**

   a. $\sqrt{-4}$

   b. $\sqrt{-12}$

   c. $5 + \sqrt{-50}$

   d. $\dfrac{6 - \sqrt{-8}}{2}$

ACTIVITY
6.3   Add, Subtract, and Multiply Complex Numbers

A complex number can be represented on the complex plane. The *x*-axis of the complex plane contains all the real numbers, and the *y*-axis contains all of the imaginary numbers.

The complex number $2 + 3i$ can be represented as shown.

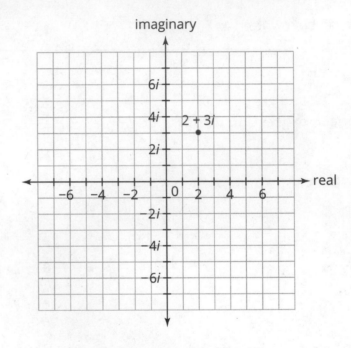

1. **Plot and label each of these complex numbers on the complex plane shown.**

   a. $5 - 3i$ b. $-3 + 4i$ c. $8 + 6i$

   d. $-6i$ e. -7 f. i

   g. $5 + 3\sqrt{-1}$ h. $-3\sqrt{-1} + 3$ i. $-4\sqrt{-1} - 3$

2. **Describe the process you can use to plot a complex number** $a + bi$ **on the complex plane.**

Let's consider the sum of two complex numbers.

The complex plane shows the sum of $(2 + 3i) + (-5 + i)$.

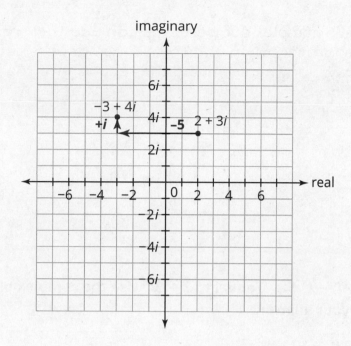

3. Suppose you start at the point $(-5 + i)$ and add $(2 + 3i)$.

   a. Show how to determine the sum on the complex plane.

   b. What do you notice about the sum? What does it suggest about the Commutative Property and complex numbers?

4. **Explain why Kimani's reasoning is correct. Illustrate your answer with an example.**

Kimani

To add two complex numbers, you can add their real parts separately, then add their imaginary parts separately, and then combine the results into the form a + bi.

Remember:

Subtracting a number is the same as adding its negative.

5. **Is $(-3 + 4i) - (-5 + i)$ equal to $2 + 3i$? Use the complex plane to confirm your answer.**

6. **Suppose you start at the point 2, or $2 + 0i$, and add $3i + (-5 + i)$.**

   a. **Show how to determine the sum on the complex plane.**

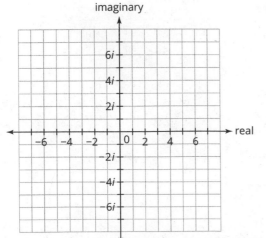

   b. **Compare the sum with $(2 + 3i) + (-5 + i)$. What do you notice? What does it suggest about the Associative Property and complex numbers?**

© Carnegie Learning, Inc.

You can multiply complex numbers by real numbers. Multiplying by a real number, k, results in a dilation of the point on the complex plane: $k(a + bi) = ka + kbi$.

7. **Consider the complex numbers plotted and labeled. Four different products can be represented. Complete each product and explain your answers.**

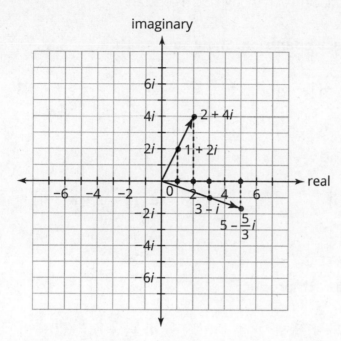

a. (_____)(1 + 2i) = (2 + 4i)

b. (_____)(2 + 4i) = (1 + 2i)

c. (_____)(3 − i) = (5 − $\frac{5}{3}i$)

d. (_____)(5 − $\frac{5}{3}i$) = (3 − i)

8. **What do these products suggest about the Distributive Property and complex numbers?**

ACTIVITY 6.4 Operations with Complex Numbers

When operating with complex numbers involving i, combine like terms by treating i as a variable (even though it is a constant).

Remember:

The value of i^2 is -1.

1. Perform each operation. Show your work.

a. $(3 + 2i) - (1 - 6i)$

b. $4i + 3 - 6 + i - 1$

c. $5i(3 - 2i)$

d. $(5 + 3i)(2 - 3i)$

2. Determine each product.

a. $(2 + i)(2 - i)$

b. $(\frac{1}{2} + i)(\frac{1}{2} - i)$

c. $(3 + 2i)(3 - 2i)$

d. $(1 - 3i)(1 + 3i)$

e. **What do you notice about each product?**

3. **What effect does multiplying a complex number by *i* have on the location of the point on the complex plane? Use examples to justify your thinking.**

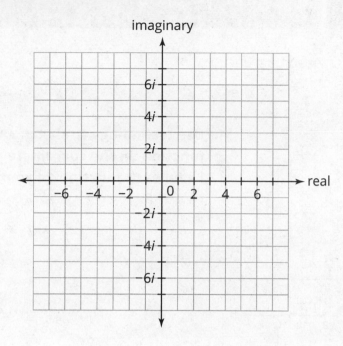

ACTIVITY 6.5

Solving Quadratics with Imaginary Zeros

Consider each quadratic function.

$$f(x) = x^2 + 9 \qquad g(x) = (x - 2)^2 + 1 \qquad h(x) = x^2 - 2x + 2$$

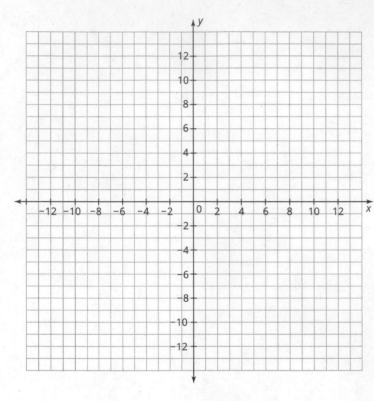

1. **Use technology to sketch each function on the coordinate plane. Label each function on your graph.**

2. **What do the solutions of the three functions have in common?**

3. **Consider the function $f(x) = x^2 + 9$.**

   a. **Describe the structure of the function. How does it compare to the function $q(x) = x^2 - 9$?**

   b. **Consider an equation written in the form $ax^2 + c = 0$. Complete the table to show when the solutions of a function are real or imaginary.**

	c is positive	c is negative
a is positive		
a is negative		

© Carnegie Learning, Inc.

c. If the factored form of a difference of squares is $a^2 - b^2 = (a - b)(a + b)$, what is the factored form of a sum of squares, $a^2 + b^2$?

d. What are the solutions to $f(x) = x^2 + 9$?

4. Consider the function $g(x) = (x - 2)^2 + 1$.

   a. How can you use the structure of the function to determine whether its zeros are real or imaginary?

Think about:

Will the graph of the function pass through the x-axis?

   b. What is the solution to $(x - 2)^2 + 1 = 0$?

5. Consider the function $h(x) = x^2 - 2x + 2$.

   a. What is the most efficient method to determine the zeros? Explain your reasoning.

Remember:

The discriminant of the function is $b^2 - 4ac$.

   b. Determine the discriminant of the function. How can you use the discriminant to know whether the solutions are real or imaginary?

c. What is the solution to $x^2 - 2x + 2 = 0$?

d. **Describe how you can check your solutions.**

You can apply the Distributive Property to determine whether an equation in factored form is equivalent to an equation in general form.

Worked Example

Consider the expression $(x - i)(x + i)$.

Multiply binomials.	$(x - i)(x + i) = x^2 + xi - xi - i^2$
Group like terms.	$= x^2 + (xi - xi) - i^2$
Combine like terms.	$= x^2 - i^2$
Use the powers of i to rewrite i^2 as -1.	$= x^2 - (-1)$
Rewrite.	$= x^2 + 1$

So, $(x - i)(x + i) = x^2 + 1$.

Recall that a quadratic function in factored form is written in the form $y = a(x - r_1)(x - r_2)$.

6. **Use your answer to Question 5 part (c) to write the function $h(x) = x^2 - 2x + 2$ in factored form.**

7. **Explain why the function you wrote in factored form is equivalent to $h(x) = x^2 - 2x + 2$.**

© Carnegie Learning, Inc.

8. Use any method to determine the zeros of each function.

a. $f(x) = -x^2 - 8x - 18$

b. $g(x) = 2x^2 - 2x + 3$

c. $h(x) = -3x^2 - 4x - 4$

TALK the TALK

Beyond Imagination

The **Fundamental Theorem of Algebra** states that any polynomial equation of degree *n* must have exactly *n* complex roots or solutions. Any root may be a multiple root.

1. Complete the table to determine the number of real and imaginary roots for different quadratic equations.

Location of Vertex	Concavity	Sketch	Number of *x*-Intercepts	Number and Type of Roots
Above the *x*-axis	Up		0	2 imaginary roots
	Down			
Below the *x*-axis	Up			
	Down			
On the *x*-axis	Up			
	Down			

2. Casey says that any quadratic equation has only one of these 3 types of solutions:

   - 2 unique real number solutions
   - 2 equal real number solutions (a double root)
   - 1 real and 1 imaginary solution

   Brandon says that any quadratic equation has only one of these 3 types of solutions:

   - 2 unique real number solutions
   - 2 equal real number solutions (a double root)
   - 2 imaginary solutions

   Karl says that any quadratic equation has only one of these 4 types of solutions:

   - 2 unique real number solutions
   - 2 equal real number solutions (a double root)
   - 2 imaginary solutions
   - 1 real and 1 imaginary solution

   Who's correct? Explain your reasoning.

3. Explain why it is not possible for a quadratic equation to have 2 equal imaginary solutions (double imaginary root).

Write

Match each definition to the corresponding term.

1. the set of all numbers written in the form $a + bi$, where a and b are real numbers
2. the set of all numbers written in the form $a + bi$, where a and b are real numbers and b is not equal to 0
3. the term bi in a complex number written as $a + bi$
4. a number equal to $\sqrt{-1}$
5. solutions to functions and equations that have a negative value for the discriminant
6. a number of the form bi where b is a real number and is not equal to 0
7. the term a in a complex number written as $a + bi$

a. imaginary roots (imaginary zeros)
b. the number i
c. imaginary numbers
d. pure imaginary number
e. complex numbers
f. real part of a complex number
g. imaginary part of a complex number

Remember

The set of complex numbers is the set of all numbers written in the form $a + bi$, where a and b are real numbers. Imaginary numbers are complex numbers where b is not equal to 0 and real numbers are complex numbers where b is equal to 0.

Practice

1. Rewrite each radical using i.

a. $\sqrt{-16}$　　　b. $\sqrt{-27}$　　　c. $\sqrt{-200}$　　　d. $5 + \sqrt{-20}$

2. Classify each number according to its most specific number set.

a. $\dfrac{-4}{\sqrt{9}}$　　　b. $\dfrac{\sqrt{-4}}{9}$　　　c. $9 - \sqrt{-4}$　　　d. $-4 - \sqrt{9}$

3. Mr. Hilbert writes the expression $(3 + i)(7 - 2i)$ on the board and asks his students to rewrite it using the Distributive Property. The work of two students is shown below. Which student simplified the expression correctly? What mistake did the other student make?

Student 1

$(3 + i)(7 - i) = 21 - 3i + 7i - i^2$
$= 21 + 4i + 1$
$= 22 + 4i$

Student 2

$(3 + i)(7 - i) = 21 - 3i + 7i - i^2$
$= 21 + 4i - 1$
$= 20 + 4i$

4. Francois claims that $\sqrt{-16} \cdot \sqrt{-4}$ is equal to 8. Jeanette claims that $\sqrt{-16} \cdot \sqrt{-4}$ is equal to -8. Who is correct? What mistake did the other student make? Support your answer with work.

5. Erika identifies $\frac{6i}{4}$ as an imaginary number and a rational number. Is Erika correct? Explain how you determined your answer.

6. Consider the functions $g(x) = x^2 - 8x - 26$ and $h(x) = x^2 - 8x + 26$ and their graphs.

   a. Describe each function. Be sure to include the number of zeros, the x-intercept(s), the y-intercept, the axis of symmetry, and the vertex.

   b. Compare the functions and their graphs. Identify any similarities and differences.

   c. Determine the zeros of both functions. Show your work.

   d. How do your answers in parts (a) and (c) compare?

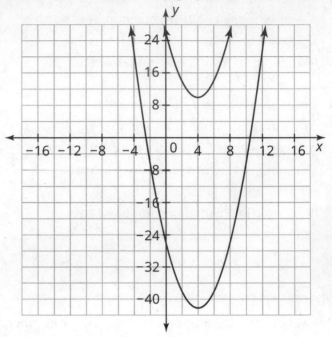

Stretch

How could you use your knowledge of quadratic functions to solve for a quadratic inequality by graphing?

Review

1. Factor each trinomial.

   a. $x^2 - 2x - 15$ b. $x^2 + 2x - 15$

2. Write each function in factored form and determine its zeros.

   a. $f(x) = 4x^2 + 8x - 12$ b. $g(x) = 15x^2 - 35x + 20$

3. Consider the function $f(x) = 3x^2 - 4$.

   a. How many zeros does the function have?

   b. What are the zeros of the function?

Exploring and Analyzing Patterns Summary

KEY TERMS

- relation
- function
- function notation
- standard form of a quadratic function
- factored form of a quadratic function
- vertex form of a quadratic function
- concavity of a parabola
- Quadratic Formula
- the number i

- imaginary zeros
- imaginary roots
- complex numbers
- real part of a complex number
- imaginary part of a complex number
- imaginary numbers
- pure imaginary number
- Fundamental Theorem of Algebra

LESSON 1	Patterns: They're Grrrrrowing!

Many patterns can be described mathematically using diagrams, algebraic expressions or functions, and words . Sequences can be used to show observable patterns. To analyze a pattern, you can draw a picture, sketch a graph, create a table, or write an equation. Analyzing a pattern can help you to recognize the pattern and extend it.

For example, consider the tile pattern shown.

Design 1   Design 2   Design 3   Design 4

The total number of tiles in each design can be described by the sequence {1, 4, 9, 16, . . .}. Each term in the sequence is a square of the term number.

A visual model, a table of values, and a graph can be used to identify patterns as linear, exponential, or quadratic.

For example, in the previous tile pattern, a table of values comparing the number of black tiles and white tiles in each design can be created to determine the number of white tiles in Design n.

Design Number	Total Number of Tiles	Number of Black Tiles	Number of White Tiles
1	1	1	0
2	4	2	2
3	9	3	6
4	16	4	12
n	n^2	n	$n^2 - n$

The pattern is quadratic.

Two or more algebraic expressions are equivalent if they produce the same output for all input values. You can verify that two expressions are equivalent by using properties to rewrite the two expressions as the same expression.

For example, Lincoln says that the number of white tiles in each row of the design is one less than the design number and expresses this pattern with the expression $n(n - 1)$. The expression $n(n - 1) = n^2 - n$ since both produce the same output for all input values.

Relationships between quantities can be represented in graphs, tables, equations, and contexts.

A **relation** is a mapping between a set of input values and a set of output values. A **function** is a relation such that for each element of the domain there exists exactly one element in the range. In **function notation**, the function $f(x)$ is read as "f of x" and indicates that x is the input and $f(x)$ is the output.

For example, in the previous tile pattern, the number of white tiles, $f(x)$, can be represented by the function $f(x) = x^2 - x$, where x represents the design number.

It can also be represented by the graph and the table shown.

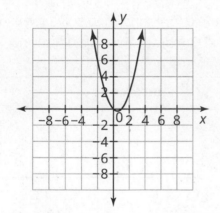

x	y
1	1
2	2
3	6
4	12

Two functions are equivalent if their algebraic or graphical representations are the same.

Quadratic functions can be written in different forms.

Standard form: $f(x) = ax^2 + bx + c$, where a does not equal 0.

Factored form: $f(x) = a(x - r_1)(x - r_2)$, where a does not equal 0.

Vertex form: $f(x) = a(x - h)^2 + k$, where a does not equal 0.

The graphs of quadratic functions can be described using key characteristics: x-intercept(s), y-intercept, vertex, axis of symmetry, and concavity. The key characteristics of a function can be determined using different methods depending on the form of the function.

Standard Form Methods to Determine Key Characteristics	
Axis of Symmetry	**x-intercept(s)**
$x = \dfrac{-b}{2a}$	Substitute 0 for y, and then solve for x using the Quadratic Formula, factoring, or graphing technology.
Vertex	**y-intercept**
Use $\dfrac{-b}{2a}$ to determine the x-coordinate of the vertex. Then substitute that value into the equation and solve for y.	c-value

Factored Form Methods to Determine Key Characteristics	
Axis of Symmetry	**x-intercept(s)**
$x = \dfrac{r_1 + r_2}{2}$	$(r_1, 0), (r_2, 0)$
Vertex	**y-intercept**
Use $\dfrac{r_1 + r_2}{2}$ to determine the x-coordinate of the vertex. Then substitute that value into the equation and solve for y.	Substitute 0 for x, and then solve for y.

© Carnegie Learning, Inc.

Vertex Form Methods to Determine Key Characteristics	
Axis of Symmetry	**x-intercept(s)**
$x = h$	Substitute 0 for y, and then solve for x using the Quadratic Formula, factoring, or graphing technology.
Vertex	**y-intercept**
(h, k)	Substitute 0 for x, and then solve for y.

Concavity of a parabola describes whether a parabola opens up or opens down. A parabola is concave up if it opens upward; a parabola is concave down if it opens downward. When the leading coefficient a is negative, the graph of the quadratic function opens downward and has a maximum. When a is positive, the graph of the quadratic function opens upward and has a minimum.

You can write a unique quadratic function given a vertex and a point on the parabola.

For example, consider a parabola with vertex (5, 2) that passes through the point (4, 9).

Substitute the given values into the vertex form of the function and solve for a.

$$f(x) = a(x - h)^2 + k$$
$$9 = a(4 - 5)^2 + 2$$
$$9 = a(-1)^2 + 2$$
$$9 = 1a + 2$$
$$7 = a$$

Finally, substitute the a-value into the function. $f(x) = 7(x - 5)^2 + 2$

You can write a unique quadratic function given the roots and a point on the parabola.

For example, consider a parabola with roots at (−2, 0) and (4, 0) that passes through the point (1, 6).

Substitute the given values into the vertex form of the function and solve for a.

$$f(x) = a(x - r_1)(x - r_2)$$
$$6 = a(1 + 2)(1 - 4)$$
$$6 = a(3)(-3)$$
$$6 = -9a$$
$$-\frac{2}{3} = a$$

Finally, substitute the a-value into the function. $f(x) = -\frac{2}{3}(x + 2)(x - 4)$

You can determine a unique quadratic function algebraically given three reference points. Substitute the x- and y-values of each point into the standard form, $y = ax^2 + bx + c$ to create a system of three equations. Then, use elimination and substitution to solve for a, b, and c.

The Root of the Problem

You can use factoring and the Zero Product Property to solve quadratics in the form $y = ax^2 + bx + c$.

For example, you can solve the quadratic equation $x^2 - 4x = -3$.

$$x^2 - 4x = -3$$
$$x^2 - 4x + 3 = -3 + 3$$
$$x^2 - 4x + 3 = 0$$
$$(x - 3)(x - 1) = 0$$

$$(x - 3) = 0 \quad \text{or} \quad (x - 1) = 0$$
$$x - 3 + 3 = 0 + 3 \quad \text{or} \quad x - 1 + 1 = 0 + 1$$
$$x = 3 \quad \text{or} \quad x = 1$$

For a quadratic function that has zeros but cannot be factored, there is another method for solving the quadratic equation. **Completing the square** is a process for writing a quadratic expression in vertex form, which then allows you to solve for the zeros.

For example, you can calculate the roots of the equation $x^2 - 4x + 2 = 0$.

Isolate $x^2 - 4x$.

$$x^2 - 4x + 2 - 2 = 0 - 2$$
$$x^2 - 4x = -2$$

Determine the constant term that would complete the square.
Add this term to both sides of the equation.

$$x^2 - 4x + ? = -2 + ?$$

$$x^2 - 4x + 4 = -2 + 4$$
$$x^2 - 4x + 4 = 2$$

Factor the left side of the equation.
Determine the square root of each side of the equation.

$$(x - 2)^2 = 2$$
$$\sqrt{(x - 2)^2} = \sqrt{2}$$
$$(x - 2) = \pm\sqrt{2}$$

Set the factor of the perfect square trinomial equal to each square root of the constant and solve for x.

$$x - 2 = \sqrt{2} \quad \text{or} \quad x - 2 = -\sqrt{2}$$
$$x = 2 + \sqrt{2} \quad \text{or} \quad x = 2 - \sqrt{2}$$

$$x \approx 3.41 \quad \text{or} \quad x \approx 0.59$$

The roots are approximately 3.41 and 0.59.

The **Quadratic Formula**, $x = \frac{-b \pm \sqrt{b^2 - 4ac}}{2a}$, can be used to calculate the solutions to any quadratic equation of the form $ax^2 + bx + c = 0$, where a, b and c represent real numbers and $a \neq 0$.

For example, given the function $f(x) = 2x^2 - 4x - 3$ you can identify the values of a, b and c.

$$a = 2; b = 24; c = -3$$

Then you use the quadratic formula to solve.

$$x = \frac{-(-4) \pm \sqrt{(-4)^2 - 4(2)(-3)}}{2(2)}$$

$$x = \frac{4 \pm \sqrt{16 - 24}}{4}$$

$$x = \frac{4 \pm \sqrt{40}}{4}$$

$$x \approx \frac{4 + 6.325}{4} \approx 2.581 \quad \text{or} \quad x \approx \frac{4 - 6.325}{4} \approx -0.581$$

The roots are $x \approx 2.581$ and $x \approx -0.581$.

You can use the same methods you used to solve a system of two linear equations to solve a system of two quadratic equations.

For example, consider the system shown.

$$\begin{cases} y = x^2 + 3x - 5 \\ y = -x^2 + 10x - 1 \end{cases}$$

Use substitution to set the two equations equal to each other. $x^2 + 3x - 5 = -x^2 + 10x - 1$

Solve for x.

$$2x^2 - 7x - 4 = 0$$
$$(2x + 1)(x - 4) = 0$$
$$x = -\frac{1}{2} \text{ or } x = 4$$

Substitute each x-value into one of the original equations to solve for y.

$$y = \left(-\frac{1}{2}\right)^2 + 3\left(-\frac{1}{2}\right) - 5 \qquad\qquad y = (4)^2 + 3(4) - 5$$
$$= \frac{1}{4} - \frac{3}{2} - 5 \qquad\qquad\qquad\quad = 16 + 12 - 5$$
$$= -6\frac{1}{4} \qquad\qquad\qquad\qquad\quad = 23$$

The solutions to the system are $(-\frac{1}{2}, -6\frac{1}{4})$ and $(4, 23)$.

i Want to Believe

In order to calculate the square root of any real number, there must be some way to calculate the square root of a negative number. That is, there must be a number such that when it is squared, it is equal to a negative number. For this reason, mathematicians defined what is called **the number *i***. The number *i* is a number such that $i^2 = -1$.

For example, you can rewrite the expression $\sqrt{-25}$ using *i*.

Factor out −1. $\qquad\qquad\qquad\qquad\qquad\qquad\sqrt{-25} = \sqrt{(-1)(25)}$

Rewrite the radical expression. $\qquad\qquad\qquad\qquad = \sqrt{-1} \cdot \sqrt{25}$

Apply the square root on $\sqrt{25}$. $\qquad\qquad\qquad\qquad = 5\sqrt{-1}$

Rewrite $\sqrt{-1}$ as *i*. $\qquad\qquad\qquad\qquad\qquad = 5i$

So, $\sqrt{-25}$ can be rewritten as $5i$.

Functions and equations that have imaginary solutions have **imaginary roots** or **imaginary zeros**, which are the solutions.

The set of **complex numbers** is the set of all numbers written in the form $a + bi$, where a and b are real numbers. The term a is called the **real part of a complex number**, and the term bi is called the **imaginary part of a complex number**.

The set of **imaginary numbers** is a subset of the set of complex numbers. A **pure imaginary number** is a number of the form $a + bi$, where b is not equal to 0.

When operating with complex numbers involving i, combine like terms by treating i as a variable (even thought it is a constant).

For example, consider the sum of $(2 + 3i) + (-5 + i)$.

$$(2 + 3i) + (-5 + i) = (2 + (-5)) + (3i + i)$$
$$= -3 + 4i$$

You can also multiply complex numbers using the Distributive Property.

For example, consider the product of $(2 + i)(2 - i)$.

$$(2 + i)(2 - i) = 2(2) + 2(-i) + i(2) + i(-i)$$
$$= 4 - 2i + 2i - i^2$$
$$= 4 - i^2$$
$$= 4 - (-1) = 5$$

You can use the same methods you used to solve quadratic equations with real solutions to solve quadratic equations with imaginary solutions.

For example, consider the function $f(x) = x^2 - 2x + 2$

$$x = \frac{-(-2) \pm \sqrt{(-2)^2 - 4(1)(2)}}{2(1)}$$

$$x = \frac{2 \pm \sqrt{4 - 8}}{2}$$

$$x = \frac{2 \pm \sqrt{-4}}{2}$$

$$x = \frac{2 \pm 2i}{2}$$

$$x = 1 \pm i$$

© Carnegie Learning, Inc.

The **Fundamental Theorem of Algebra** states that any polynomial equation of degree n must have, exactly n complex roots or solutions.

Any root may be a multiple root. The table shows the number of real and imaginary roots for different quadratic equations.

Location of Vertex	Concavity	Sketch	Number of x-Intercepts	Number and Type of Roots
Above the x-axis	Up		0	2 imaginary roots
	Down		2	2 real roots
Below the x-axis	Up		2	2 real roots
	Down		0	2 imaginary roots
On the x-axis	Up		1	1 unique root
	Down		1	1 unique root

Composing and Decomposing Functions

Tubes for producing musical sounds may be cylindrical, conical, or a combination, and are often coiled to make an instrument easier to carry. The musician opens and closes valves to change the tube length and diameter, thereby changing the pitch of the note. How might you calculate the volume of air moving through a sousaphone?

Module 1: Analyzing Structure

TOPIC 2: COMPOSING AND DECOMPOSING FUNCTIONS

This topic introduces students to the concept of building new functions on the coordinate plane by operating on or translating functions. Students review the modeling process—Notice and Wonder, Organize and Mathematize, Predict and Analyze, and Test and Interpret—which can be used to solve real-world problems. Familiar with translating and dilating functions by a constant, students explore the higher-degree functions that result when translating and dilating functions by non-constant amounts. After building functions from linear and quadratic factors, students then decompose functions.

Where have we been?

Beginning in middle school, students have studied the key characteristics of linear functions, including the x- and y-intercept and slope. In earlier high school courses, students examined the graphs of linear and quadratic functions and learned that the x-intercepts of a graph are the zeros of the function. They have used the linear factors of a quadratic function to demonstrate the Zero Product Property and have used this property to solve quadratic equations.

Where are we going?

In the upcoming topics in this course, students will continue to analyze the structure of polynomial functions. Understanding zeros graphically lays the foundation for understanding and solving for zeros algebraically, and the connection to graphical representations of functions helps students to factor polynomials using long division or synthetic division.

Building Functions

You can use the product of linear functions to build a polynomial. The graph shows the product of two functions, $h(x) \cdot l(x) = A(x)$.

The new function crosses the x-axis at each of its factor's x-intercepts.

The graph increases or decreases depending on whether the output is positive or negative as it moves from one interval to the next.

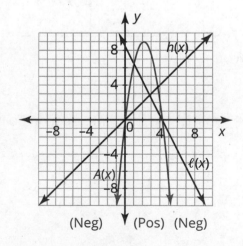

Escher Time

M.C. Escher was a well-known artist with a unique visual perspective. Many of his works display elusive connections, peculiar symmetry, and tessellations. Tessellations are symmetric designs with a repeated pattern. You can find many images of Escher's work on the World Wide Web. Take a look and enjoy! Make sure to take a close look, because things may not be as straightforward as they seem.

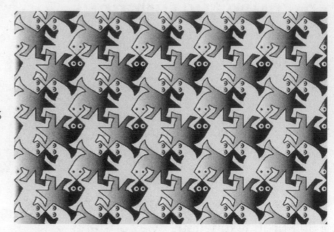

Talking Points

Cubic functions can be an important topic to know about for college admissions tests.

Here is an example of a sample question:

The graph of a cubic function and the graph of $y = x + 1$ in the *xy*-plane can intersect in at most how many points?

You can visualize the linear function and a cubic function as shown:

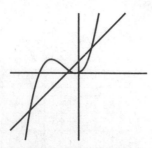

At most, there are 3 intersection points.

Key Terms

cubic function

A cubic function is a function that can be written in the standard form $f(x) = ax^3 + bx^2 + cx + d$, where $a \neq 0$. A cubic function is a polynomial function of degree 3.

multiplicity

Multiplicity is how many times a particular number is a zero for a given function.

Fundamental Theorem of Algebra

The Fundamental Theorem of Algebra states that a degree n polynomial has, counted with multiplicity, exactly n zeros.

Blame It on the Rain

Modeling with Functions

Warm Up

The table of values shown describes a function.

x	y
−5	24
−4	22
0	14
1	12
5	4

Write an equation using function notation to represent the table of values.

Learning Goals

- Use multiple representations of functions to model and solve problems.
- Use multiple representations of functions to analyze problems.

You have calculated the area of various geometric figures. How can you use what you know about area to build an algebraic function?

Brain Drain

A nearby town hired Ms. Farrelli, a civil engineer, to rebuild its storm drainage system. The drains in this town are open at the top to allow water to flow directly into them. While designing the drains, the engineer must keep in mind the height and the width of the drain. She needs to consider the height because the water cannot rise above the drain or it will flood the town and cause major destruction. However, the drain must also be wide enough that it will not get clogged by debris.

Rectangular sheets of metal will be used to build the drains. These sheets are bent up on both sides to represent the height of the drain. An end view of the drain is shown.

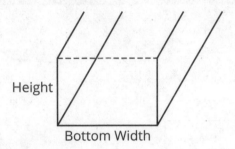

1. **Use a sheet of paper to model a drain.**

   a. **Compare your model of a drain to your classmates' models. Identify similarities and differences between your models.**

   b. **How does folding the sides of the drain affect the bottom width of the drain?**

   c. **Describe the drain that you think best fits the needs of the town. Explain your reasoning.**

The sheets of metal being used to create the drain are 8.5 feet wide. The engineer wants to identify possible heights and bottom width measurements she could use to construct the drains.

1. **Determine the bottom width for each given height. Then, define a function *w*(*h*) for the bottom width given a height of *h* feet.**

Height of the Drain (feet)	Bottom Width of the Drain (feet)
0	
1.5	
3	
5	

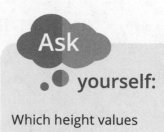

Ask yourself:

Which height values make sense for this situation?

2. **The engineer needs to identify the measurements that allow the most water to flow through the drain. What does the engineer need to calculate? What does she need to consider?**

To determine the drain dimensions that allow the most water to flow through, the engineer must calculate the cross-sectional area. The cross-sectional area of a drain is shown.

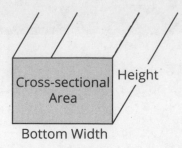

Cross-sectional Area

Height

Bottom Width

3. **Describe how to determine the cross-sectional area of any drain.**

4. **Predict and describe the drain with the maximum cross-sectional area.**

5. **Define a function $A(h)$ for the cross-sectional area of the drain with a height of h feet.**

6. **Use technology to graph the function $A(h)$. Then sketch the graph.**

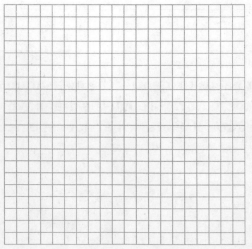

Remember:

Don't forget to label your axes.

7. Analyze and interpret your graph.

a. What is the maximum cross-sectional area for the drain pipe? Explain your reasoning.

b. Identify and label the intercepts of $A(h)$ on your graph. Then describe the meaning of each in terms of this problem situation.

c. Identify and label the equation of the axis of symmetry on the graph. Then describe the relationship between the axis of symmetry and the maximum cross-sectional area.

Think about:

Is there a way to determine the maximum cross-sectional area using the *x*-intercepts?

8. Draw and label the drain with the greatest cross-sectional area.

9. In this problem, you built a new function $A(h) = h(8.5 - 2h)$ using two existing functions.

a. Identify the first factor in this function and its function family. Then describe what it represents in terms of this problem situation.

b. Identify the second factor in this function and its function family. Then describe what it represents in terms of this problem situation.

c. Identify the type of function created by the product of these two factors. Why does this happen?

When you solve real-world problems using mathematics, you can use a process to model situations.

The Modeling Process

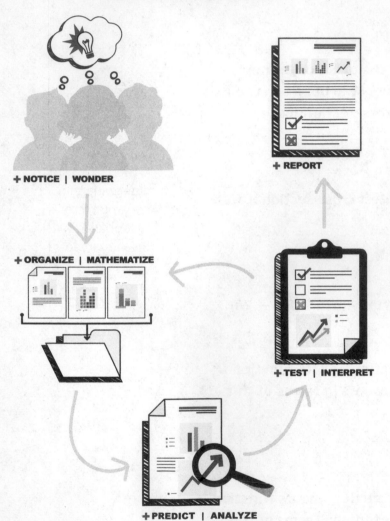

+ NOTICE | WONDER

+ ORGANIZE | MATHEMATIZE

+ PREDICT | ANALYZE

+ TEST | INTERPRET

+ REPORT

Notice and Wonder
Gather information, notice patterns, and formulate mathematical questions about what you notice.

Organize and Mathematize
Organize your information and represent it using mathematical notation.

Predict and Analyze
Extend the patterns created, complete operations, make predictions, and analyze the mathematical results.

Test and Interpret
Interpret your results and test your mathematical predictions in the real world. Make adjustments necessary.

If your predictions are incorrect, you can revisit your mathematical work and make adjustments—or start over!

1. How did you Notice and Wonder when you started to think about the rain drain in the previous activity?

2. Explain how you organized information and represented this information mathematically.

3. How did you Predict and Analyze in the activity?

4. How did you Test and Interpret in the rain drain activity?

TALK the TALK

Determine the Best Design

A civil engineering company is hired to design a new drainage system for your town. To construct one of the storm drains, a sheet of metal that is 15.25 feet wide is folded on both sides.

1. **Describe the drain that has the maximum cross-sectional area. Include at least two different representations in your description. Show all work and explain your reasoning.**

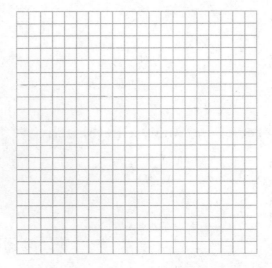

Think

about:

Use the modeling process as you solve this problem.

· Notice and Wonder
· Organize and Mathematize
· Predict and Analyze
· Test and Interpret

Assignment

Write

1. In your own words, explain the four steps of the mathematical modeling process.
   - Notice and Wonder
   - Organize and Mathematize
   - Predict and Analyze
   - Test and Interpret

Remember

Tables, graphs, and equations can be used to model situations. A function created by the product of two linear factors is a quadratic function.

Practice

1. Mr. Jones wants to fence in a rectangular field for his horse using the 600 feet of fence he has stored in his barn. He wants to maximize the area of the field in order to give his horse the most pasture possible. Help Mr. Jones design his field to achieve the maximum area.

   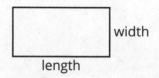

   a. Complete the table to show the length of the field for each given width.

Width (feet)	0	50	100	150	200	250	300
Length (feet)							

   b. Define the function $l(w)$ to represent the length of the field as a function of the width. Explain your reasoning.

   c. Define the function $A(w)$ to represent the area of the field as a function of the width. Explain your reasoning.

   d. Determine the maximum area of the field as well as the length and width that will result in the maximum area. Explain your reasoning.

2. Ms. Williams wants to fence in a rectangular area of her field using the 1200 feet of fence she has. She wants the area to have four congruent sections. She is trying to decide which of the two designs shown will give her animals the maximum fenced area.

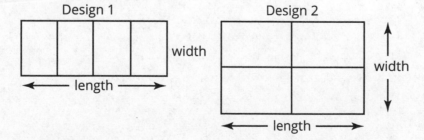

Determine the design and the dimensions of the design that will give Ms. Williams the maximum fenced area. Show your work and explain your reasoning.

© Carnegie Learning, Inc.

Stretch

1. A team of engineers is going to build a recreational field with a path around it. The field will be rectangular in shape with a semicircle at each end. The path will be 1320 feet long. Determine the dimensions for the length and width that will give the greatest possible area for the rectangular section of the field. Round your answers to the nearest tenth.

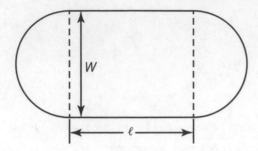

Review

1. Use properties to rewrite each expression.

   a. $(8 - 3i) - (8 + 3i)$

   b. $(8 - 3i)(8 + 3i)$

2. A baseball is hit from an initial height of 3 feet. The baseball reaches its maximum height of 81 feet when it is 156 feet from home plate.

   a. Write a quadratic function to represent the height of the baseball as a function of its distance from home plate.

   b. Determine the height of the baseball when it is 180 feet from home plate. Round your answer to the nearest tenth.

3. Solve the equation $7x^2 - 11x + 3 = 0$. Round your answer(s) to the nearest hundredth, if necessary.

Folds, Turns, and Zeros

Transforming Function Shapes

Warm Up

Use the Distributive Property to rewrite each expression.

1. $x(x^2 - 5)$

2. $(x - 1)(x + 4)$

3. $x(x + 1)\left(\frac{1}{2}x + 1\right)$

4. $(2x + 1)(x + 2)(x + 2)$

Learning Goals

- Translate and dilate functions by non-constant values to create higher-degree functions.
- Describe the relationship between the linear factors of a function and its zeros.
- Describe how the linear factors of a function combine to produce intervals of increase and decrease in the product function.
- Explain the behavior of function graphs at zeros represented by degree-1 factors and zeros represented by degree-2 factors.
- Sketch graphs of degree-3 functions given their linear factors.

You have transformed functions by constant values to create new functions of the same degree. How can you use transformations to create higher-degree functions?

A Functional Transformation

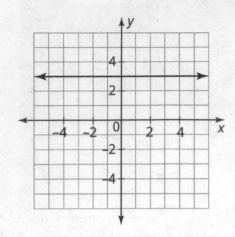

Consider the constant function $f(x) = 3$. The graph of this function is a horizontal line crossing the y-axis at $(0, 3)$.

Recall that you can translate this function vertically by adding a constant: $f(x) = 3 + D$. Every point on the line is translated vertically by the constant. But think about a transformation in which the D-value is not a constant. Suppose the function $f(x) = 3$ is translated by x to form $f(x) = 3 + x$. This would mean that the y-value of every point on the line $y = 3$ is translated by its corresponding x-value.

1. **Consider the point of the original function at $x = 1$. This point has coordinates (1, 3). Plot the location of the point after a vertical translation of x.**

2. **Consider the point of the original function at $x = -1$. This point has coordinates $(-1, 3)$. Plot the location of the point after a vertical translation of x.**

3. **Plot other points after applying a vertical translation of x. What function is formed by translating all the points on the line $f(x) = 3$ by x?**

4. **What point does not change its location from the original function to the new function? Explain why.**

5. **Identify the zero of the new function. Explain how the zero is created.**

Recall that you can dilate a function vertically by multiplying the function by a constant. For example, if the function is $f(x) = x$, then $f(x) = A \cdot x$ represents a vertical dilation of the original function.

What happens when you transform a function by an A-value that is not a constant? Suppose the function $f(x) = x + 3$ is dilated by x, or $x \cdot f(x)$. This would mean that the y-value of every point on the line $y = x + 3$ is dilated according to its corresponding x-value.

1. **The graph shows the function $f(x) = x + 3$.**
   Choose several points on $f(x)$ and dilate each by multiplying by the x-value of that particular point. Then sketch the graph. Two points have already been dilated.

Think
about:

How can you use a table to help organize your calculations?

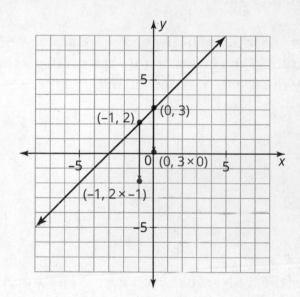

2. **Write the equation to represent the new function $g(x) = x \cdot f(x)$. How did the dilation change the degree of the new function?**

3. **Identify the zeros of $g(x)$. How are these related to the two linear factors, $x + 3$ and x?**

The graph shows the product of the linear factors used to create the new function $g(x) = x \cdot f(x)$. As you analyze the graph from left to right, consider that the new function $g(x)$ changes from decreasing to increasing at the point $(-1.5, -2.25)$.

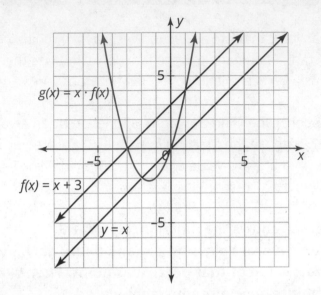

$g(x) = x \cdot f(x)$

$f(x) = x + 3$

$y = x$

4. **Analyze two intervals.**

   a. **Consider the interval between $x = -8$ and $x = -3$. Explain why the product of the linear factors results in $g(x)$ being positive and why the function is decreasing.**

   b. **Consider the interval between $x = -3$ and $x = 0$. Explain why the product of the linear factors results in $g(x)$ being negative and why the function changes from decreasing to increasing.**

Suppose the function $h(x) = -(x + 3)$ is dilated by x, or $x \cdot h(x)$.

5. The graph shows the function $h(x) = -(x + 3)$. Choose several points on $h(x)$ and dilate each by multiplying by the x-value of that particular point. Then sketch the graph.

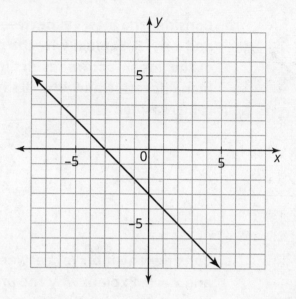

6. Write the equation to represent the new function $j(x) = x \cdot h(x)$. What function family does the new function belong to?

7. Identify the zeros of $j(x)$. How are these related to the two linear factors, $-(x + 3)$ and x?

The graph shows the product of the linear factors used to create the new function $j(x) = x \cdot h(x)$. As you analyze the graph from left to right, consider that the new function $j(x)$ changes from decreasing to increasing at the point $(-1.5, 2.25)$.

8. **Analyze the two intervals.**

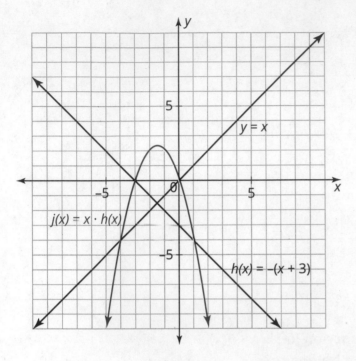

a. **Consider the interval between $x = -10$ and $x = -3$. Explain why the product of the linear factors results in $j(x)$ being negative and why the function is increasing.**

b. **Consider the interval between $x = -3$ and $x = 0$. Explain why the product of the linear factors results in $j(x)$ being positive and why the function changes from increasing to decreasing.**

9. **What do you know about the linear function factors when the resulting quadratic function:**

a. **Has a positive A-value?**

b. **Has a negative A-value?**

Let's create a function of degree 3. Start with the linear function $f(x) = x - 1$,
as shown on the coordinate plane.

1. **Dilate the function $f(x)$ by a factor of $x + 3$,
   or $(x + 3) \cdot f(x)$. Sketch the graph of the new
   function, $m(x)$. Write the equation for $m(x)$
   and identify the zeros of the new function.**

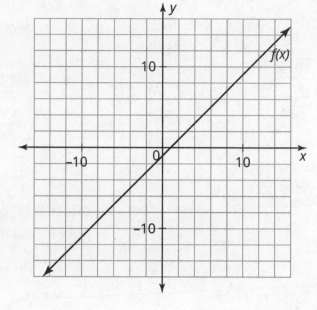

2. **Dilate $m(x)$ by a factor of $x + 2$, or $(x + 2) \cdot m(x)$.
   Sketch the graph of the new function, $p(x)$.
   Write the equation for $p(x)$ and identify the
   zeros of the new function.**

3. **Analyze the changes between each original function and each
   new function.**

   a. **What do you notice about the dilations of each function and
      the zeros of each new function?**

   b. **How do the zeros appear to be related to the increasing and
      decreasing behavior of the function? Explain why you think
      this behavior occurs.**

4. The graph shows the function $m(x) = (x - 1)(x + 3)$.

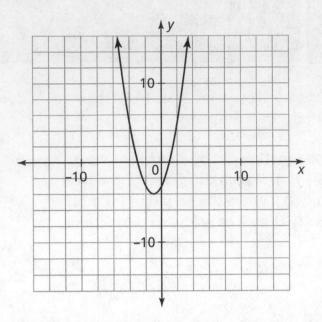

a. Dilate $m(x)$ by another factor of $x + 3$. Sketch the graph of the new function, $r(x) = (x + 3) \cdot m(x)$.

b. Compare the degree-3 function $r(x)$ with the degree-3 function $p(x)$ you created in Question 2. How are the two functions similar and different?

Let's continue to explore the dilation of quadratic functions.

1. **Dilate each given function to create a new function of a higher degree. Sketch the graph and then identify the zeros of each new function.**

a. $f(x) = (x - 1)(x + 1)$
   Sketch $x \cdot f(x)$.

b. $g(x) = (2x + 1)(x - 2)$
   Sketch $(x - 2) \cdot g(x)$.

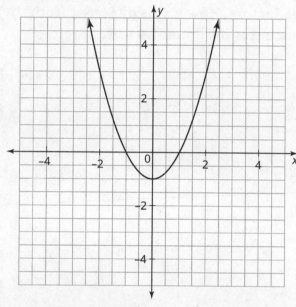

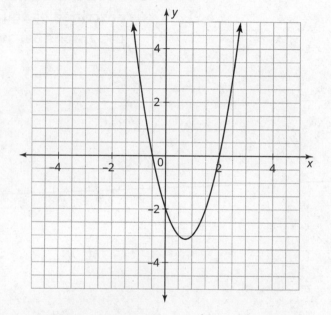

c. $h(x) = \left(\frac{1}{2}x - 1\right)(x + 4)$
   Sketch $(x + 4) \cdot h(x)$.

d. $j(x) = (x - 4)(x + 4)$
   Sketch $(x - 2) \cdot j(x)$.

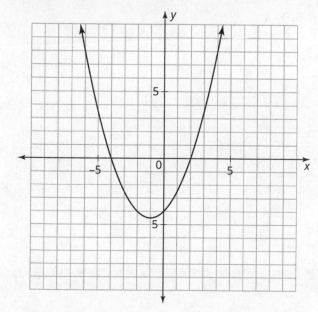

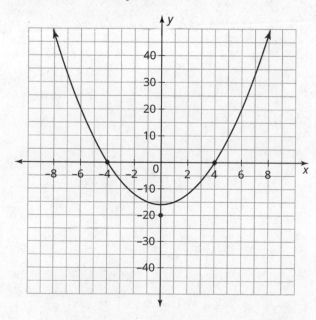

2. **How do the factors of each equation in Question 1 describe the locations of the zeros of the function?**

When the function $g(x)$ is dilated by $x - 2$, the new function contains a square factor, $(x - 2)^2$. Similarly, when the function $h(x)$ is dilated by $x + 4$, the new function contains a square factor, $(x + 4)^2$.

3. **Describe how the graphs of the functions behave at zeros described by square factors. How is this different from the way the graphs behave at zeros described by linear factors?**

TALK the TALK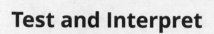

Test and Interpret

1. **Predict the shape of each function. Sketch it on the coordinate plane and label the zeros. Use graphing technology to test each prediction.**

   a. $f(x) = x(x - 10)(x + 4)$

   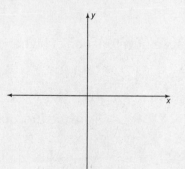

   b. $g(x) = (x + 3)(x - 3)(x + 3)$

   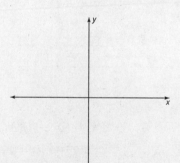

   c. $h(x) = (x^2)(x)$

   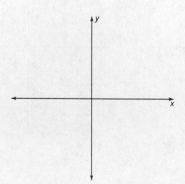

Assignment

Write

Write the transformation form for a function $f(x)$. Then, in your own words, describe how each of the values A and D affects the graph of the function.

Remember

Functions can be translated and dilated by non-constant values, which apply a different transformation to each point of the function.

Practice

Dilate each function to create a new function of higher degree. Sketch the graph and then identify the zeros of each new function.

1. $f(x) = (x + 2)(x - 1)$

   Dilate the function by x.

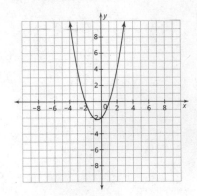

2. $g(x) = (x + 1)(2x - 1)$

   Dilate the function by $x - 1$.

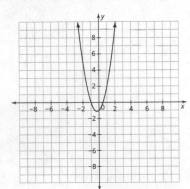

3. $h(x) = (x + 3)(x - 3)$

   Dilate the function by $\left(x + \frac{1}{2}\right)$.

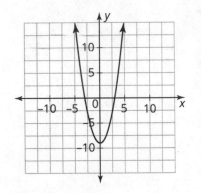

4. $m(x) = \left(\frac{1}{3}x - 2\right)(x + 1)$

   Dilate the function by x.

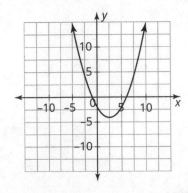

5. $f(x) = (3x - 1)(3x + 1)$

   Dilate the function by $x - 2$.

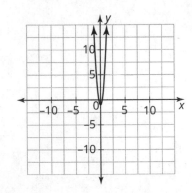

6. $g(x) = (x + 4)(x - 5)$

   Dilate the function by $x + 3$.

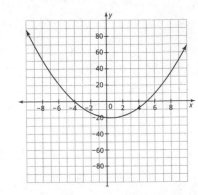

Stretch

1. Consider the graph of a cubic function.

   a. Determine a quadratic function that could have been dilated to produce the cubic function. State the function used to dilate the quadratic function.

   b. Determine a linear function that could have been dilated to produce the cubic function. State the function used to dilate the linear function.

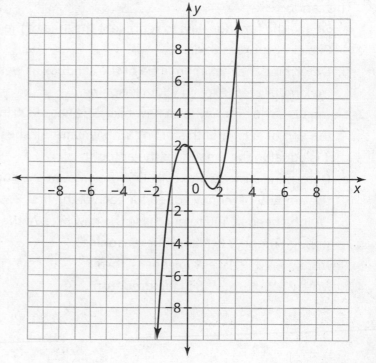

2. Consider the function $f(x) = x^3 + 2x^2 - 5x - 6$.

   a. Use technology to graph the function, and then sketch it on the grid.

   b. Determine the domain and range of the function.

   c. Determine the intervals over which the function is increasing and decreasing.

   d. Determine the x- and y-intercepts of the graph of $f(x)$.

   e. Determine the values of x for which $f(x) = -4$.

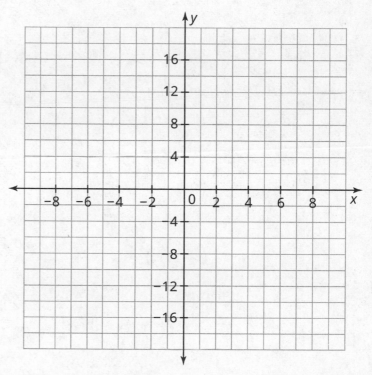

Review

1. Alton is making a sandbox for his kids in the backyard. He has 400 feet of board for the sides of the sandbox.
   a. Define the function $A(w)$ to represent the area of the sandbox as a function of the width. Explain your reasoning.
   b. Determine the maximum area of the sandbox as well as the length and width that will result in the maximum area. Explain your reasoning.

2. Quinna is saving money for a new bike. She has $5.00 in her savings account as of January 1. At the end of each month starting with January 31, she is planning to add to her account an amount that is equal to the amount in the account.
   a. Determine a method to calculate the amount she adds each month. Use that method to calculate the amount of money added for each of the first 5 months.
   b. Quinna needs $400 to purchase the new bike. At the end of which month will she have enough money? Explain your reasoning.

3. Rewrite $y = 2(x - 1)^2 - 9$ in general form.

4. Rewrite $y = 5x^2 - x - 18$ in factored form.

Planting the Seeds

Exploring Cubic Functions

Warm Up

Use the Distributive Property to rewrite each expression.

1. $a(2a - 1)(5 + a)$

2. $(9 - x)(x + 3)$

3. $b^2(10 - b) + b^2$

4. $(w - 2)(w + 3)(w + 1)$

Learning Goals

- Represent cubic functions using words, tables, equations, and graphs.
- Interpret the key characteristics of the graphs of cubic functions.
- Analyze cubic functions in terms of their mathematical context and problem context.
- Connect the characteristics and behaviors of a cubic function to its factors.
- Compare cubic functions with linear and quadratic functions.
- Build cubic functions from linear and quadratic functions.

Key Terms

- cubic function
- relative maximum
- relative minimum

You have calculated the volume of various geometric figures. How can you use what you know about volume to build an algebraic function?

Our Business Is Growing

The Plant-A-Seed Planter Company produces planter boxes. To make the boxes, a square is cut from each corner of a rectangular copper sheet. The sides are bent to form a rectangular prism without a top. Cutting different sized squares from the corners results in differently sized planter boxes. Plant-A-Seed takes sales orders from customers who request a sized planter box.

It may help to create a model of the planter by cutting squares out of the corners of a sheet of paper and folding.

Each rectangular copper sheet is 12 inches by 18 inches. In the diagram, the solid lines indicate where the square corners are cut, and the dotted lines represent where the sides are bent for each planter box.

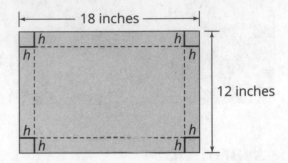

1. **Complete the table given each planter box is made from a 12 inch by 18 inch copper sheet. Include an expression for each planter box's height, width, length, and volume for a square corner side of length *h*.**

Square Corner Side Length (inches)	Height (inches)	Width (inches)	Length (inches)	Volume (cubic inches)
0				
1				
2				
3				
4				
5				
6				
7				
h				

2. **Analyze the relationship between the height, length, and width of each planter box. What are the dimensions of the largest sized square corner that can be cut to make a planter box? Explain your reasoning.**

Ask yourself:

What patterns do you notice in the table?

3. **Write a function $V(h)$ to represent the volume of the planter box in terms of the corner side length h.**

Let's consider the graph of the *cubic function* you created.

1. **Louis, Ahmed, and Heidi each used graphing technology to analyze the volume function, *V*(*h*), and to sketch the graph. They disagree about the shape of the graph.**

A **cubic function** is a function that can be written in the general form $f(x) = ax^3 + bx^2 + cx + d$, where $a \neq 0$.

Louis

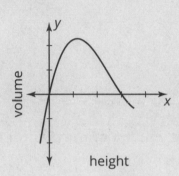

The graph increases and then decreases. It is a parabola.

Ahmed

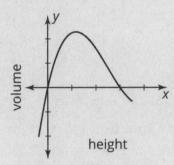

The graph lacks a line of symmetry, so it can't be a parabola.

Heidi

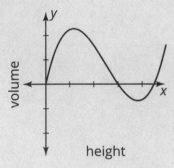

I noticed the graph curves back up so it can't be a parabola.

Evaluate each student's sketch and rationale to determine who is correct. For the student(s) who is/are not correct, explain why the rationale is not correct.

2. Represent the cubic function using graphing technology with the settings $[-10, 15] \times [-400, 400]$.

   a. Describe the key characteristics of the graph.

Think about:

In this problem, you are determining the maximum value graphically. How will your solution strategy change when using the table or equation?

   b. What is the maximum volume of a planter box? State the dimensions of this planter box. Explain your reasoning.

   c. Identify the domain of the function $V(h)$. Is the domain the same or different in terms of the context of this problem? Explain your reasoning.

   d. Identify the range of the function $V(h)$. Is the range the same or different in terms of the context of this problem? Explain your reasoning.

   e. What do the *x*-intercepts represent in this problem situation? Do these values make sense in terms of this problem situation? Explain your reasoning.

A graph may reveal different key characteristics within a given domain. The function $V(h) = h(12 - 2h)(18 - 2h)$ has x-intercepts at $x = 0$, $x = 6$, and $x = 9$.

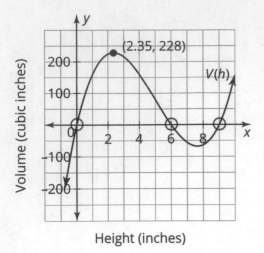

As the input values for height increase, the output values for volume approach infinity. Therefore, the function doesn't have a maximum; however, the point (2.35, 228) is a *relative maximum* within the domain interval of (0, 6). A **relative maximum** is the highest point in a particular section of a graph.

Similarly, as the values for height decrease, the output values approach negative infinity. Therefore, a *relative minimum* occurs at (7.65, −68.16). A **relative minimum** is the lowest point in a particular section of a graph.

The function $V(h)$ represents all of the possible volumes for a given height h. A horizontal line is a powerful tool for working backwards to determine the possible values for the height when the volume is known.

Suppose a customer ordered a particular planter box with a volume of 100 cubic inches, but did not specify the height of the planter box.

Worked Example

You can determine the possible heights from the graph of $V(h)$. Suppose the given volume of a planter box is 100 cubic inches.

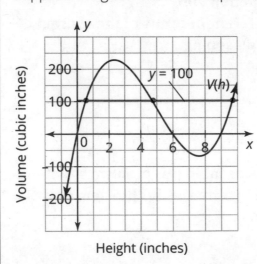

- Draw a horizontal line at $y = 100$.
- Identify each point where $V(h)$ intersects with $y = 100$, or where $V(h) = 100$.

The first point of intersection is represented using function notation as $V(0.54) = 100$.

3. Consider the worked example.

   a. Use graphing technology to determine where $V(h) = 100$. Then write the intersection points in function notation. What do the intersection points mean in terms of this problem situation?

   b. How many differently sized planter boxes can Plant-A-Seed make to fill this order? Explain your reasoning.

4. A neighborhood beautifying committee would like to purchase a variety of planter boxes with volumes of 175 cubic inches to add to business windowsill store fronts. Determine the planter box dimensions that the Plant-A-Seed Company can create for the committee. Show all work and explain your reasoning.

5. **Plant-A-Seed's intern claims that he can no longer complete an order because he spilled a cup of coffee on the sales ticket. Help him complete the order by determining the missing dimensions from the information that is still visible. Explain how you determined possible unknown dimensions of each planter box.**

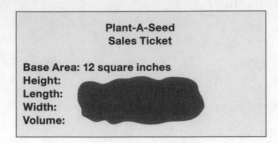

**Plant-A-Seed
Sales Ticket**

Base Area: 12 square inches
Height:
Length:
Width:
Volume:

A customer sent this email:

To Whom It May Concern,
I would like to purchase several planter boxes, all with a height of 5 inches. Can you make one that holds 100 cubic inches of dirt? Please contact me at your earliest convenience.

Thank you,
Muriel Jenkins

Think about:

How is the volume function built in this problem?

6. Write a response to this customer, showing all calculations.

ACTIVITY
3.2

Building a Cubic Function from a Quadratic and Linear Function

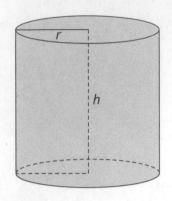

The Plant-A-Seed Company also makes cylindrical planters for city sidewalks and store fronts. The cylindrical planters come in a variety of sizes, but all have a height that is twice the radius.

1. **Why do you think Plant-A-Seed might want to manufacture different sizes of a product, but maintain a constant ratio of height to radius?**

Remember:

A constant ratio makes the cylindrical planters similar.

Volume of a cylinder:
$V = $ (base area)(height)
Area of a circle: $A = \pi r^2$

2. **Consider differently sized cylindrical planters.**

   a. **Complete the table.**

Radius	Height (inches)	Base Area (square inches)	Volume (cubic inches)
0			
1			
2			
3			
4			
			2000
x			

   b. **Describe how you determined the volume when you are given the radius.**

c. Describe your method to determine the base area and the
    height when you are given the volume.

d. Analyze your table of values. For every unit increase in the
    radius, describe the rate of change in the height, area of the
    base, and volume of each planter.

The base area function $A(x) = \pi x^2$ and the height function $h(x) = 2x$ are
multiplied to build the volume function $V(x) = (\pi x^2)(2x)$.

3. Use technology to sketch and label the functions $A(x)$, $h(x)$, and
    $V(x)$ on the coordinate plane shown.

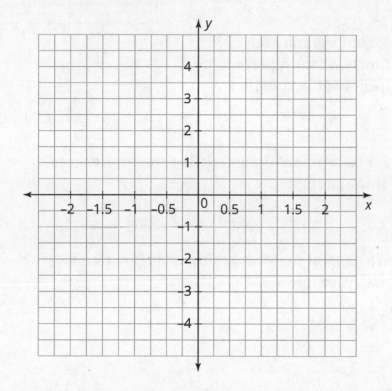

The two cubic functions you have sketched in this lesson represent the two
general shapes of a cubic function.

4. How can you describe these two general shapes?

A cubic function is a
function that can be
written in the general
form $f(x) = ax^3 + bx^2 +
cx + d$, where $a \neq 0$.

TALK the TALK

Cubism

Consider a cube, which has equal length, width, and height, *x*.

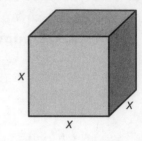

1. **Recall that one way to determine the volume of a cube is to multiply the area of the base by its height.**

   a. **Sketch a graph of the function that represents the area of the base of the cube.**

   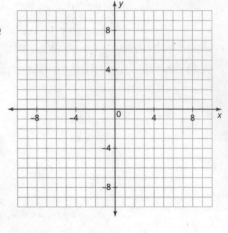

   b. **Sketch a graph of the function that represents the height of the cube.**

   c. **Sketch a graph of the function that represents the volume of the cube.**

2. **Which general shape does this cubic function match? Explain your reasoning.**

Assignment

Write

Provide an example of each key term.

1. relative minimum
2. relative maximum
3. cubic function

Remember

A cubic function is a polynomial function of degree 3 that can be written in the form $f(x) = ax^3 + bx^2 + cx + d$, where $a \neq 0$. The graph has 2 general shapes.

Practice

1. Cynthia is an engineer at a manufacturing plant. Her boss asks her to use rectangular metal sheets to build storage bins with the greatest possible volume. Each rectangular sheet is 8 feet by 10 feet. Cynthia's sketch shows the squares to be removed from the corners of each sheet. The dashed lines indicate where the metal sheets will be folded before they are welded to form the prism-shaped storage bins without tops.

   a. Write a function $V(x)$ to represent the volume of a bin in terms of the side length, x, of the removed squares. Explain your reasoning.

   b. Represent the function $V(x)$ using technology. Determine the domain and range of the function. Determine the domain and range of the function as they relate to this problem situation. Explain your reasoning.

   c. Determine the maximum volume of a bin. What are the dimensions of a bin with the maximum volume?

   d. Determine any relative maximums or relative minimums of $V(x)$. Then, determine the intervals over which the function is increasing and decreasing.

   e. Determine the x- and y-intercepts of the graph of $V(x)$. What do they represent in this problem situation?

   f. Cynthia's boss asks her to make several bins with volumes of exactly 40 cubic feet. Determine the bin dimensions that will work.

Stretch

1. Nikki is an engineer at a manufacturing plant. Her boss asks her to use rectangular sheets of metal to build storage bins with the greatest possible volume. Each rectangular sheet is 14 feet by 12 feet. Nikki's sketch shows the squares to be removed from each sheet. The dashed lines indicate where the metal

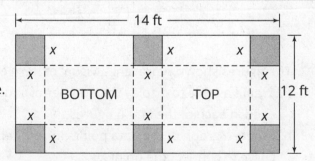

   sheets will be folded before they are welded to form the prism-shaped storage bins with tops.

   a. Write a function $V(x)$ to represent the volume of a bin in terms of the side length, x, of the removed squares. Explain your reasoning.

   b. Represent the function $V(x)$ using technology. Determine the domain and range of the function. Determine the domain and range of the function as they relate to this problem situation. Explain your reasoning.

c. Determine the maximum volume of a bin. What are the dimensions of a bin with the maximum volume?

d. Determine any relative maximums or relative minimums of $V(x)$. Then, determine the intervals over which the function is increasing and decreasing.

e. Determine the x- and y-intercepts of the graph of $V(x)$. What do they represent in this problem situation?

f. Nikki's boss asks her to make several bins with volumes of exactly 40 cubic feet. Determine the bin dimensions that will work.

Review

1. Dilate each function by the given factor to create a new function of higher degree. Sketch the graph and then identify the zeros of the new function.

a. $f(x) = \left(\frac{1}{2}x + 1\right)(x - 3)$

Sketch $(x + 1) \cdot f(x)$.

b. $g(x) = (3x + 4)\left(\frac{1}{4}x + 2\right)$

Sketch $(x - 1) \cdot f(x)$.

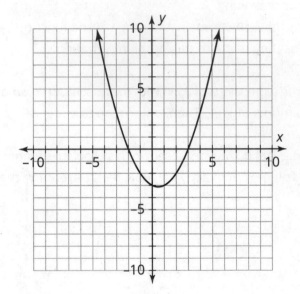

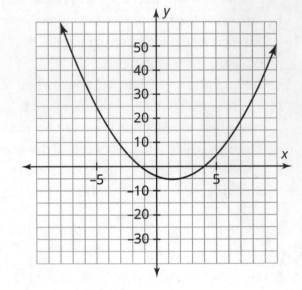

2. The figures shown represent a visual pattern of tiles.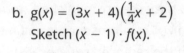

a. Create a table to display the number of squares used in each of the first 6 figures.

b. Create a graph of the data points in your table on the coordinate plane shown. Draw a smooth curve to connect the points.

c. Describe the pattern as linear, exponential, quadratic, or none of these. Explain your reasoning.

3. Solve the equation $x^2 - 6x + 35 = 10$.

The Zero's the Hero

Decomposing Cubic Functions

Warm Up

Determine the possible values for x in each equation.

1. $2x - 5 = 0$

2. $(x + 4)(x - 4) = 0$

3. $x(x + 3) = 0$

4. $(x - 5)(x + 1)(x - 2) = 0$

Learning Goals

- Connect the characteristics and behaviors of quadratic and cubic functions to their factors.
- Build cubic functions from linear and quadratic functions graphically.
- Determine the zeros of functions and the multiplicity of the functions' zeros.
- Compare cubic functions with linear and quadratic functions.
- Show how linear, quadratic, and cubic functions demonstrate the Fundamental Theorem of Algebra.

Key Term

- multiplicity

You have built functions to represent two- and three-dimensional shapes. What does the structure of the equation reveal about the graph of the function?

A Difference in Degree

You know that another name for a linear function that is not a constant function is a polynomial of degree 1, because the greatest exponent in a linear function equation is 1. A quadratic function is a polynomial of degree 2, and a cubic function is a polynomial of degree 3.

1. **Determine the degree of each function.**

   a. $f(x) = x$

   b. $g(x) = x - 1$

   c. $h(x) = x(x - 1)$

   d. $j(x) = (x - 1)(x - 1)$

   e. $k(x) = x(x - 1)(x - 1)$

   f. $m(x) = (x)(x)(x - 1)$

Recall that the zeros of a function are the points on the graph of the function where the function's value is zero. For example, given the function $f(x) = x$, the value of the function is 0 when $x = 0$. Likewise, given $g(x) = x - 1$, the value of the function is 0 when $x = 1$.

Multiplicity is how many times a particular number is a zero for a given function. The zero in each of the functions f and g, for example, has a multiplicity of 1.

2. **For the functions given in parts (c) through (f), identify the number of zeros and the multiplicity of each zero.**

3. **What do you notice about the zeros of a function, counted with multiplicity, and the degree of the function?**

Decomposing a Quadratic Function

Consider the quadratic function you created to represent the cross-sectional area of the rain gutter in a previous lesson. This function was written as a product of two linear functions: one representing the height, $h(x) = x$, and one representing the length, $\ell(x) = -2x + 8.5$. Let's consider how to sketch the graph of the quadratic function without technology using the two linear functions.

The graph shows the two linear functions. Dashed lines are drawn through each x-intercept to divide the graph into three regions.

- Region A: From negative infinity to the leftmost zero.
- Region B: The region between the two zeros.
- Region C: From the rightmost zero to positive infinity.

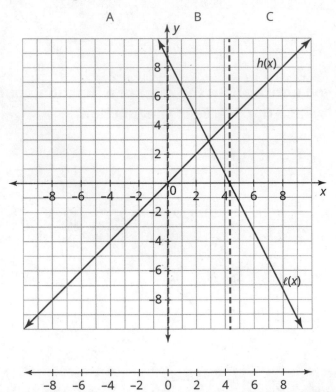

Ask yourself:

How many zeros, counted with multiplicity, should the product function have?

1. **Label the zeros of each function with open points on the coordinate plane and on the number line below the coordinate plane.**

2. **Consider the three regions. For each region:**

   a. **Determine whether the output values of the product of the functions, $h(x) \cdot \ell(x)$ is positive or negative. Label the number line accordingly.**

Ask yourself:

Is the product positive, negative, or zero? Does the point representing the product fall above, below, or on the x-axis?

   b. **Choose an x-value in the region. Evaluate the functions $h(x)$, $\ell(x)$, and $h(x) \cdot \ell(x)$ for that x-value. Plot each point on the coordinate plane.**

3. **Describe the product $h(x) \cdot \ell(x)$ at the intersection point of the two linear functions. Plot the point that represents the product of the two functions at this point on the coordinate plane.**

4. **Describe the product $h(x) \cdot \ell(x)$ at the zeros of the two linear functions. Plot the point that represents the products of the two functions at these points on the coordinate plane.**

5. **Use the information from Questions 2 and 3 to sketch the function $h(x) \cdot \ell(x)$ on the coordinate plane.**

Remember:

The Zero Product Property states that if the product of two or more factors is equal to zero, then at least one factor must be equal to zero.

6. **How does the Zero Product Property relate to the x-intercepts of the three functions?**

© Carnegie Learning, Inc.

7. **Analyze the graphs of s(x) and v(x).**

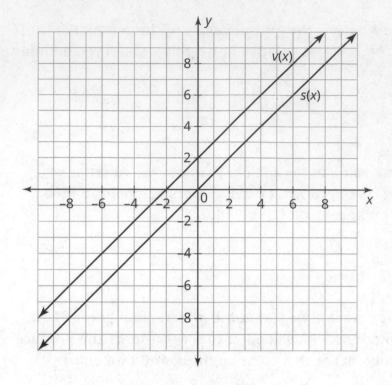

a. **Sketch the graph of p(x) if p(x) = s(x) · v(x).**

b. **Identify the x-intercepts of p(x). Explain the relationship
between the x-intercepts of p(x) and the x-intercepts of
s(x) and v(x).**

c. **Identify the vertex of p(x). What is the relationship between
the vertex of p(x) and the functions s(x) and v(x)?**

Decomposing Cubic Functions

Let's now use three linear functions to sketch their cubic function product.

Recall that the volume function $V(x) = x(18 - 2x)(12 - 2x)$ for the planter boxes in a previous lesson was built by multiplying three linear functions representing length, width, and height.

You can sketch the graph of this cubic function without technology using the three linear functions. The linear functions that represent the length, width, and height of the planter boxes from Plant-A-Seed are shown on the graph.

> **Think about:**
>
> How do the zeros help you construct a sketch of the function defined by the factors of the polynomial?

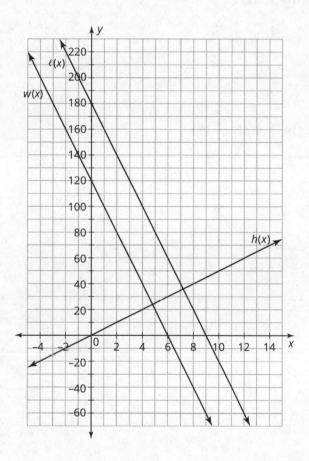

1. **Follow the instructions to compose the graph of $V(x)$ using $w(x)$, $\ell(x)$, and $h(x)$.**

   a. **Draw dashed vertical lines through the x-intercepts to divide the coordinate plane into regions.**

b. **Determine whether the output values for the product are positive or negative in each region. Label each region. Explain how you know where $V(x)$ lies, above or below the x-axis.**

c. **How do you know where $V(x)$ crosses the x-axis?**

d. **Choose an x-value in each region. Evaluate each function and then determine the product. Plot each point on the coordinate plane.**

Think about:

Which x-values do you want to choose in each region to help you understand the shape of the graph? Is one value enough?

e. **Sketch the graph of $V(x)$.**

Recall that the volume function for the cylindrical planter in a previous lesson was built from a quadratic function, $A(x) = \pi x^2$, representing the area of the base and a linear function, $h(x) = 2x$, representing the height.

2. **Sketch the graph of the cubic volume function that is the product of the quadratic and linear functions. Show all your work and explain your reasoning.**

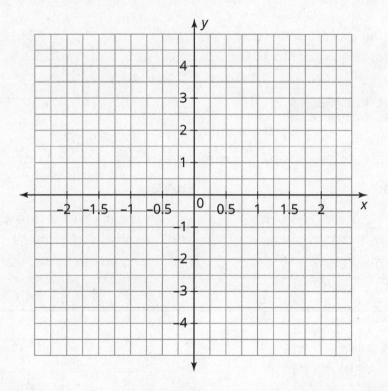

3. **Explain how the two cubic functions presented in this activity demonstrate the Fundamental Theorem of Algebra.**

Remember:

The Fundamental Theorem of Algebra states that a degree n polynomial has, counted with multiplicity, exactly n zeros.

ACTIVITY

4.3 Multiplying to Create Polynomials

You can multiply to determine whether a product written in factored form is equivalent to a quadratic or cubic function written in general form.

Consider, for example, the cubic function $f(x) = 3x^3 + 16x^2 + 12x - 16$. Is the function equivalent to $g(x) = (x + 2)(3x - 2)(x + 4)$?

Worked Example

You can determine the product of the linear factors $(x + 2)(3x - 2)(x + 4)$ using multiplication tables.

Step 1:

Choose 2 of the binomials, multiply, and then combine like terms.

·	x	2
$3x$	$3x^2$	$6x$
-2	$-2x$	-4

Step 2:

Multiply the product from step 1 with the remaining binomial. Then combine like terms.

·	x	4
$3x^2$	$3x^3$	$12x^2$
$4x$	$4x^2$	$16x$
-4	$-4x$	-16

$$(x + 2)(3x - 2)(x + 4) = 3x^3 + 16x^2 + 12x - 16$$

---

1. **Analyze the worked example for the multiplication of three binomials.**

   a. **How can you use graphing technology to verify that the expression in factored form is equivalent to the product written in general form?**

   b. **How does the cubic function demonstrate the Fundamental Theorem of Algebra? Explain your reasoning.**

2. **Determine each product algebraically. Show all your work and then use technology to verify your product is correct. Finally, sketch the graph and explain how the function demonstrates the Fundamental Theorem of Algebra.**

Ask yourself:

How do the factors of the given expression relate to the zeros of the graph?

a. $(x + 2)(-3x + 2)(2x + 1)$

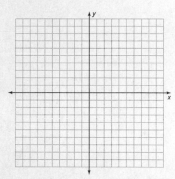

b. $(x + 2)(5x + 1)$

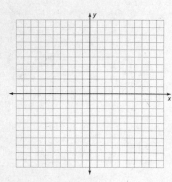

c. $(2x - 1)(x - 1)$

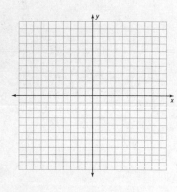

d. $(x + 2)^3$

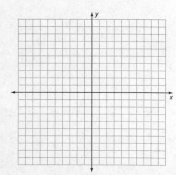

© Carnegie Learning, Inc.

3. Max determined the product of three linear factors.

> Max
> The function $f(x) = (x + 2)^3$ is equivalent to $f(x) = x^3 + 8$.

a. Explain why Max is incorrect.

b. How many x-intercepts does the function $f(x) = (x + 2)^3$ have? How many zeros, counted with multiplicity? Explain your reasoning.

TALK the TALK

A Difference in Kind

In this lesson, you sketched polynomial functions using factors and rewrote them in general form.

1. **Use the factors to sketch each cubic function and label the zeros. Then rewrite the function in general form.**

    a. $f(x) = (x + 3)(-x + 5)(2 - 2x)$

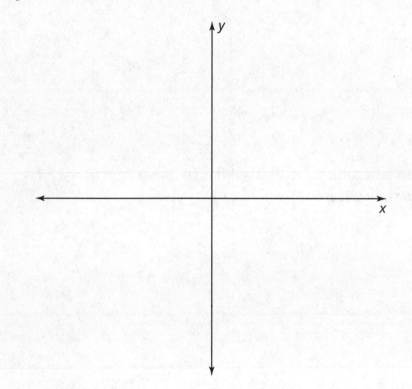

b. $g(x) = (x - 2)^3$

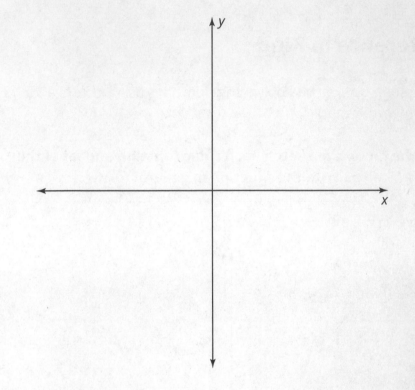

2. **How are cubic functions similar to linear functions? How are they different?**

Think about:

Consider the functions as graphs, tables, equations, and situations. What is the degree of the function? How many zeros, counted with multiplicity, does it have?

3. **How are cubic functions similar to quadratic functions? How are they different?**

Assignment

Write

In your own words, explain what the term *multiplicity* means.

Remember

The Zero Product Property states that if the product of two or more factors is equal to zero, then at least one factor must be equal to zero. The Fundamental Theorem of Algebra states that a degree n polynomial has, counted with multiplicity, exactly n zeros.

Practice

1. Consider the functions $k(x) = x - 1$, $m(x) = x + 2$, $n(x) = x - 3$, and $f(x) = k(x) \cdot m(x) \cdot n(x)$.

   a. Graph $k(x)$, $m(x)$, and $n(x)$.

   b. Determine the degree of the function $f(x)$. Explain your reasoning.

   c. Determine the zeros of $f(x)$. Explain your reasoning.

   d. Determine the intervals over which the value of $f(x)$ is positive. Determine the intervals over which the value of $f(x)$ is negative. Explain your reasoning.

   e. Sketch $f(x)$.

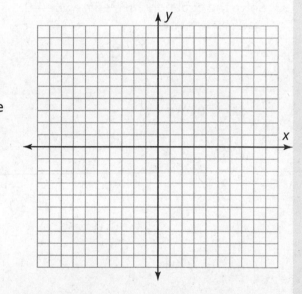

Stretch

1. Consider the function $f(x) = 3x^3 + 5x^2 - 16x - 12$.

   a. Graph the function.

   b. Determine the zeros of the function from the graph.

   c. Rewrite the function into factored form.

   d. Determine the intervals over which the value of $f(x)$ is positive. Determine the intervals over which the value of $f(x)$ is negative. Explain your reasoning.

Review

1. An open box is to be made from a rectangular piece of cardboard, 30 inches by 24 inches, by cutting equal squares from the corners and turning up the sides.

   a. Write a function $V(x)$ to represent the volume of a box in terms of the side length, x, of the removed squares. Explain your reasoning.

   b. Represent the function $V(x)$ using graphing technology. Determine the domain and range of the function and of this problem situation. Explain your reasoning.

2. Write an quadratic equation that includes the the given points.

   a. vertex $(4, -3)$; point $(6, -1)$

   b. points $(-2, 8)$, $(1, 14)$, and $(0, 10)$

3. Solve the equation $2m^2 - 6m + 14 = 0$.

Composing and Decomposing Functions Summary

KEY TERMS

- cubic function
- relative maximum
- relative minimum
- multiplicity

Blame It on the Rain

A physical model or drawing is often helpful when describing and analyzing a real-world problem.

A quadratic function is used to model area. You can determine the maximum area by identifying and interpreting the coordinates of the vertex of the graph.

For example, consider a situation in which Siwoo wants to build a rectangular pen for her rabbit from a length of foldable mesh wire. She has a total length of 30 feet of mesh wire and wants to determine the maximum area for the pen.

The function $A(w) = w(15 - w)$, or $A(w) = -w^2 + 15w$, models the area of the pen where w represents the width of the pen.

The graph of the function has a vertex at (7.5, 56.25). This means that the maximum area the pen can be is 56.25 square feet when the width of the pen is 7.5 feet.

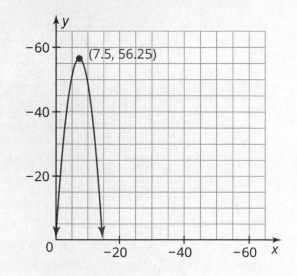

(7.5, 56.25)

When you solve real-world problems using mathematics, you can use a process to model situations. The first step in modeling a situation mathematically is to gather information, notice patterns, and formulate mathematical questions about what you notice. The second step in the modeling process is to organize your information and represent it using mathematical notation. The third step of the modeling process is to extend the patterns you created, complete operations, make predictions, and analyze the mathematical results. The final step in the modeling process, before reporting your results, is to interpret your results and test your mathematical predictions in the real world. If your predictions are incorrect, you can revisit your mathematical work and make adjustments—or start over.

LESSON

2

Folds, Turns, and Zeros

Recall that you can dilate a function vertically by multiplying the function by a constant, the A-value. If the function is $f(x) = x$, then $f(x) = Ax$ represents a vertical dilation of the original function. When a linear function is dilated vertically by multiplying the function by a linear function that is not a constant function, the resulting function is a second degree function.

For example, consider the graphs of $k(x) = -2x + 1$, $m(x) = x - 1$, and $n(x) = m(x) \cdot k(x)$. In this case, the A-value in $n(x)$ representing the vertical dilation of $k(x)$ is $m(x)$, or $(x - 1)$.

Since $n(x)$ is a vertical dilation of $k(x)$ by a linear function, $m(x)$, the resulting function is a second degree function. Written as an equation, $n(x) = (x - 1)(-2x + 1)$, or $n(x) = -2x^2 + 3x - 1$.

The graph of $n(x)$ shares zeros with both $k(x)$ and $m(x)$.

When a quadratic function is dilated vertically by multiplying the function by a linear function that is not a constant function, the resulting function is a third degree function.

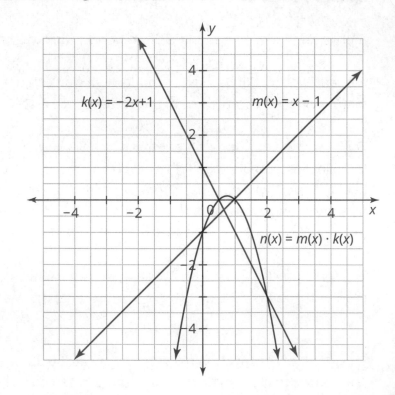

For example, consider the graphs of $q(x) = x^2 - 1$, $r(x) = 3x + 2$, and $s(x) = r(x) \cdot q(x)$. In this case, the A-value in $s(x)$ representing the vertical dilation of $q(x)$ is $r(x)$, or $(3x + 2)$.

Since $s(x)$ is a vertical dilation of $q(x)$ by a linear function, $r(x)$, the resulting function is a third degree function. Written as an equation, $s(x) = (3x + 2)(x^2 - 1)$, or $s(x) = 3x^3 + 2x^2 - 3x - 2$.

The graph of $s(x)$ shares zeros with both $q(x)$ and $r(x)$.

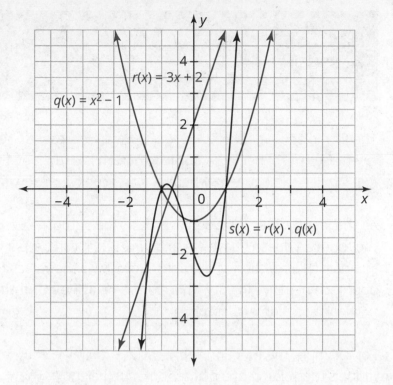

When functions are written in factored form, the zeros are observable, and the intervals of increase and decrease are determined by the sign of the A-value.

The shape of the graph of functions can be predicted using observable characteristics of the equation when the equation is written in factored form. Somewhere between any two zeros of a function, the graph changes directions from increasing to decreasing or vice versa. The graph must change directions to intersect with the x-axis.

Planting the Seeds

The formula for volume, $V = l \times w \times h$, can represent a cubic function when length and width are given in terms of height. A **cubic function** is a function that can be written in the general form $f(x) = ax^3 + bx^2 + cx + d$, where $a \neq 0$. A cubic function is a polynomial function of degree 3.

As the input values for height increase, the output values for volume approach infinity. Therefore, the function doesn't have a maximum. But, it can have a **relative maximum**, or a highest point in a particular section of a graph. Similarly, as the values for height decrease, the output values approach negative infinity. Therefore, a **relative minimum** can occur at the lowest point in that particular section of a graph.

For example, the function $V(h) = h(12 - 2h)(18 - 2h)$ models the volume of a planter box with height, h. The graph of the function is shown. The function has a relative maximum at (2.35, 228) and a relative minimum at (7.65, −68.16). The relative maximum can be interpreted in the context of the situation. A height of 2.35 inches will produce a prism with a maximum volume of 228 cubic inches.

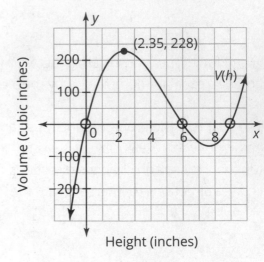

A horizontal line is a powerful tool for working backwards to determine the possible values for height when the volume is known.

For example, consider a situation in which someone wants a planter box with a volume of 100 cubic inches. You can determine the possible heights for the planter from the graph of $V(h)$.

Draw a horizontal line at $y = 100$ and identify each point where $V(h)$ intersects with $y = 100$, or where $V(h) = 100$.

The points of intersection are (0, 0.54), (0, 4.76), and (0, 9.7). The planter box can have a height of 0.54 inch, 4.76 inches, or 9.7 inches and have a volume of 100 cubic inches.

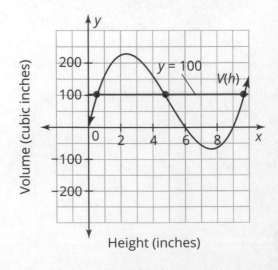

LESSON 4

The Zero's the Hero

Recall that the zeros of a function are the points on the graph of the function where the function's value is zero. **Multiplicity** is how many times a particular number is a zero for a given function.

For example, for $f(x) = x - 5$, the value of the function f is 0 when $x = 5$. This zero has a multiplicity of 1. For $g(x) = (x - 3)(x - 3)$, the value of the function g is 0 when $x = 3$. This zero has a multiplicity of 2.

The Zero Product Property can be used to identify when a factor is equal to 0. At the x-intercepts, the values of linear functions are zero, so the product of one linear function and another at a zero point will be zero.

Recall that the Fundamental Theorem of Algebra states that a degree n polynomial has, counted with multiplicity, exactly n zeros. Cubic functions have exactly 3 zeros, with multiplicity.

You can use two linear functions to sketch their quadratic function product.

For example, consider the functions $\ell(x) = -2x + 8.5$ and $h(x) = x$. Use each linear function to sketch the graph of $A(x) = \ell(x) \cdot h(x)$.

Description	Graphical Display
Graph each factor as an individual function. • The x-intercepts for each function are circled.	

Draw dashed vertical lines through the x-intercepts.

- The coordinate plane is now divided into 3 sections: $(-\infty, 0)$, $(0, 4.25)$, and $(4.25, \infty)$.

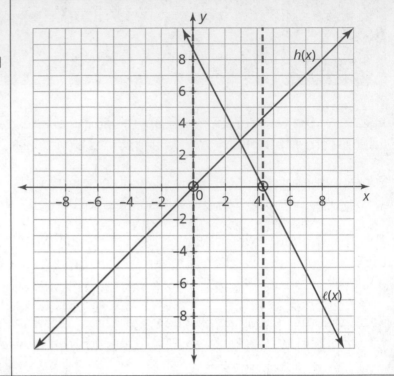

Determine whether the output values for each function in the interval are positive or negative.

- Values above the x-axis are positive.
- Values below the x-axis are negative.
- Determine the location of the quadratic function by calculating whether the product of the factors is positive or negative over each interval.

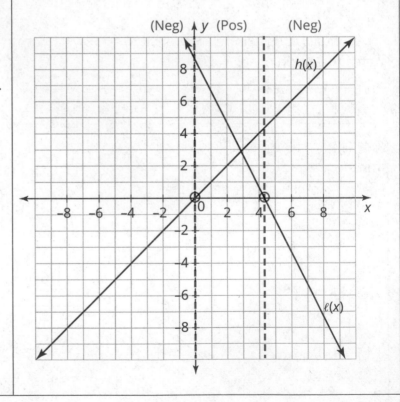

- Use the *x*-intercepts and the sign of the output value over each interval to sketch the graph.
- The new function will cross the *x*-axis with each of the *x*-intercepts becoming the factors.
- The graph will increase or decrease depending on whether the output is positive or negative as it moves from one interval to the next.

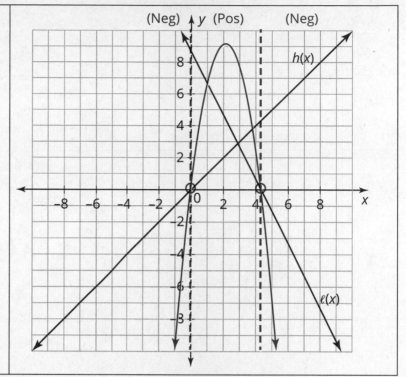

When multiplying three linear factors, the result is always a cubic function. First choose two of the factors to multiply and combine like terms. Then, multiply that product with the remaining factor and combine like terms. The original expression and the new expression can be graphed to verify that they are equivalent.

For example, consider the cubic function, $V(x) = x(12 - 2x)(18 - 2x)$. Multiply the factors to rewrite it as a polynomial with degree 3.

$$x(12 - 3x)(18 - 2x) = (12x - 3x^2)(18 - 2x)$$

$$= 216x - 24x^2 - 54x^2 + 6x^3$$

$$= 6x^3 - 78x^2 + 216x$$

The product of a quadratic function and a linear function is also a cubic function.

Characteristics of Polynomial Functions

Container ships carry cargo in standard 20-foot or 40-foot containers for efficient loading and unloading.

Module 1: Analyzing Structure

TOPIC 3: CHARACTERISTICS OF POLYNOMIAL FUNCTIONS

This topic opens with a study of power functions of the form $P(x) = ax^n$ and even- and odd-degree functions. Students are then introduced to polynomial functions and their transformations. They build cubic and quartic functions both graphically and algebraically and then close the topic by analyzing polynomial functions and applying polynomial functions to a variety of real-world situations. Throughout, students use their prior knowledge of function characteristics and transformations to generalize to polynomial functions.

Where have we been?

Students have extensive experience analyzing nonlinear functions, such as quadratic functions, identifying their key characteristics, and graphing their transformations. They have used functions to model situations and data and have built functions from other functions. Students have manipulated and solved basic polynomial equations.

Where are we going?

Students will work with polynomial functions and equations closely in the next two topics. Polynomial functions are used throughout the sciences and in engineering to model complex real-world situations and datasets.

Polynomial Functions Representing Data

You can use polynomial functions to represent real-world data.

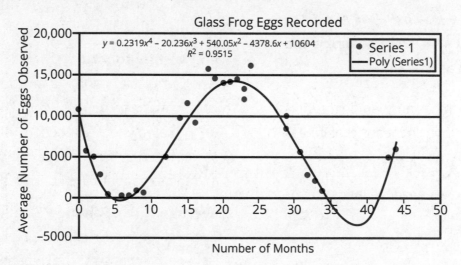

The data shown represent the average number of frog eggs over the span of 44 months in a population of a rare, endangered species of frog called the glass frog. A quartic polynomial function can be graphed to fit these data.

The Double Helix

Children typically resemble their parents because of the inheritance of genes from parents to offspring. Scientists know of over 200 hereditary traits that are transmitted across generations of families. The genes that carry these traits are in specific strands of DNA. When you look at a species, you can determine or predict what the offspring may look like. The same thing is true for polynomials! If you know certain characteristics about the polynomial, you can predict what the graph will look like, as well as other key characteristics.

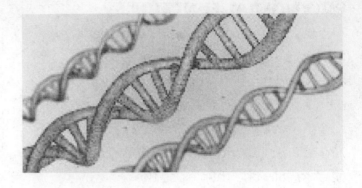

Talking Points

Polynomial functions can be an important topic to know about for college admissions tests.

Here is an example of a sample question:

Let $C(x) = ax^4 + x^3 − bx^2 − 4x + c$.
If $C(x) \to \infty$ as $x \to \infty$, then describe the change in $C(x)$ as $x \to -\infty$.

Since the function has an even degree, it is an even function, which means that it has a symmetry about the y-axis.

So, as x approaches negative infinity, $C(x)$ approaches infinity.

Key Terms

even function
An even function has a graph symmetric about the y-axis, thus $f(x) = f(-x)$.

odd function
An odd function has a graph symmetric about the origin, thus $f(x) = -f(-x)$.

polynomial function
A polynomial function is a function that can be written in the form $[\ ]x^n + [\ ]x^{n-1} + \ldots [\ ]x^2 + [\ ]x + [\ ]$. In a polynomial function, the coefficients, represented by each $[\ ]$, are complex numbers and the exponents are nonnegative integers.

average rate of change
The average rate of change of a function is the ratio of the change in the dependent variable to the change in the independent variable over a specific interval.

So Odd, I Can't Even

Power Functions

Warm Up

Evaluate each expression for $x = 2$ and $x = -3$.

1. x^4

2. $-x^2 + 1$

3. $(-x)^2 - 1$

4. x^8

Learning Goals

- Describe the general behavior of the graph of even and odd degree power functions.
- Describe how the graph of a power function changes as the value of the power increases.
- Use graphs and transformations to determine the symmetry of even and odd functions.
- Determine whether a function is even or odd based on a function equation or graph.

Key Terms

- power function
- end behavior
- symmetric about a line
- symmetric about a point
- even function
- odd function

You have analyzed and built quadratic and cubic functions from functions of lesser degree. What are the characteristics of the graphs of power functions?

Flat in the Middle

You have studied linear functions, quadratic functions, and now you will explore more polynomial functions. A common type of polynomial function, which you have also studied, is a *power function*. A **power function** is a function of the form $P(x) = ax^n$, where n is a non-negative integer.

1. **Consider each power function and its graph in the sequence shown.**

$y = x$

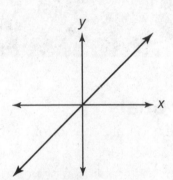

$y = x^2$

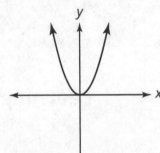

$y = x^3$

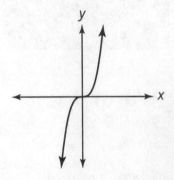

$y = x^4$

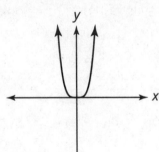

$y = x^5$

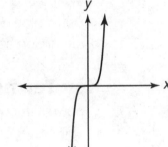

$y = x^6$

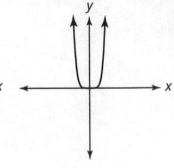

a. Sketch and label the next two graphs in the sequence.

b. State any observations or patterns that you notice about the graphs in the sequence.

Consider the power functions graphed in the Getting Started. The tables show values of each function for different domain values.

Odd Degree			
x	x^1	x^3	x^5
-2	-2	-8	-32
-1	-1	-1	-1
$-\frac{1}{2}$	$-\frac{1}{2}$	$-\frac{1}{8}$	$-\frac{1}{32}$
0	0	0	0
$\frac{1}{2}$	$\frac{1}{2}$	$\frac{1}{8}$	$\frac{1}{32}$
1	1	1	1
2	2	8	32

Even Degree			
x	x^2	x^4	x^6
-2	4	16	64
-1	1	1	1
$-\frac{1}{2}$	$\frac{1}{4}$	$\frac{1}{16}$	$\frac{1}{64}$
0	0	0	0
$\frac{1}{2}$	$\frac{1}{4}$	$\frac{1}{16}$	$\frac{1}{64}$
1	1	1	1
2	4	16	64

1. **For both the odd- and even-degree functions, observe the change in the values between −1 and 1. How does this change compare with the change in the values less than −1 and greater than 1?**

2. Observe the behavior of each function on either side of 0, using the tables and graphs.

   a. Describe the behavior of a function of odd degree on either side of 0.

   b. Describe the behavior of a function of even degree on either side of 0.

3. For both the odd- and even-degree functions:

   a. Explain why the graphs flatten as the degree increases, for values of x between -1 and 1.

   b. Explain why the graphs steepen as the degree increases, for values of x less than -1 and greater than 1.

Exploring End Behavior and Symmetry of Power Functions

The **end behavior** of a graph of a function is the behavior of the graph as x approaches infinity and as x approaches negative infinity.

> **Worked Example**
>
> You can write the end behavior of the polynomial function shown using this notation.
>
> As $x \rightarrow \infty$, $f(x) \rightarrow \infty$.
> As $x \rightarrow -\infty$, $f(x) \rightarrow -\infty$.
>
>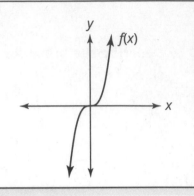

1. **Consider the sequence of graphs shown.**

$$f_1(x) = x \qquad\qquad f_2(x) = x^2 \qquad\qquad f_3(x) = x^3$$

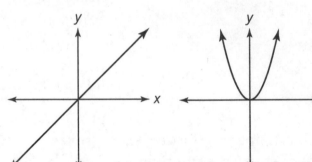

a. **What happens when the A-value is negative? Write each function in terms of x, and then sketch it.**

$$-f_1(x) = \underline{\qquad} \qquad -f_2(x) = \underline{\qquad} \qquad -f_3(x) = \underline{\qquad}$$

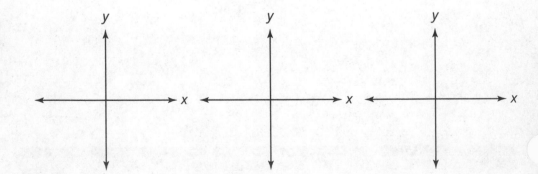

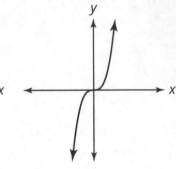

Remember:

Changes to the A-value in the transformation form of a function can cause a vertical dilation of the function and/or a reflection across the x-axis.

Changes to the B-value of a function can cause a horizontal dilation of the function and/or a reflection across the y-axis.

b. What happens when the *B*-value is negative? Write each function in terms of *x*, and then sketch it.

$f_1(-x) =$ _____ $f_2(-x) =$ _____ $f_3(-x) =$ _____

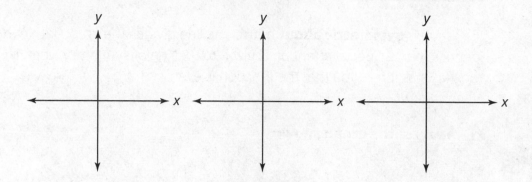

c. Complete the table to describe the end behavior for any polynomial function.

	Odd Degree Power Function	Even Degree Power Function
A > 0		
A < 0		
B > 0		
B < 0		

| ACTIVITY **1.3** | Investigating Characteristics of Even and Odd Functions |

If a graph is **symmetric about a line**, the line divides the graph into two identical parts. Special attention is given to the line of symmetry when it is the y-axis as it tells you that the function is even.

1. **Analyze the graph shown.**

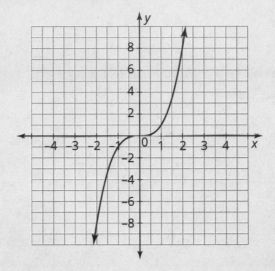

Olivia says that the graph has no line of symmetry because if she reflected the graph across the x- or y-axis, it would not be a mirror image.

Randall says that the graph has no line of symmetry because if he looks at the x-values 1 and −1, the y-values are not the same, so there can't be symmetry about the y-axis. Also, if he looks at the y-values 8 and −8, the x-values are not the same, so there can't be symmetry about the x-axis.

Shedrick said that there is some type of symmetry. He looks at the point (2, 8) and notices that the point (−2, −8) is also on the graph. Likewise he looks at the point (1, 1) and notices that the point (−1, −1) is also on the graph. He concluded that it must have a reflection across the x- and y-axis at the same time.

Who's correct? Explain your reasoning.

The graph of an odd degree basic power function is *symmetric about a point*, in particular the origin. A function is **symmetric about a point** if each point on the graph has a point the same distance from the central point, but in the opposite direction. Special attention is given when the central point is the origin as it determines that the function is odd. When the point of symmetry is the origin, the graph is reflected across the x-axis and the y-axis. If you replace both (x, y) with $(-x, -y)$, the function remains the same.

Worked Example

Consider the function $f(x) = x^3$. You can think of the point of symmetry about the origin as a double reflection.

$$f_1(x) = x^3 \qquad\qquad f_2(x) = f_1(-x) \qquad\qquad f_3(x) = -f_2(x)$$
$$ = (-x)^3 \qquad\qquad\quad = -((-x)^3)$$
$$ = x^3$$

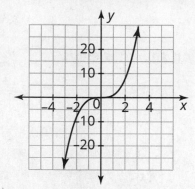

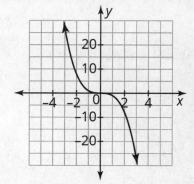

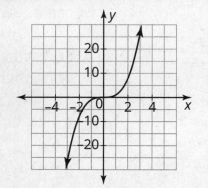

The function $f_1(x)$ is shown.

The function $f_1(x)$ is reflected across the y-axis to produce f_2.

The function $f_2(x)$ is reflected across the x-axis to produce f_3.

An **even function** has a graph symmetric about the y-axis, thus $f(x) = f(-x)$.

An **odd function** has a graph symmetric about the origin, thus $f(x) = -f(-x)$.

2. **Use what you know about A and B-value transformations to describe even and odd functions in your own words.**

> Odd and even functions are NOT the same as odd- and even-degree functions. A function must have an odd or even degree. But a function is not necessarily odd or even.

3. **Explain why Claire is correct. Use function notation to write her conclusion.**

> ### Claire
> The reflection of an odd function across the y-axis produces the same graph as its reflection across the x-axis.

You determine algebraically whether a function is even by evaluating the function at $f(-x)$. If $f(-x) = f(x)$, then the function is even. You can also evaluate the function at $-f(x)$. If $-f(-x) = f(x)$, or $-f(x) = f(-x)$, then the function is odd.

4. **State whether the graph of each function shown is even, odd, or neither.**

a.

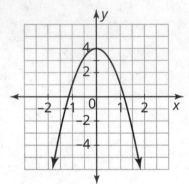

b.

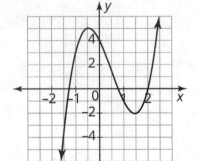

c.

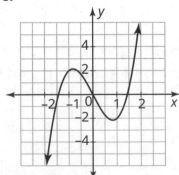

5. **Determine algebraically whether each function is even, odd, or neither. Describe the end behavior of the function.**

   a. $f(x) = 2x^3 - 3x$

Think

about:

Take your time and check your substitutions.

   b. $g(x) = 6x^2 + 10$

   c. $h(x) = x^3 - 3x^2 - 2x + 7$

TALK the TALK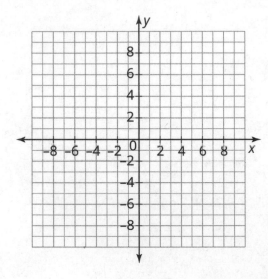

To Be Number One, You Have to Be Odd

1. Graph and label each function.

   $f(x) = x^2$

   $g(x) = (x - 3)^2$

   $h(x) = 3x^2$

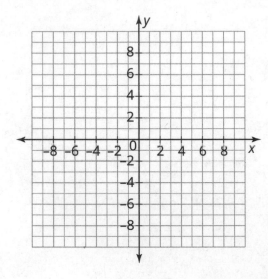

2. Determine whether each function is an even function, an odd function, or neither. Then describe the end behavior.

Assignment

Write

Choose the term from the box that best completes each statement.

even function	end behavior	symmetric about a point
power function	symmetric about a line	odd function

1. A function is _____ if the line divides the graph into two identical parts.
2. The _____ of a graph of a function is the behavior of the graph as x approaches infinity and as x approaches negative infinity.
3. A(n) _____ has a graph symmetric about the origin, thus $f(x) = -f(-x)$.
4. A function is _____ if each point on the graph has a point the same distance from the central point but in the opposite direction.
5. A(n) _____ has a graph symmetric about the y-axis, thus $f(x) = f(-x)$.
6. A(n) _____ is a function of the form $P(x) = ax^n$, where n is a non-negative integer.

Remember

A power function is a function of the form $P(x) = ax^n$, where n is a non-negative integer.

An even function has a graph symmetric about the y-axis, thus $f(x) = f(-x)$, and an odd function has a graph symmetric about the origin, thus $f(x) = -f(-x)$.

Practice

1. Graph each function. Determine whether the function is even, odd, or neither. Then describe the end behavior of the graph.
   a. $f(x) = x^3 + x$.
   b. $f(x) = x^3 + x^2 - 6x$.
2. Sketch each function and describe the end behavior of each graph.
   a. $f(x) = x^{20}$
   b. $f(x) = x^{25}$
3. Determine algebraically whether each function is even, odd, or neither.
   a. $f(x) = x^3 - 4x + 3$
   b. $f(x) = 2x^4 - x^2 + 9$

Stretch

1. Consider the function $f(x) = 3x^6 - 5x^4 + 2x^2 - 100$. Determine whether the function is even, odd, or neither. Then describe the end behavior of the graph.

2. Rewrite the function $f(x) = x^3$ for each transformation.

   a. The graph is shifted down 3 units.

   b. The graph is shifted to the left 5 units.

   c. The graph is vertically stretched by a factor of 2.

   d. The graph is reflected across the x-axis.

Review

1. Consider the functions $k(x) = x + 1$, $m(x) = x - 4$, $n(x) = x + 5$, and $f(x) = k(x) \cdot m(x) \cdot n(x)$.

   a. Determine the degree of the function $f(x)$. Explain your reasoning.

   b. Determine the zeros of $f(x)$. Explain your reasoning.

   c. Determine the intervals over which the value of $f(x)$ is positive. Determine the intervals over which the value of $f(x)$ is negative. Explain your reasoning.

2. Nina has a piece of wire 18 feet long that she wants to bend into a rectangle that she will then run yarn across to form artwork.

   a. Define the function $A(w)$ to represent the area of the wire artwork as a function of the length. Explain your reasoning.

   b. Determine the maximum area of the wire artwork as well as the length and width that will result in the maximum area. Explain your reasoning.

3. Add or subtract each expression.

   a. $(5 + 3i) + (8 - 9i)$ b. $(-10 - 7i) - (4 - 15i)$

Math Class Needs a Makeover

Transformations of Polynomial Functions

2

Warm Up

1. Describe the graph of the equation $y = x^n$, where n is an even integer.

2. Describe the graph of the equation $y = x^n$, where n is an odd integer.

Learning Goals

- Dilate and translate cubic and quartic functions.
- Explore differences between even and odd functions and even and odd degree functions with regard to transformations.
- Use power functions to build cubic, quartic, and quintic functions.
- Explore the possible graphs of cubic, quartic, and quintic functions and extend graphical properties to higher-degree functions.

Key Terms

- polynomial function
- quartic function
- quintic function

You have explored the behaviors and characteristics of different power functions. How do these behaviors relate to polynomial functions built using power functions?

Applying Some Foundation

Consider the basic quadratic function, $f(x) = x^2$. Three key points are identified that demonstrate how the function grows.

The basic quadratic function is symmetric about the *y*-axis. Thus, $f(x) = f(-x)$.

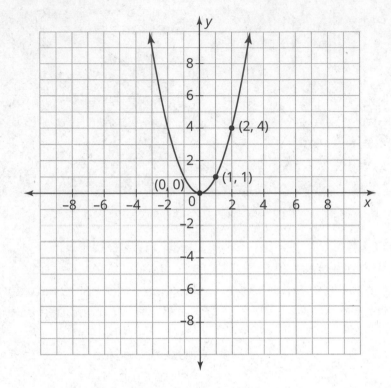

1. **Use the symmetry of the basic quadratic function to graph two other points of the function. Explain how these points demonstrate the property that $f(x) = f(-x)$.**

Let's consider a set of key points and the property of symmetry to graph the basic cubic function, $f(x) = x^3$.

2. **Complete the table for the given key points. Then graph the points on the coordinate plane shown.**

x	$f(x) = x^3$
0	
1	
2	

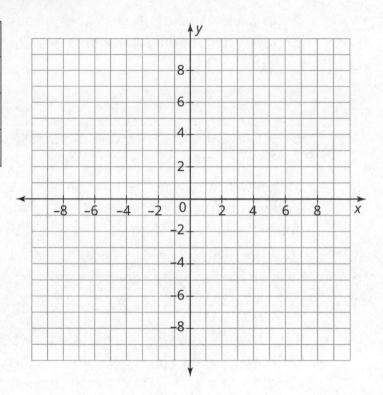

3. **Use the property of symmetry to determine two points other than the key points. Then, use these points to graph the basic cubic function on the coordinate plane shown.**

The graph of the basic cubic function is symmetric about the origin. So, $f(x) = -f(-x)$.

Linear, quadratic, and cubic functions are all examples of *polynomial functions*. A **polynomial function** is a function that can be written in the form

$$\blacksquare x^n + \blacksquare x^{n-1} + \ldots \blacksquare x^2 + \blacksquare x + \blacksquare$$

In a polynomial function, the coefficients, represented by each $\blacksquare$, are complex numbers and the exponents of the variables are nonnegative integers.

You know that a polynomial function of degree 3 is a cubic function. A **quartic function** is a fourth degree polynomial function, while a **quintic function** is a fifth degree polynomial function.

Transformations performed on any polynomial function $f(x)$ to form a new function $g(x)$ can be described by the transformational function:

$$g(x) = Af(B(x - C)) + D$$

Recall that the constants A and D affect the outside of the function (the output values). For example, if $A = 2$, then you can multiply each y-coordinate of $f(x)$ by 2 to determine the y-coordinates of $g(x)$. The constants B and C affect the inside of the function (the input values). For example, if $B = 2$, then you can multiply each x-coordinate of $f(x)$ by $\frac{1}{2}$ to determine the x-coordinates of $g(x)$.

Function Form	Equation Information	Description of Transformation of Graph
$y = Af(x)$	$\lvert A \rvert > 1$	vertical stretch of the graph by a factor of A units
	$0 < \lvert A \rvert < 1$	vertical compression of the graph by a factor of A units
	$A < 0$	reflection across the x-axis
$y = f(Bx)$	$\lvert B \rvert > 1$	compressed horizontally by a factor of $\frac{1}{\lvert B \rvert}$
	$0 < \lvert B \rvert < 1$	stretched horizontally by a factor of $\frac{1}{\lvert B \rvert}$
	$B < 0$	reflection across the y-axis
$y = f(x - C)$	$C > 0$	horizontal shift right C units
	$C < 0$	horizontal shift left C units
$y = f(x) + D$	$D > 0$	vertical shift up D units
	$D < 0$	vertical shift down D units

1. **Cut out the Function Transformation Cards located at the end of the lesson. Match the function representation with its corresponding coordinate pair. For each function representation or coordinate pair that does not have a match, provide a match by writing the appropriate equation or coordinate pair on a blank card.**

2. **Explain why Sanjay's reasoning is not correct. Rewrite the transformation to identify the correct *B*- and *C*-values.**

> ## Sanjay
> I can tell from the expression that the transformation given by f(2x + 5) has a B-value of 2 and a C-value of 5.

3. **Complete the table to show the coordinates of $g(x) = Af(B(x - C)) + D$ after each type of transformation performed on $f(x)$.**

Type of Transformation Performed on $f(x)$	Coordinates of $f(x) \rightarrow$ Coordinates of $g(x)$
Vertical Dilation by a Factor of A	$(x, y) \rightarrow ($ _____ , _____ $)$
Horizontal Dilation by a Factor of B	$(x, y) \rightarrow ($ _____ , _____ $)$
Horizontal Translation of C units	$(x, y) \rightarrow ($ _____ , _____ $)$
Vertical Translation of D units	$(x, y) \rightarrow ($ _____ , _____ $)$
All four transformations: A, B, C, and D	$(x, y) \rightarrow ($ _____ , _____ $)$

© Carnegie Learning, Inc.

ACTIVITY 2.2 Building and Sketching Transformations of Polynomial Functions

Let's use what you know about function transformations to graph polynomials.

1. The graph of the function $f(x) = x^3 - 2x$ is shown.

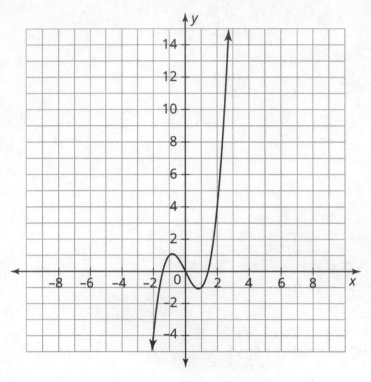

a. Determine whether $f(x)$ is an even function, an odd function, or neither. Show your work.

b. Suppose that $g(x) = 2f(x)$. Use the given reference points to complete the table of values for $g(x)$. Then, use properties of symmetry to graph and label $g(x)$ on the same coordinate plane as $f(x)$.

Reference Point on $f(x)$	Corresponding Point on $g(x)$
(0, 0)	
(1, −1)	
(2, 4)	

c. Suppose that $h(x) = \frac{1}{2}f(x)$.
Use the given reference points to complete the table of values for $h(x)$. Then, use properties of symmetry to graph and label $h(x)$ on the same coordinate plane as $f(x)$.

Reference Point on $f(x)$	Corresponding Point on $h(x)$
(0, 0)	
(1, −1)	
(2, 4)	

© Carnegie Learning, Inc.

2. The graph of the function $d(x) = x^3 + \frac{1}{2}x$ is shown.

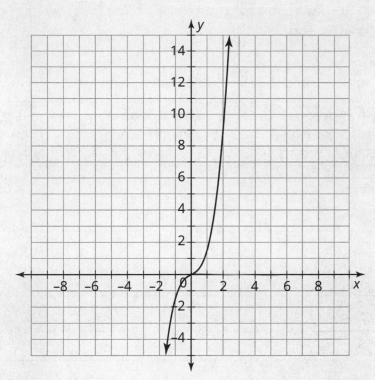

a. Verify that $d(x)$ is an odd function. Show your work.

b. Suppose that $j(x) = d(2x)$.
   Use the given reference points to complete the table
   of values for $j(x)$. Then, use properties of symmetry to
   graph and label $j(x)$ on the same coordinate plane as $d(x)$.

Reference Point on $d(x)$	Corresponding Point on $j(x)$
$(0, 0)$	
$\left(1, \frac{3}{2}\right)$	
$(2, 9)$	

c. Suppose that $k(x) = d\left(\frac{1}{2}x\right)$.
   Use reference points to complete the table of values
   for $k(x)$. Then, use properties of symmetry to graph
   and label $k(x)$ on the same coordinate plane as $d(x)$.

Reference Point on $d(x)$	Corresponding Point on $k(x)$
$(0, 0)$	
$\left(1, \frac{3}{2}\right)$	
$(2, 9)$	

3. Complete the table to summarize the effects that transformations have on the basic cubic function $c(x) = x^3$. The first row has been completed for you.

Effects of Transformations on the Basic Cubic Function $c(x) = x^3$			
Rigid Motion	New Transformed Function $p(x)$ in Terms of $c(x)$	Description of Symmetry of $p(x)$	Is $p(x)$ Even, Odd, or Neither?
Vertical Stretch Dilation	$p(x) = Ac(x)$, $\|A\| > 1$	Symmetric about the point (0, 0)	Odd
Vertical Compression Dilation			
Horizontal Stretch Dilation			
Horizontal Compression Dilation			
Reflection across x-axis			
Reflection across y-axis			
Vertical Translation			
Horizontal Translation			

4. Do you think that your results in Question 3 are the same for any odd-degree power function? Explain your reasoning.

The graph of the basic quartic function $q(x) = x^4$ and reference points are shown.

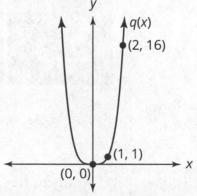

5. **Use the graph to sketch the function after dilations, reflections, and translations. Pay special attention to the symmetry after the transformations. Record your conclusions by completing the table. The first row has been completed for you.**

Effects of Transformations on the Basic Quartic Function $q(x) = x^4$			
Rigid Motion	**New Transformed Function $p(x)$ in Terms of $q(x)$**	**Description of Symmetry of $p(x)$**	**Is $p(x)$ Even, Odd, or Neither?**
Vertical Stretch Dilation	$p(x) = Aq(x),$ $|A| > 1$	Symmetric about the y-axis	Even
Vertical Compression Dilation			
Horizontal Stretch Dilation			
Horizontal Compression Dilation			
Reflection across x-axis			
Reflection across y-axis			
Vertical Translation			
Horizontal Translation			

6. **Do you think that your results in Question 5 would be the same for any even-degree power function? Explain your reasoning.**

You have graphed transformations of functions. In this activity, you will interpret the transformation given the graph.

1. **Analyze the graphs of $f(x)$ and $g(x)$. For each reference point on $f(x)$, the corresponding points after the transformations are shown on $g(x)$. Describe the transformations performed on $f(x)$ to create $g(x)$. Then, write an equation for $g(x)$ in terms of $f(x)$.**

   a. $g(x) = $ _____

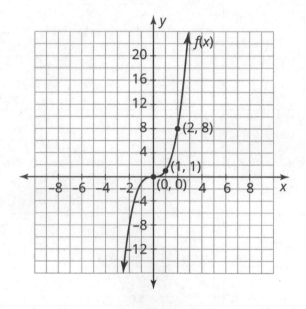
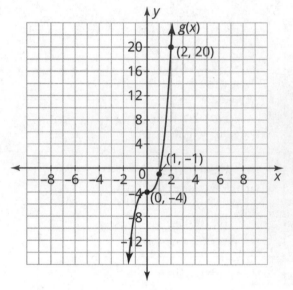

   b. $g(x) = $ _____

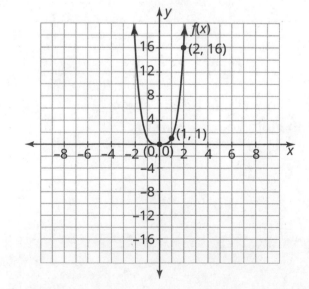
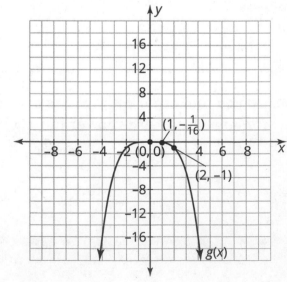

c. $g(x) =$ _____

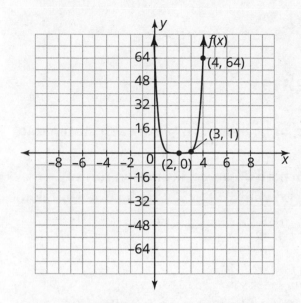 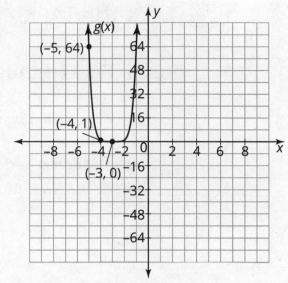

2. The equation for a polynomial function $p(x)$ is given. The equation for the transformed function $t(x)$ in terms of $p(x)$ is also given. Describe the transformation(s) performed on $p(x)$ that produced $t(x)$. Then, write an equation for $t(x)$ in terms of x.

a. $p(x) = x^5$
   $t(x) = 0.5p(-x)$

b. $p(x) = x^4$
   $t(x) = 2p(x + 3)$

c. $p(x) = x^3$
   $t(x) = -p(x - 2) + 4$

TALK the TALK

Just a Few Highlights

1. Use *always*, *sometimes*, or *never* to complete each statement.

   a. If a dilation is performed on an odd function $f(x)$ to produce $g(x)$, then $g(x)$ will _____ be an odd function.

   b. If a reflection is performed on an even function $f(x)$ to produce $g(x)$, then $g(x)$ will _____ be an even function.

   c. If a translation is performed on an odd function $f(x)$ to produce $g(x)$, then $g(x)$ will _____ be an odd function.

   d. If a translation is performed on an even function $f(x)$ to produce $g(x)$, then $g(x)$ will _____ be an even function.

Function Transformation Cards

$f\left(\frac{1}{2}x\right)$	$f(x - 5)$	$f(2x + 5)$	$f(x) + 5$	$f(-x)$
$f(x) - 5$	$-f(x)$	$\frac{1}{2}f(x)$	$2f(x)$	$f(2x)$
$\left(x, \frac{1}{2}y\right)$	$(-x, y)$	$(x, 2y)$	$(x + 5, y)$	$\left(\frac{1}{2}x, y\right)$
$(x, y + 5)$	$(x, -y)$	$(2x, y)$	$(-x, -y)$	$(x - 5, y)$
$(x, y - 5)$				

Assignment

Write

Provide an example of each type of function.

1. polynomial function
2. quartic function
3. quintic function

Remember

The function $g(x) = Af(B(x - C)) + D$ is the transformation function where the constants A and D affect the output values of the function and the constants B and C affect the input values of the function.

Practice

1. Analyze the graphs of the functions $f(x)$ and $g(x)$.

   a. Write the equation for $f(x)$.

   b. The function $g(x)$ is a transformation of the function $f(x)$. Describe the transformations performed on $f(x)$ that result in the function $g(x)$. Explain your reasoning.

   c. Write the equation for $g(x)$.

   d. Is the function $g(x)$ even, odd, or neither? Explain your reasoning.

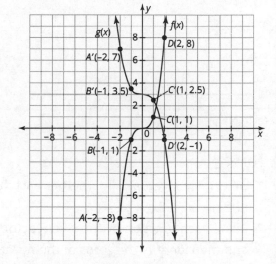

2. The graph of the basic quartic function $m(x) = x^4$ is shown.

   a. The function $h(x) = \frac{1}{4}(x - 6)^4$ is a transformation of $m(x)$. Complete the table.

Reference Points on $m(x)$	→	Corresponding Points on $h(x)$
(x, y)	→	
$(-2, 16)$	→	
$(-1, 1)$	→	
$(0, 0)$	→	
$(1, 1)$	→	
$(2, 16)$	→	

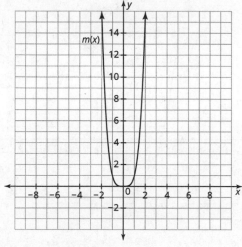

   b. Graph the function $h(x) = \frac{1}{4}(x - 6)^4$ on the same coordinate plane as $m(x)$.

   c. Is the function $h(x)$ even, odd, or neither? Explain your reasoning.

Stretch

1. Consider the graph of $f(x)$.

   a. Determine the end behavior of $f(x)$.

   b. Determine the x-intercepts.

   c. Determine the domain and range of $f(x)$.

   d. If the domain is restricted to $-3 < x < 2$, what are the maximum and minimum values of the function?

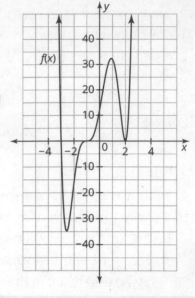

Review

1. Determine algebraically whether each function is even, odd, or neither.

   a. $f(x) = x^5 - 2x^3 + x$

   b. $f(x) = 3x^6 - 5x^4 - 1$

2. Dilate each function by the given factor to create a new function of higher degree. Sketch the graph and then identify the zeros of the new function.

   a. $f(x) = (x + 3)(4x - 1)$

      Dilate by $(x - 1)$.

   b. $f(x) = (x + 2)(x - 2)$

      Dilate by x.

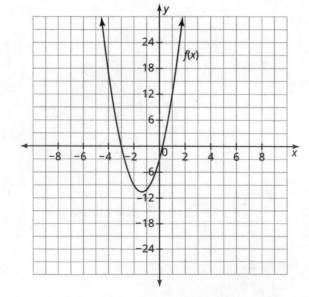

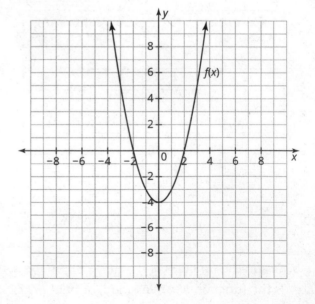

3. Rewrite each expression using multiplication.

   a. $(3 - 2i)(4 + 5i)$

   b. $(7 - 6i)^2$

Poly-Wog

Key Characteristics of Polynomial Functions

Warm Up

1. Sketch graphs of cubic functions with the given number of zeros. Describe the domain, range, and zeros of each function.

   a. 1 zero

   b. 2 zeros

   c. 3 zeros

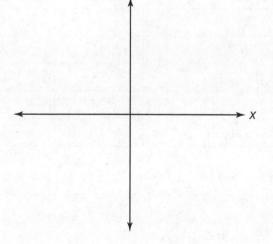

Learning Goals

- Interpret key characteristics of a polynomial function in the context of a problem situation.
- Generalize about the key characteristics of polynomial functions.
- Determine the possible number of real and imaginary zeros for quartic and quintic polynomials.
- Sketch the graph of a polynomial function given certain key characteristics.

Key Terms

- absolute maximum
- absolute minimum
- extrema

You have investigated power functions and polynomial functions. What are some of the key characteristics of these functions?

© Carnegie Learning, Inc.

Math World vs. Real World

The data shown represents the population of a rare, endangered species of frog called the glass frog. To better understand the glass frog's fertilization habits, scientists performed a study and recorded the average number of frog eggs over the span of 44 months.

Month of Study	Average Number of Glass Frog Eggs	Month of Study	Average Number of Glass Frog Eggs
0	10,534	19	14,330.5
1	5500	20	13,845.1
2	5033	21	13,893.1
3	2600	22	14,546.3
4	239.4	23	11,815.8
6	137.3	23	13,086.2
7	108.4	24	15,966.9
8	667.1	29	9904.4
9	387.4	29	8257.3
12	4813.1	31	5297.5
14	9539.5	32	2494.1
15	11,318.6	33	1805.4
16	8953.3	34	665
18	15,402.5	43	4813

The data has been plotted for you and a quartic regression was used to generate the polynomial function that best represents the data. The quartic regression option calculates the best-fit equation of the form $y = ax^4 + bx^3 + cx^2 + dx + e$.

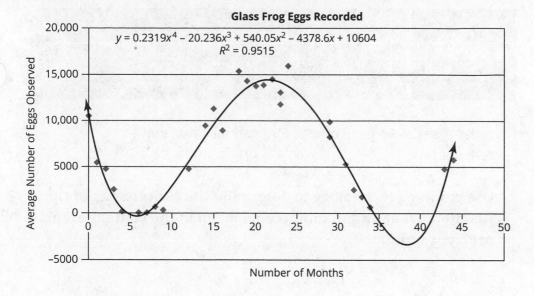

Glass Frog Eggs Recorded

$y = 0.2319x^4 - 20.236x^3 + 540.05x^2 - 4378.6x + 10604$

$R^2 = 0.9515$

Average Number of Eggs Observed

Number of Months

1. Consider the graph and equation to answer each question.

   a. What is the domain and range of the study? Explain what the domain and range represent in the context of this problem.

   b. What is the domain and range of the function?

   c. In which month of the study were the most frog eggs observed? In which month of the study were the fewest frog eggs observed? Write the maximum and minimum values.

   d. If the study lasted for 50 months, how many frog eggs would there be according to the function?

   e. How many frog eggs appeared between months 35 and 40?

   f. In which month(s) of the study were approximately 4800 frog eggs observed?

Consider the situation and quartic function modeled in the
Getting Started.

1. **Use graphing technology to determine the *x*-intercepts of the
   function. What do the *x*-intercepts mean in the context of this
   problem situation?**

2. **State the end behavior of the function. Does this make sense in
   the context of this problem scenario? Explain your reasoning.**

3. **How many frog eggs were observed at the beginning of the
   study? Explain the mathematical meaning of your answer.**

4. **Describe the interval(s) when the frog's egg population is:**

   a. **Increasing.**

   b. **Decreasing.**

You have learned about minimums, maximums, zeros, end behavior, and
the general shape of a graph. Now, you will combine all that information to
generalize the key characteristics for a polynomial of any degree.

Recall that a relative maximum is the highest point in a particular section of a function's graph, and a relative minimum is the lowest point in a particular section of the graph. Similarly, the **absolute maximum** is the highest point in the entire graph, and the **absolute minimum** is the lowest point in the entire graph. The set of relative maximums, relative minimums, absolute maximums, and absolute minimums may also be referred to as **extrema**. The extrema are also called *extreme points* and *extremum*.

5. **Consider the graph that represents the average number of glass frog eggs in the Getting Started.**

   a. **Identify all relative maximums and relative minimums.**

   b. **Identify all absolute maximums and absolute minimums.**

An absolute maximum can also be considered a relative maximum. Usually only the more significant label of absolute maximum is used, with the term relative maximum implied. The same reasoning can be applied to an absolute minimum and a relative minimum.

Let's investigate the shape of graphs of polynomial functions when the end behavior is known.

1. **Cut out the graph pieces and axes located at the end of the lesson.**

You can rotate the cards to any orientation as necessary.

2. **Use the arrow cutouts to demonstrate the different possible types of end behavior of polynomial functions. Make a sketch and use notation to describe each case.**

Now let's consider the possible graphs of polynomial functions with this end behavior.

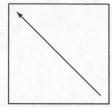 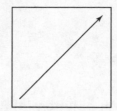

Pearl

I can create this shape.

This is a degree-2 polynomial with 1 extrema—an absolute minimum—and vertical symmetry through the vertex.

This function may have 0, 1, or 2 x-intercepts, depending on how it crosses the x-axis.

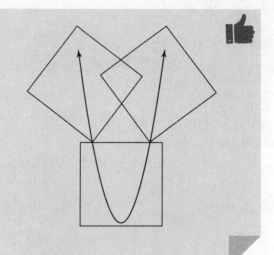

3. **Create Pearl's polynomial. Use the axis to show how the graph could have 0, 1, or 2 intercepts.**

4. **Novena created a graph of a fourth degree polynomial. Armondo placed the *x*-axis on the graph and said that she is incorrect, that it is a fifth degree polynomial. Who is correct? For the student who is incorrect, explain the error in their thinking.**

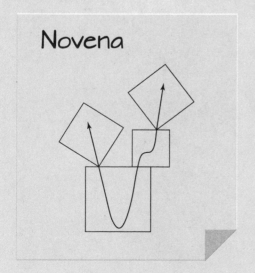

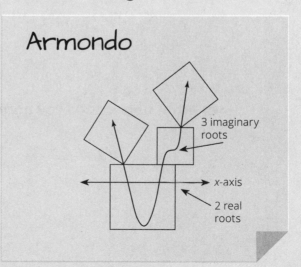

© Carnegie Learning, Inc.

5. What other types of polynomial functions can you build with this end behavior? Create and then draw examples using the cutouts.

Ask yourself:

How can this information be transferred to a function with both arrows facing upward?

6. Analyze each polynomial function that you built.

   a. How many extrema does each function have?

   b. Describe whether the function is even, odd, or neither.

   c. Use the axis cutout to describe the polynomial's number of possible *x*-intercepts.

   d. Consider the intervals of increase or decrease. How many times does the function change direction?

   e. What patterns do you notice?

Now let's consider graphs of polynomial functions whose end behavior looks like this.

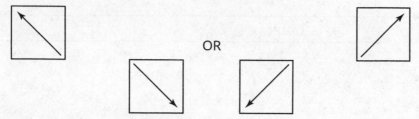

OR

7. **Create and draw polynomials with this end behavior.**

8. **Analyze each polynomial function that you built.**

   a. **How many extrema does each function have?**

   b. **Describe whether the function is even, odd, or neither.**

   c. **Use the axis cutout to describe the polynomial's number of possible *x*-intercepts.**

   d. **Consider the intervals of increase or decrease. How many times does the function change direction?**

   e. **What patterns do you notice?**

9. **Complete each table to summarize the key characteristics for quartics and quintics. The cubics table has been done for you.**

Cubics	
All possible end behavior	As $x \to \infty, f(x) \to \infty$. As $x \to -\infty, f(x) \to -\infty$. As $x \to \infty, f(x) \to -\infty$. As $x \to -\infty, f(x) \to \infty$.
Possible number of x-intercept(s)	3, 2, or 1
Number of possible extrema	2 or none
Possible intervals of increase and decrease	• Always increasing • Always decreasing • Increasing, decreasing, increasing • Decreasing, increasing, decreasing

Quartics	
All possible end behavior	
Possible number of x-intercept(s)	
Number of possible extrema	
Possible intervals of increase and decrease	

Quintics	
All possible end behavior	
Possible number of x-intercept(s)	
Number of possible extrema	
Possible intervals of increase and decrease	

10. Consider the types of functions you created.

    a. What conclusions can you make about the domain and range of all even degree polynomial functions?

    b. What conclusions can you make about the domain and range of all odd degree polynomial functions?

11. Write *always*, *sometimes*, or *never* to complete each statement. Justify your answer with a sketch or explanation.

    a. An odd degree function _____ has an absolute extrema.

    b. An even degree function _____ has an absolute extrema.

    c. An even degree function _____ has 3 or more relative extrema.

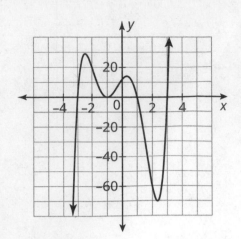

12. Consider the graph shown.

    a. Determine whether the *a*-value of this function is positive or negative.

    b. Is the degree of this function even or odd?

    c. Can this function be a cubic function? Explain why or why not.

    d. State the domain of this function.

    e. State the range of this function.

    f. Determine the number of relative extrema in this graph.

    g. Determine the number of absolute extrema in this graph.

    h. Use estimation to identify the intervals where the graph is increasing.

    i. Use estimation to identify the intervals where the graph is decreasing.

13. **Consider the graph shown.**

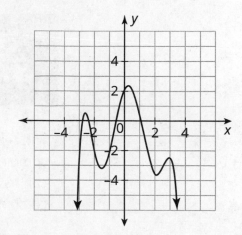

    a. Determine whether the *a*-value of this function is positive or negative.

    b. Is the degree of this function even or odd?

    c. Can this function be a 6th degree polynomial function? Explain why or why not.

    d. State the domain of this function.

    e. State the range of this function.

    f. Determine the number of relative extrema in this graph.

    g. Determine the number of absolute extrema in this graph.

    h. Use estimation to identify the intervals where the graph is increasing.

    i. Use estimation to identify the intervals where the graph is decreasing.

Zeros of Polynomial Functions

The zeros of a polynomial function can be real, imaginary, or a combination of both. The real zeros of the function may all be distinct, or can have varying degrees of multiplicity. The tables summarize all possible combinations of zeros for a linear, quadratic, and a cubic function.

Linear Function	
Zeros	**Graph**
1 real	

Quadratic Function	
Zeros	**Graph**
2 real distinct	
1 real (multiplicity 2)	
2 imaginary	

Cubic Function	
Zeros	**Graph**
3 real distinct	
1 real (multiplicity 3)	
1 real (multiplicity 1) 1 real (multiplicity 2)	
1 real 2 imaginary	

1. **Analyze the tables.**

   a. **Describe any similarities or differences you notice.**

   b. **Describe the number of graphs of each function you could sketch given the combination of zeros. Explain your reasoning.**

2. **Complete the table to show all the possible combinations of zeros for a quartic function by filling in the missing values and sketching the basic shape on each set of axes.**

Quartic Function	
Zeros	**Graph**
_____ real distinct	
1 real (multiplicity _____)	
1 real (multiplicity 1) 1 real (multiplicity _____)	
_____ real (multiplicity 1) 1 real (multiplicity 2)	
2 real (multiplicity _____)	
_____ imaginary	
2 real distinct _____ imaginary)	
1 real (multiplicity _____) 2 imaginary	

3. Complete the table to show all the possible combinations of zeros for a quintic function by filling in the missing values and sketching the basic shape on each set of axes.

Quintic Function	
Zeros	**Graph**
_____ real distinct	
1 real (multiplicity _____)	
_____ real distinct 1 real (multiplicity 2)	
3 real distinct _____ imaginary	
1 real (multiplicity 1) _____ real (multiplicity 2)	
1 real (multiplicity 1) 1 real (multiplicity _____)	
1 real (multiplicity 1) _____ imaginary	
1 real (multiplicity 1) 1 real (multiplicity _____) _____ imaginary	

4. Compare your tables from Questions 2 and 3 with those of your classmates. Describe any similarities or differences.

5. How does the combination of zeros help you decide on the shape of the graph?

© Carnegie Learning, Inc.

Sketching Polynomial Functions

You have composed and decomposed various polynomial functions. In this activity, you will sketch polynomials given key characteristics.

1. Use the coordinate plane to sketch each polynomial function. If the graph is not possible to sketch, explain why.

a. Characteristics:

- **degree 4**

- **has an a-value less than 0**

- **relative maximum at $x = -4$**

- **absolute maximum at $x = 3$**

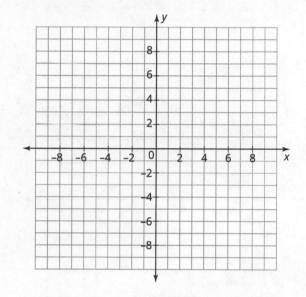

b. Characteristics:

- **always increasing**

- **y-intercept at 5**

- **x-intercept at −1.7**

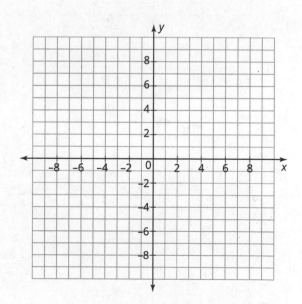

© Carnegie Learning, Inc.

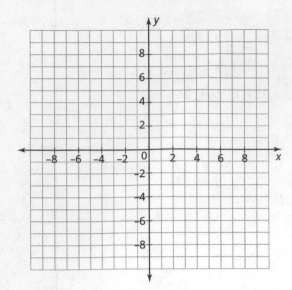

c. **Characteristics:**

- **odd degree**

- **increases to $x = -3$, then decreases to $x = 3$, then increases**

- **absolute maximum at $y = 4$**

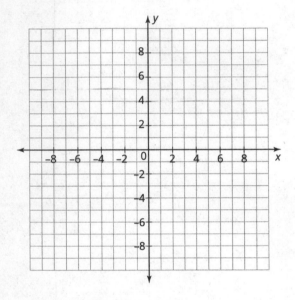

d. **Characteristics:**

- **as $x \to \infty$, $f(x) \to \infty$**
  as $x \to -\infty$, $f(x) \to \infty$

- **four x-intercepts**

- **relative maximum at $y = 3$**

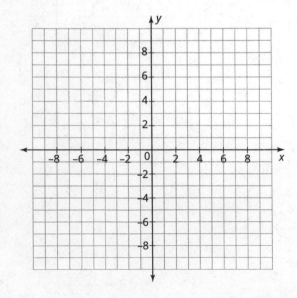

e. **Characteristics:**

- **x-intercepts at -2, 2, and 5**

- **negative a-value**

- **degree 2**

TALK the TALK

Shapeshifting

Consider all the different shapes of graphs of polynomial functions you saw in this lesson.

1. **Describe what each characteristic of the graph tells you about the polynomial function.**

   a. **end behavior**

   b. **x-intercept(s)**

   c. **extrema**

2. **Choose the possible graph(s) for each given polynomial function $f(x)$.**

   a. **Which graph(s) could be the graph of $f(x) = 2x^2$?**

   Graph A   Graph B   Graph C

   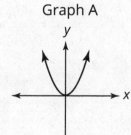 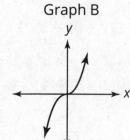 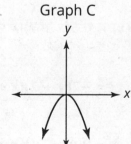

b. Which graph(s) could be the graph of $f(x) = -x^3 - x^2 + 6x$?

Graph A   Graph B   Graph C

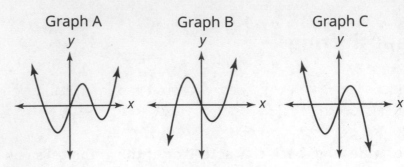

c. Which graph(s) could be the graph of $f(x) = x^4 + 1$?

Graph A   Graph B   Graph C

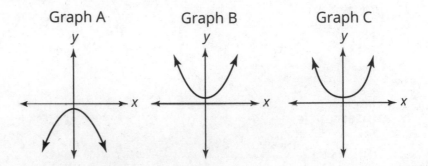

3. **Analyze each graph. Circle the function(s) which could model the graph. Describe your reasoning to either eliminate or choose each function.**

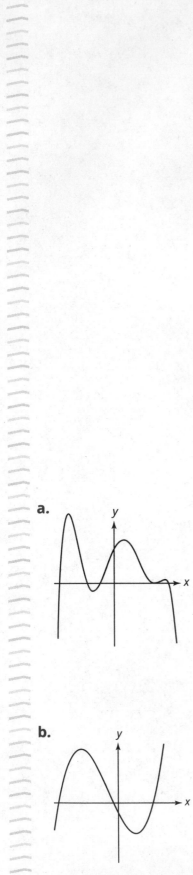

a.

$f_1(x) = -3x^5 - 2x^2 + 4x + 7$

$f_2(x) = -(x + 2)(x + 1.5)(x + 0.5)(x - 2.5)^2 (x - 3)$

$f_3(x) = -3x^4 - 2x^2 + 4x + 7$

b.

$f_1(x) = 0.5(x + 7)(x + 1)(x - 5) - 3$

$f_2(x) = -2(x + 7)(x + 1)(x - 5) - 3$

$f_3(x) = 2(x + 7)(x + 1)(x - 5)(x - 3)$

Graph Pieces and Axes

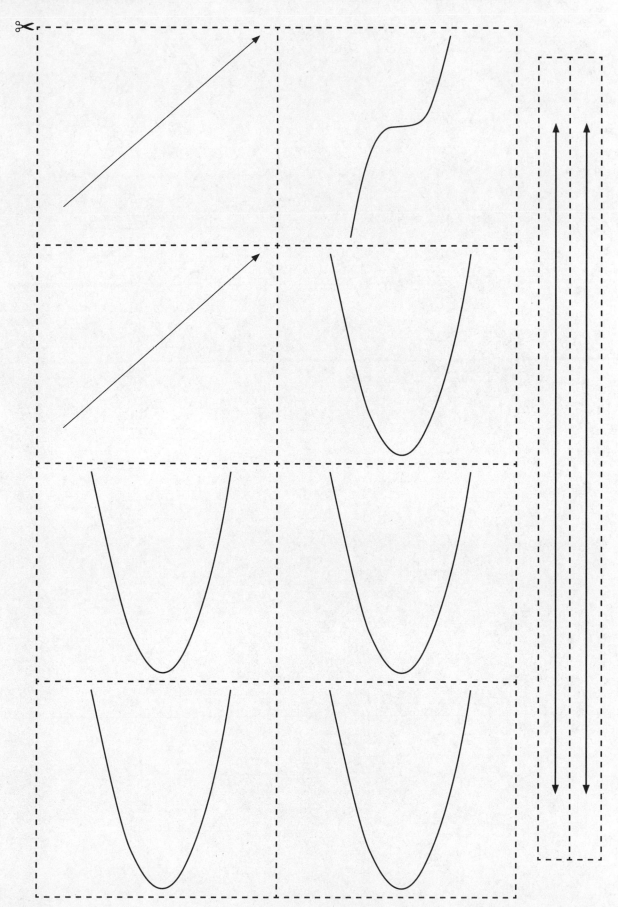

Assignment

Write

Define each term in your own words.

1. absolute maximum
2. absolute minimum
3. extrema

Remember

- The maximum number of extrema in a polynomial function $f(x) = x^n$ is $n - 1$.
- The maximum number of x-intercepts is the same as the degree of the function.
- The combination of real and imaginary roots of a polynomial function are equal to the degree of the polynomial and can be used to determine the shape of its graph.

Practice

1. Describe the combination of real and imaginary roots for each graphed function. Include the multiplicity of each real root.

   a. Quartic

   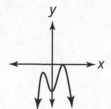

   b. Quintic

   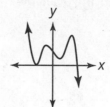

2. Sketch a graph of a polynomial function with the characteristics given. If the graph is not possible to sketch, explain why.

   a. Characteristics:
   - degree 4
   - absolute minimum at $x = -2$
   - 2 real roots
   - as $x \to \infty$, $f(x) \to \infty$
     as $x \to -\infty$, $f(x) \to \infty$

   b. Characteristics:
   - negative a value
   - even degree
   - absolute minimum at $x = 4$
   - as $x \to \infty$, $f(x) \to \infty$
     as $x \to -\infty$, $f(x) \to \infty$

Stretch

Sketch a graph of a polynomial function with the characteristics given. If the graph is not possible to sketch, explain why.

Characteristics:
- degree 6
- two real roots
- relative maximum at $y = 1$
- absolute minimum at $x = -4$

Review

1. Analyze the graphs of the functions $f(x)$ and $g(x)$.

   a. Write the equation for $f(x)$.

   b. The function $g(x)$ is a transformation of the function $f(x)$. Describe the transformations performed on $f(x)$ that result in the function $g(x)$. Explain your reasoning.

   c. Write the equation for $g(x)$.

   d. Is the function $g(x)$ even, odd, or neither? Explain your reasoning.

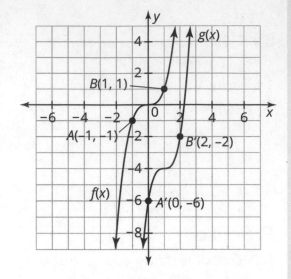

2. A farmer is going to fence in an area next to the barn into a rectangle split into two equal pens. The farmer has 165 yards of fencing available.

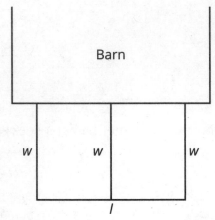

   a. Define the function $A(w)$ to represent the fenced in area as a function of the width. Explain your reasoning.

   b. Determine the maximum area of the entire fenced in area as well as the width and length that will result in the maximum area. Explain your reasoning.

3. Solve the equation $b(b + 3) = -12$.

Function Construction

Building Cubic and Quartic Functions

4

Warm Up

Calculate the zeros of each function.

1. $f(x) = -3x + 2$

2. $f(x) = x^2 - 3x + 2$

3. $f(x) = (x - 2)(x^2 - 1)$

Learning Goals

- Connect graphical behavior of cubic and quartic functions to key characteristics of their factors.
- Construct cubic and quartic functions given key characteristics of their factors.
- Determine the number of real and imaginary zeros for a polynomial function based on its factors.

You have analyzed the characteristics of the graphs of functions that represent factors and used those characteristics to sketch the resulting product. You have built functions with known end behavior and summarized your results. How can you build the graph of a cubic or a quartic function given a description of its key characteristics?

Don't Be a Cubics Rube

You previously built a cubic function by multiplying three linear functions and by multiplying a linear function and a quadratic function. Let's explore how the properties of linear and quadratic functions determine the key characteristics of cubic functions.

Precise drawings are not necessary here, just sketches with key characteristics. If you are unsure, experiment on your calculator, discuss with partners, and try a few things . . . That's how mathematicians work!

1. **Sketch a set of functions whose product builds a cubic function with the given characteristics. Explain your reasoning. Then list similarities and differences between your graphs and your classmates' graphs.**

   a. **zeros: $x = 0$, $x = 2$, and $x = -5$**
      Explanation:

      Similarities/Differences:

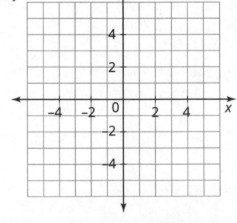

Ask yourself:

Which mathematical property guarantees that the zeros of a function must be the same as the zeros of its factors?

   b. **zeros: $x = -3$, $x = 4$ (multiplicity 2)**
      Explanation:

      Similarities/Differences:

2. Derek and Alex disagree over which functions (when multiplied together) build a cubic function with zeros $x = 5$, $x = -1$ (multiplicity 2).

Derek

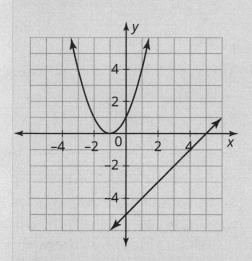

I sketched a parabola with vertex (–1, 0) and a line with x-intercept at (5, 0).

Alex

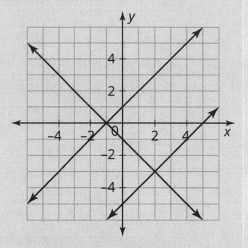

I sketched three linear functions, each with an x-intercept that matches the zero.

Who is correct? Explain your reasoning.

Building a Cubic Function

The key characteristics of the individual functions that build a cubic function reveal properties of the polynomial.

1. Analyze the linear and quadratic functions that are shown.

$f(x) = x$ $g(x) = x + 1$ $h(x) = x - 1$ $j(x) = -x + 1$

$m(x) = x^2$ $p(x) = x^2 + 1$ $r(x) = (x - 1)^2$ $w(x) = -(x - 1)(x + 1)$

Choose a set of functions from the functions provided whose product builds a cubic function with the given characteristics. Explain your reasoning. Then list similarities and differences between your graphs and your classmates' graphs.

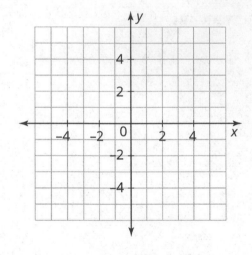

a. two imaginary zeros and a real zero
   Explanation:

   Similarities/Differences:

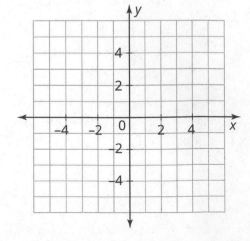

b. *y*-intercept of (0, −1)
   Explanation:

   Similarities/Differences:

c. **zero: $x = 1$ (multiplicity 3)**
Explanation:

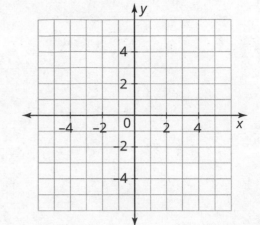

Similarities/Differences:

d. **three distinct real zeros**
Explanation:

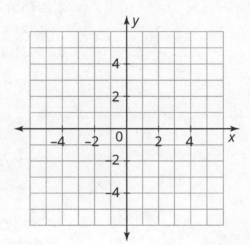

Similarities/Differences:

e. **located in Quadrants I and III only**
Explanation:

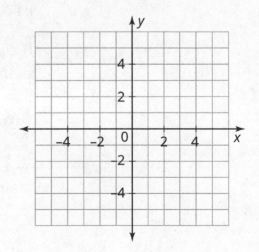

Similarities/Differences:

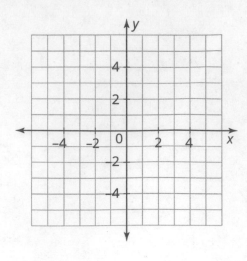

f. 3 imaginary zeros
   Explanation:

   Similarities/Differences:

2. What are the possible combinations of real and imaginary zeros
   that a cubic function can have? Explain your reasoning in terms
   of the functions that can build a cubic function.

3. Emily makes an observation about the number of imaginary
   zeros a cubic function may have.

> **Emily**
>
> A cubic function must have three zeros. I know this
> from the Fundamental Theorem of Algebra. However,
> the number of real and imaginary zeros can vary. The
> function may have 0, 1, 2, or 3 imaginary zeros.

Explain the error in Emily's reasoning.

4. **Augie, Kathryn, and Chili each wrote a cubic function with zeros at $x = 3$, $x = 1$, and $x = -4$.**

Augie
The cubic function $f(x) = (x - 3)(x - 1)(x + 4)$ has the three zeros given. I can verify this by solving the equations $x - 3 = 0$, $x - 1 = 0$, and $x + 4 = 0$.

Kathryn
The cubic function $g(x) = 5(x - 3)(x - 1)(x + 4)$ has the three zeros given.

Chili
The cubic function $j(x) = (2x - 6)(3x - 3)(x + 4)$ has the three zeros given.

a. **How does multiplying by a constant affect the graph of the function?**

b. **Why do the zeros remain the same after multiplying by a constant?**

c. **How many different cubic functions can you write from a given set of zeros?**

5. **Write two different cubic functions with the given characteristics.**

   a. zeros: $x = 2$, $x = 0$, and $x = -4$

   b. zeros: $x = 0$, $x = 2i$, $x = -2i$

   c. zeros: $x = 6$ (multiplicity 2) and $x = -5$

   d. zeros: $x = 2$, $x = 3$, $x = 1$ and a y-intercept $(0, -24)$

Analyzing Functions that Build a Quartic Function

You have determined that a cubic function has 3 zeros. The zeros may be real, imaginary, or have multiplicity depending on the key characteristics of the functions that built it. Similarly, the Fundamental Theorem of Algebra guarantees that a quartic function has 4 zeros.

1. **List different combinations of function types that multiply to build a quartic function.**

2. **Analyze the table shown. The function $h(x)$ is the product of $f(x)$ and $g(x)$.**

x	$f(x)$	$g(x)$	$h(x) = f(x) \cdot g(x)$
−2	8	4	32
−1	5	1	5
0	4	0	0
1	5	1	5
2	8	4	32
3	13	9	117

Think about:

What would the graph of $f(x)$ and the graph of $g(x)$ look like?

a. **Determine whether $h(x)$ is a quartic function. Explain your reasoning.**

b. **Determine the number of real and imaginary zeros of $h(x)$. Explain your reasoning.**

c. **Describe the end behavior of $h(x)$. How does this help you determine whether the function is quartic or not?**

3. **Analyze the table shown. The function $m(x)$ is the product of $j(x)$ and $k(x)$.**

x	$j(x)$	$k(x)$	$m(x) = j(x) \cdot k(x)$
−2	4	−1	−4
−1	0	0	0
0	−2	1	−2
1	−2	2	−4
2	0	3	0
3	4	4	16

a. **Determine whether $m(x)$ is a quartic function. Explain your reasoning.**

b. **Determine the number of real and imaginary zeros of $m(x)$. Explain your reasoning.**

c. **Describe the end behavior of $m(x)$. How does this help you determine whether the function is quartic or not?**

4. **Analyze the table shown. The function _v(x)_ is the product of _t(x)_ and _w(x)_.**

x	t(x)	w(x)	v(x) = t(x) · w(x)
−2	4	−11	−44
−1	3	−6	−18
0	4	−3	−12
1	7	−2	−14
2	12	−3	−36
3	19	−6	−114

a. **Determine whether _v(x)_ is a quartic function. Explain your reasoning.**

b. **Determine the number of real and imaginary zeros of _v(x)_. Explain your reasoning.**

c. **Describe the end behavior of _v(x)_. How does this help you determine whether the function is quartic or not?**

5. Gavin explains the relationship between the imaginary zeros of a polynomial function and the table of values for that function. Henry disagrees.

Gavin
A polynomial function with imaginary zeros has imaginary numbers in the table of values. For example, the function $x^2 + 4$ has 2 imaginary zeros. These values appear in the table.

Henry
It is impossible for a polynomial function to have imaginary numbers in the table of values. A real input value must have a real output value.

Who is correct? Explain your reasoning.

Just as with a cubic function, the key characteristics of a quartic function vary depending on the functions that built it.

1. **Analyze the linear, quadratic, and cubic functions that are shown.**

$f(x) = x$ $g(x) = -x + 2$ $m(x) = x^2 - 4x + 5$

$n(x) = -x^2 + 1$ $p(x) = x^2 + 4$ $r(x) = (x + 2)^2$ $w(x) = x^3$

Choose a set of functions from the functions provided whose product builds a quartic function with the given characteristics. Explain your reasoning. Then list similarities and differences between your graphs and your classmates' graphs.

a. **two imaginary zeros and a double zero**
   Explanation:

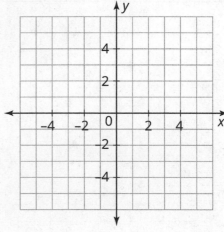

   Similarities/Differences:

b. **four distinct real zeros**
   Explanation:

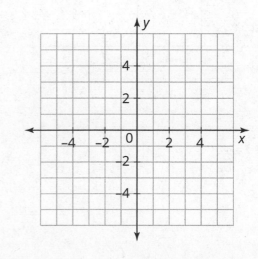

   Similarities/Differences:

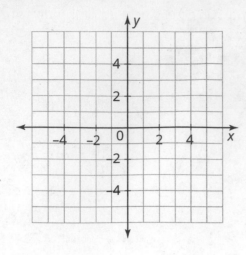

c. no *x*-Intercepts
Explanation:

Similarities/Differences:

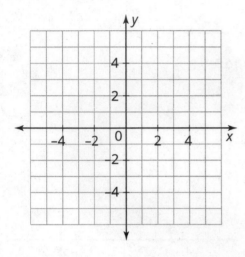

d. located in Quadrants II and IV only
Explanation:

Similarities/Differences:

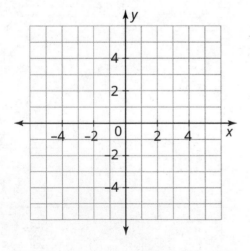

e. zero with multiplicity 4
Explanation:

Similarities/Differences:

2. The zeros of a polynomial function are −1 , 2, 3, and 4.

- Use the zeros to write the polynomial in factored form.

- Write the equation of the polynomial function by multiplying the factors.

- Determine the degree of the polynomial function.

- Describe the end behavior of the polynomial function.

- Determine the *y*-intercept(s) of the polynomial function.

- Sketch a graph of the polynomial function.

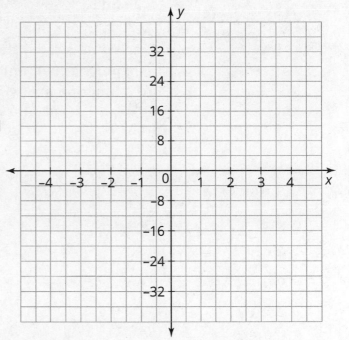

3. The graph of a polynomial function is shown.

- Use the zeros to write the polynomial in factored form.

- Write the equation of the polynomial function by multiplying the factors.

- Determine the degree of the polynomial function.

- Describe the end behavior of the polynomial function.

- Determine the *y*-intercept(s) of the polynomial function.

- Identify the domain and range of the polynomial function.

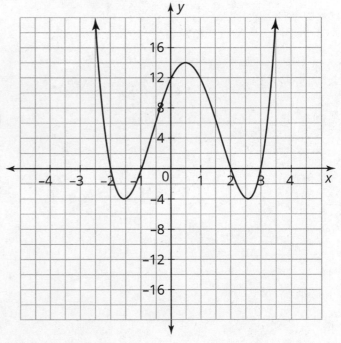

4. Analyze the polynomial functions you wrote for Questions 2 and 3.

   a. What is the difference between writing the equation for the polynomial function when you are given the zeros of the function and when you are given the graph of the function?

   b. Can you identify the domain and range of the polynomial function in Question 2? Explain your reasoning.

TALK the TALK

A Rootin'-Tootin' Good Time!

1. Complete each statement with *always*, *sometimes*, or *never*. Explain your reasoning.

   a. A function of the *n*th degree _____ has *n* zeros.

   b. The number of *x*-intercepts _____ matches the number of zeros of a function.

   c. A function _____ has imaginary zeros.

   d. A function _____ has an odd number of imaginary zeros.

   e. An odd-degree function _____ has at least one real zero.

2. **What function types can be multiplied together to build a new function of degree 5? How many total zeros will the function have? How many can be imaginary?**

3. **Explain the possible ways to build a function of degree *n*.**

Assignment

Write

Explain how you can determine the combination of the three zeros of a cubic function from a graph of the function.

Remember

The characteristics of a polynomial function are formed by the characteristics of the functions that are its factors.

A polynomial function may have a combination or real and imaginary zeros, as long as the imaginary zeros are in pairs.

Practice

1. Consider the functions $k(x) = x - 1$, $m(x) = x + 2$, $n(x) = x - 3$, and $f(x) = k(x) \cdot m(x) \cdot n(x)$.

   a. Graph $k(x)$, $m(x)$, and $n(x)$.

   b. Determine the degree of the function $f(x)$. Explain your reasoning.

   c. Determine the zeros of $f(x)$. Explain your reasoning.

   d. Determine the y-intercept of $f(x)$. Explain your reasoning.

2. Consider the graphs of the quadratic function $g(x) = (x - 2)^2$ and the cubic function $f(x) = g(x) \cdot h(x)$.

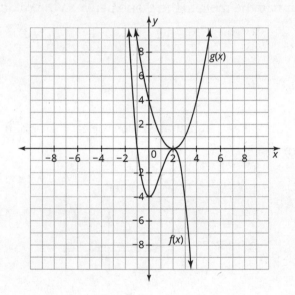

   a. Determine the degree of the function $h(x)$. Explain your reasoning.

   b. Determine the x-intercept(s) of $h(x)$. Explain your reasoning.

   c. Determine the y-intercept of $h(x)$. Explain your reasoning.

   d. Determine the equation of the function $h(x)$.

3. Determine 2 linear functions and 1 quadratic function such that the product of the 3 functions will build a quartic function with a double zero at -1 and a y-intercept at $(0, -3)$. Write the equation of the quartic function. Explain your reasoning.

4. Determine 2 quadratic functions such that the product of the 2 functions will build a quartic function with only 2 x-intercepts at $(-2, 0)$ and $(1, 0)$ and a y-intercept at $(0, -8)$. Write the equation of the quartic function. Explain your reasoning.

Stretch

1. Determine 2 quadratic functions and a linear function such that the product of the 3 functions will build a quintic function with 3 x-intercepts at (−1, 0), (2, 0) and (3, 0) and a y-intercept at (0, 12). Write the equation of the quintic function. Explain your reasoning.

2. Consider the function $f(x) = x^4 − 4x^3 − 2x^2 + 12x − 3$.

   a. Graph the function.

   b. Complete the table of values for the function.

x_1	x_2	$f(x_1)$	$f(x_2)$	$f(x_2) − f(x_1)$	$x_2 − x_1$	$\dfrac{f(x_2) − f(x_1)}{x_2 − x_1}$
−2	−1					
3	4					

   c. Compare the last column of the table to the graph between the values x_1 and x_2. What do you notice?

Review

1. Describe the combination of real and imaginary zeros for each graphed function. Include the multiplicity of each real zero.

   a. Quartic

   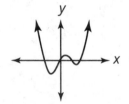

   b. Quintic

   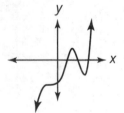

2. An open topped bin is to be made from a piece of metal by cutting equal squares from the corners and turning up the sides. The piece of metal is 5 meters by 8 meters. The function $V(x) = x(5 − 2x)(8 − 2x)$ represents the volume of a bin in terms of the side length, x, of the removed squares.

   a. Determine the maximum volume of a bin. What are the dimensions of a bin with the maximum volume?

   b. Determine any relative maximums or relative minimums of $V(x)$. Then, determine the intervals over which the function is increasing and decreasing.

3. Perform each operation.

   a. $(25 + 17i) − (−24 + 18i)$

   b. $(12 + 2i)(12 − 2i)$

Level Up

Analyzing Polynomial Functions

5

Warm Up

Determine each function's average rate of change for the interval (0, 2).

1. $f(x) = \frac{1}{2}x$

2. $g(x) = 3x^2$

3. $h(x) = 2^x$

Learning Goals

- Analyze the key characteristics of polynomial functions in a problem situation.
- Solve equations and inequalities graphically.
- Determine the average rate of change of a polynomial function.

Key Term

- average rate of change

You have explored the key characteristics of polynomial functions of different degrees. How can you interpret these characteristics in terms of a problem situation that is modeled by a polynomial function?

Play Is Our Work

The polynomial function $p(x)$ models the profits of Zorzansa, a video game company, from its original business plan through its first few years in business.

Zorzansa's Profits

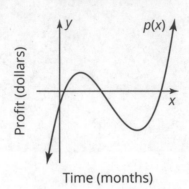

1. **Label the portion(s) of the graph that model each of the memorable events in the company's history by writing the letter directly on the graph. Explain your reasoning.**

   a. **The Chief Executive Officer anxiously meets with her accountant.**

   b. **The highly anticipated game, *Zephyr's Zenith II*, is released.**

   c. **The company opens its doors for business for the first time.**

d. The company reaches its first short-term sales goal just as the holiday shopping season ends.

e. The company breaks even.

f. Members of the Board of Directors get in a heated debate over the next move the company should make.

g. The game design team is fired after two game releases, *Leisurely Sunday Drive* and *Peaceful Resolution*, delight many parents but sell poorly.

h. A large conglomerate buys the company.

2. Do you think this cubic function is an appropriate model for this scenario? Explain your reasoning.

Ask yourself:

In what ways does this cubic model make sense? In what ways does it not make sense?

ACTIVITY 5.1 Interpreting Graphs of Polynomial Models

The cubic function $p(x)$ models Zorzansa's total profits over the first five years of business.

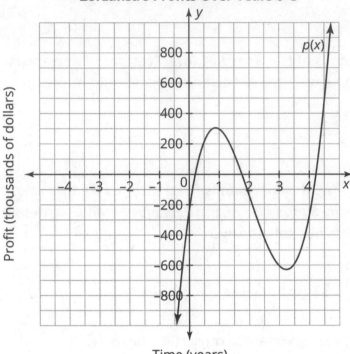

Think about:

What is the maximum number of solutions for a given profit?

1. **Use the graph to estimate when Zorzansa's achieved each profit. Then explain how you determined your estimate.**

   a. **$800,000**

   b. **$200,000**

   c. **Greater than $200,000**

   d. **The company is losing money**

   e. **The company is making a profit**

© Carnegie Learning, Inc.

2. Avi and Ariella disagree about the end behavior of the function.

Avi
The end behavior is incorrect. As time increases, profit approaches infinity. It doesn't make sense that the profits are increasing before the company even opens.

Ariella
The end behavior is correct. The function is cubic with a positive a-value. This means as x approaches infinity, y approaches infinity. As x approaches negative infinity, y also approaches negative infinity.

Who is correct? Explain your reasoning.

3. Costas makes the statement about Zorzansa's profits. Explain the error in Costas's reasoning.

Costas
Zorzansa is making a profit after 3.5 years because the graph is increasing.

ACTIVITY

5.2 Average Rate of Change

The **average rate of change** of a function is the ratio of the change in the dependent variable to the change in the independent variable over a specific interval. The formula for average rate of change is $\frac{f(b) - f(a)}{b - a}$ for the interval (a, b). The expression $b - a$ represents the change in the input values of the function f. The expression $f(b) - f(a)$ represents the change in the output values of the function f as the input values change from a to b.

Worked Example

You can determine the average rate of change of Zorzansa's profit for the time interval (3.25, 4.25).

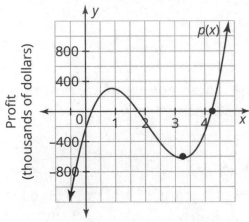

Zorzansa's Profits Over Years 0–5

Profit (thousands of dollars) vs *Time (years)*

Substitute the input and output values into the average rate of change formula.

Evaluate the expression.

$$\frac{f(b) - f(a)}{b - a} = \frac{f(4.25) - f(3.25)}{4.25 - 3.25}$$

$$= \frac{0 - (-600)}{1}$$

$$= \frac{600}{1} = 600$$

The average rate of change for the time interval (3.25, 4.25) is approximately $600,000 per year.

© Carnegie Learning, Inc.

1. **Analyze the worked example.**

   a. Explain why the average rate of change is $600,000 per year, and not $600 per year.

   b. Explain why the average rate of change is positive over this interval.

   c. What does the average rate of change represent in this problem situation?

2. **Determine the average rate of change of Zorzansa's profits for the time interval (1, 3).**

3. **Sam has a theory about the average rate of change. Describe the error in Sam's reasoning.**

   > Sam
   >
   > I can quickly estimate the average rate of change for intervals that are above and below the x-axis because they add to zero. For example, at year 1, the profit is about $300,000 and at year 2.25 the profit is about −$300,000. Therefore, the average rate of change for the time interval (1, 2.25) is approximately $0.

4. Is it possible for an interval to have an average rate of change equal to 0? Use an interval from the graph of $p(x)$ to justify your reasoning.

5. After 4.5 years, would you consider Zorzansa a successful business? Explain your reasoning.

TALK the TALK

Achievement Unlocked

In the game *Zephyr's Zenith II*, a player gains experience points by solving puzzles and defeating enemies. A player loses experience points by incorrectly solving puzzles or being defeated by an enemy. When a player first gains a certain minimum number of experience points, they earn a special bonus item that helps them advance in the game.

The function $z(x)$ models the experience points of a player over the first 2.5 hours of playing the game.

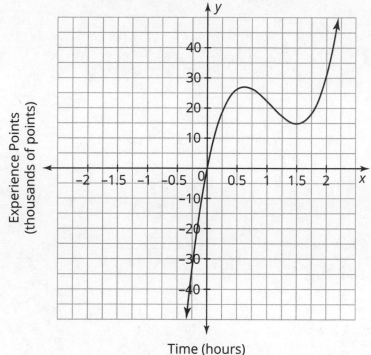

Player's Experience Points Over Time

1. **Write a scenario to match the graph.**

2. Estimate the minimum number of experience points needed to earn the special bonus item and when the player earned it. Use the graph to justify your answer.

3. Estimate the average rate of change for each time interval.

   a. (0, 0.6)   b. (0.6, 1.5)

Assignment

Write

Write a definition for the term *average rate of change* in your own words.

Remember

The formula for average rate of change is $\frac{f(b) - f(a)}{b - a}$ for an interval (a, b). The expression $b - a$ represents the change in the input of the function f. The expression $f(b) - f(a)$ represents the change in the function f as the input changes form a to b.

Practice

1. Biologists conducted a 20-year study of fruit bat populations in a small African country. The polynomial function $p(x)$ models the fruit bat population from the year 1990 (when $x = 0$) to the year 2010 (when $x = 20$).

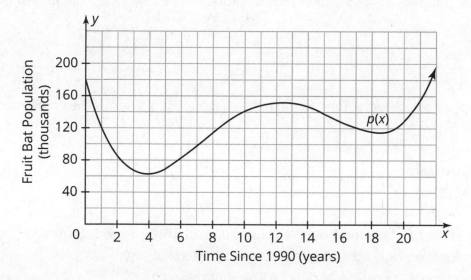

a. Determine the intervals over which the fruit bat population increased.

b. Determine the intervals over which the fruit bat population decreased.

c. During the 20-year study, a law was passed that banned the use of a pesticide known to be harmful to the fruit bat. Predict the year in which the law was passed. Explain your reasoning.

d. During the 20-year study, a logging company signed a 6-year government contract to harvest the timber from a large forest known to be the habitat of the fruit bat. Predict the year in which the company started harvesting the timber. Explain your reasoning.

e. Estimate when the fruit bat population was 100,000. Explain your reasoning.

f. At what point during the 20-year study was the fruit bat population the highest? What was the population at that time?

g. Determine the average rate of change of the fruit bat population from the year 1994 to the year 2002. Explain the meaning of your answer in terms of the problem situation.

h. Determine the average rate of change of the fruit bat population over the entire 20-year study. Explain the meaning of your answer in terms of the problem situation.

Stretch

A biologist studied the population of mosquitoes over a 10-year period from 2000 to 2010 in a rural county of her state. The population of mosquitoes had the following characteristics:

- The population first increased, then decreased, then increased, and then decreased.
- The average rate of change of the population of mosquitoes over the 10-year period was 10,000 mosquitoes per year.
- The average rate of change of the population of mosquitoes from 2003 to 2005 was −10, 000 per year.
- The maximum number of mosquitoes during the 10-year period was 175,000.
- The number of mosquitoes in the year 2007 was 150,000, which was the same as the year 2010.

Draw a possible graph for the population of mosquitoes that has the given characteristics.

Review

1. Sketch a graph of a polynomial function with the characteristics given. If the graph is not possible to sketch, explain why.

   Characteristics:

   - 4 imaginary zeros
   - as $x \to \infty$, $f(x) \to -\infty$

     as $x \to -\infty$, $f(x) \to -\infty$

2. Determine 1 linear function and 1 quadratic function such that the product of the 2 functions will build a cubic function with a double zero at 2 and a y-intercept at $(0, -4)$.

   Write the equation of the cubic function. Explain your reasoning.

3. Consider the functions $k(x) = x + 2$, $m(x) = x - \frac{1}{2}$, $n(x) = x - 1$, and $f(x) = k(x) \cdot m(x) \cdot n(x)$.

   a. Graph $k(x)$, $m(x)$, $n(x)$, and $f(x)$.   b. Determine the zeros of $f(x)$. Explain your reasoning.

4. Solve each equation.

   a. $x^2 - 8x + 18 = 0$ b. $x^2 + 49 = 0$

To a Greater or Lesser Degree

Comparing Polynomial Functions

6

Warm Up

Use technology to evaluate each polynomial expression for $x = 5$.

1. $x^3 + 10x^2 - 1$

2. $2x^5 - 6x^4 - x + 2$

3. $\dfrac{2x^5 - 6x^4 - x + 2}{x^3 + 10x^2 - 1}$

Learning Goals

- Compare polynomial functions by their key characteristics.
- Compare polynomial functions using multiple representations.

You know how to represent a polynomial function using a graph, a table of values, and key characteristics. How can you compare polynomials using these different representations?

The Lesser Degree

You know that the degree of a polynomial function is the greatest exponent of a term in the polynomial. Let's investigate polynomial functions with greater and lesser degrees.

1. **Given each polynomial function and its graph, determine a function of lesser degree using the same coefficients. Write the equation and then use technology to sketch the graph of the function.**

a.

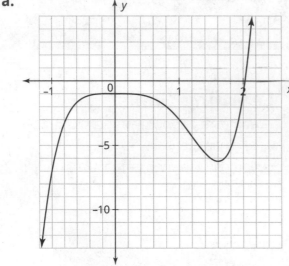

$f(x) = 2x^5 - 4x^4 - 1$

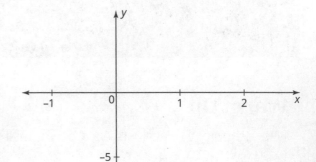

Function of lesser degree: _____

b.

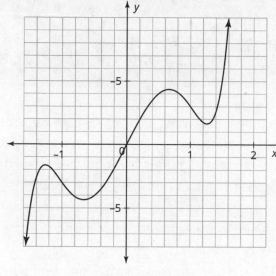

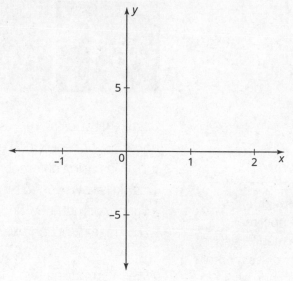

$g(x) = x^7 - 8x^3 + 10x$

Function of lesser degree: _____

2. Compare your functions with your classmates' functions. Did everyone write the same equations?

3. Compare your functions with the corresponding functions of lesser degree. What do you notice?

Recall that you can represent a polynomial using a graph, table of values, equation, or description of its key characteristics. The ability to compare functions using different representations is an important mathematical habit. This skill allows you to model problems in different ways, solve problems using a variety of methods, and more easily identify patterns. At times, you may need to compare functions when they are in different representations.

When comparing two functions in different forms, it may be helpful to ask yourself a series of questions. Examples include:
- What information is given?
- What is the degree of each function?
- What do I know about all functions of this degree?
- What key characteristics do I need to know?
- How do the functions compare?

Metacognition is an important mathematical habit that involves mentally asking yourself a series of questions to determine what you know about a problem and how you can reason your way to a solution.

Worked Example

Consider two polynomial functions $f(x)$ and $g(x)$. Which polynomial has a greater number of real zeros? Justify your choice.

$f(x) = -2(x - 1)^3$

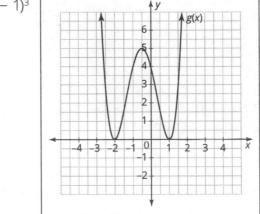

- The Fundamental Theorem of Algebra states that the number of zeros must be equal to the degree of the function. Therefore, $f(x)$ has 3 zeros.
- The function $f(x)$ has a real zero at 1 (multiplicity 3), so all zeros are real.
- The graph of $g(x)$ shows each zero has multiplicity 2, for a total of 4 real zeros.

The function $g(x)$ has 4 real zeros, while $f(x)$ has 3. Therefore, the correct choice is $g(x)$.

1. Toby compared the table of values for $f(x)$ and the graph of $g(x)$ to determine which polynomial function has the greater number of real zeros.

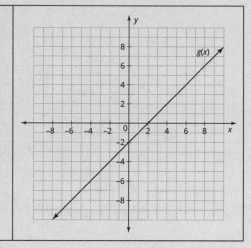

x	f(x)
−2	3
−1	−2
0	−5
1	−6
2	−5
3	−2
4	3

Toby

Function g(x) has the greater number of real zeros. The graph has 1 zero at x = 2 while the table of values has no output value of 0, and therefore no zeros.

Is Toby correct? Explain your reasoning.

2. **Analyze each pair of representations. Then, answer each question and justify your reasoning.**

   a. Which function has a greater degree?

A polynomial function $h(x)$ has 1 absolute maximum and 1 relative maximum.	$j(x) = -40(x - 7)^2 + 30x^2 - 17x + 1$

b. Which function has a greater degree?

x	m(x)
−2	9
−1	3
0	1
1	3
2	9

A polynomial function $n(x)$ has a real zero and imaginary zeros.

c. Which function has a degree divisible by 2?

x	p(x)
−2	2
−1	4
0	6
1	8
2	10

The function $q(x)$ has only imaginary zeros.

d. Determine which function has the greater output as *x* approaches infinity.

An odd function $r(x)$ with $a < 0$.	$k(x) = x^6 + x^4 + 3x^2 + 5x - 10{,}000$

e. Determine which function has the greater output as *x* approaches negative infinity.

$t(x) = -3(x - 4)^8 + 130$	A quartic function $s(x)$ with y-intercept $(0, 5)$ and all imaginary roots.

3. **Sam and Otis disagree when they compared the two functions shown to determine which one has an odd degree.**

| The function $f(x)$ has an absolute maximum value. | $g(x) = x^4(3 - x)(2x^2 + 3)(x^4 + 4)$ |

Sam

The function f(x) has an odd degree because odd functions approach positive infinity as x either increases or decreases. This means f(x) has a maximum value.

Otis

The function g(x) has an odd degree. When I multiplied the factors, I got a term with a highest exponent of 11:
$x^4(-x)(2x^2)(x^4) = -2x^{11}$.
Therefore, g(x) is odd.

Who is correct? Justify your reasoning.

Multiple Representations of Polynomial Functions

As you consider additional questions in this lesson, it may be helpful to compare the problems to ones that you have already completed.

Worked Example

Consider the representations shown. Which function has a greater *y*-intercept? Justify your reasoning.

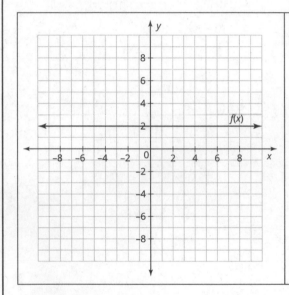

A function $g(x)$ has an *a*-value less than zero and all roots have multiplicity 2.

Solution:

This problem is similar to previous problems in that you must consider functions with restrictions on the *a*-value and functions with multiple zeros. The problem is also similar in that you must consider an output value for a given input. In this case, the input is 0.

In function $f(x)$, the output value is 2 for any given input. Analyzing function $g(x)$, the multiplicity 2 tells you that the function is even, and the negative *a*-value indicates that the function opens downward. The multiplicity of the zeros also tells you that the function does not cross the *x*-axis. Instead, it reflects at a given point where the double zero occurs.

Comparing the two functions, you know that function $g(x)$ is always below the *x*-axis and function $f(x)$ is above the *x*-axis. Therefore, $f(x)$ has a greater *y*-intercept.

1. Isaac and Tina disagree over which function has a greater *y*-intercept.

$g(x) = 2(x - 2)(x + 2)(x - 3) - 4$			

x	h(x)
−2	−2
−1	0
0	4
1	10
2	18

Isaac
Function g(x) has a greater y-intercept. I calculated the y-intercept by substituting 0 for x. This value is greater than (0, 4) shown in the table for the function h(x).

Tina
Function h(x) has a greater y-intercept. The y-intercept of h(x) is (0, 4) and the y-intercept of g(x) is (0, −4).

Who is correct? Justify your reasoning.

2. **Analyze each pair of representations. Then, answer each question and justify your reasoning.**

a. **Which function has a greater average rate of change for the interval (−4, 4)?**

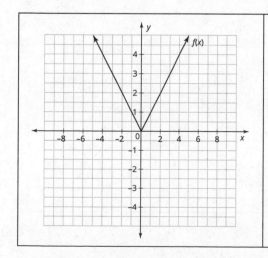

$g(x) = x$

b. Which function has a greater average rate of change for the interval (−1, 1)?

x	j(x)
−2	4
−1	1
0	0
1	1
2	4

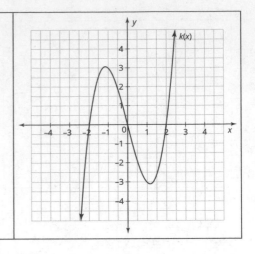

c. Which function has a greater relative minimum?

A cubic function $a(x)$ with $a > 0$ and 3 distinct real roots.

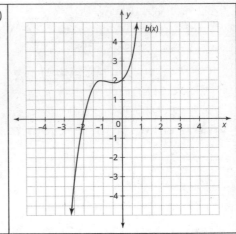

d. Which function's axis of symmetry has a greater x-value?

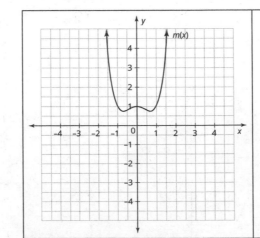

$$n(x) = x^2 - 3x + 1$$

3. **Emilio studied the table of values and description of the key characteristics to determine which function has a greater minimum.**

x	d(x)
−2	5
−1	2
0	1
1	2
2	5

A quartic function m(x) has a < 0 and 2 real zeros (each of multiplicity 2).

Emilio

Function d(x) has a greater minimum. This function is a parabola opening up, with its vertex at (0, 1). Function m(x) opens down because a < 0. Since the real zeros have multiplicity 2, I know any real zeros occur when the function reflects off the x-axis. Therefore, the output values of m(x) never reach a point greater than y = 0.

Is Emilio correct? Justify your reasoning.

Recall that a basic function is a function in its simplest form. The basic power function is $f(x) = x^n$ for any natural number n. Transformations of a basic function are performed by changing the A-, B-, C-, and D-values in the form $g(x) = Af(B(x) - C) + D$. Remember, each value describes different transformations of the graph: the A-value vertically stretches or compresses the graph, the B-value horizontally stretches or compresses the graph, the C-value horizontally shifts the graph right or left, and the D-value vertically shifts the graph up or down.

4. **Analyze the transformations of the basic functions. Then answer each question and justify your reasoning.**

a. **Which function has a greater output for a given input?**

The basic quadratic function $f(x) = x^2$.	$g(x) = f(x - 2) + 1$

b. **Which function has a lower minimum?**

x	$j(x)$
−2	16
−1	1
0	0
1	1
2	16

$k(x) = 5f(x - 4) + 2$

c. **Which function has the greater input for a given output value?**

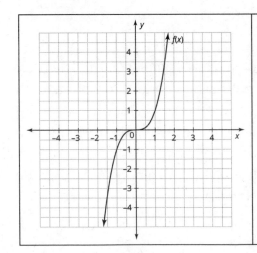

$g(x) = 3f(x - 5) + 1$

TALK the TALK

The Greater Degree

1. Which polynomial function has a greater degree?

A polynomial function $b(x)$ with 2 absolute minimums and 1 relative maximum.	$c(x) = -2(3 - x^2)(x - 4) + 9$

2. Which polynomial function has a greater number of real zeros?

$d(x) = x^2 - x - 6$		
	x	**f(x)**
	−5	−8
	−4	−1
	−3	0
	−2	1
	−1	8
	0	27
	1	64

3. Which function has an odd degree?

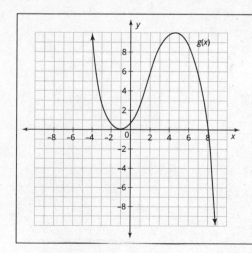

	A polynomial function $h(x)$ with 2 real zeros and an imaginary zero.

Write

List the key characteristics of a polynomial function.

Remember

The key characteristics of polynomial functions can be compared even when the representations are different.

Practice

1. Analyze the given representations of the polynomial functions $f(x)$, $g(x)$, $h(x)$ and $k(x)$. Then, answer each question and justify your reasoning.

<table>
<tr>
<td>

The cubic function $f(x)$ with x-intercepts $(-4, 0)$, $(-1, 0)$, and $(2, 0)$ and y-intercept $(0, 8)$.

</td>
<td>

$$g(x) = (x - 3)^2(x + 2)^2$$

</td>
</tr>
<tr>
<td>

x	h(x)
−2	−7
−1	−4
0	−3
1	−4
2	−7

</td>
<td>

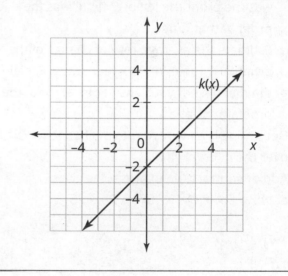

</td>
</tr>
</table>

a. Consider $f(x)$ and $g(x)$. Which function has the smaller output as x approaches infinity?

b. Consider $f(x)$ and $h(x)$. Which function has the greatest number of imaginary zeros?

c. Consider $f(x)$ and $h(x)$. Which function has a greater degree?

d. Consider $g(x)$ and $k(x)$. Which function has the greater y-intercept?

e. Consider $f(x)$ and $g(x)$. Which function has the lowest relative minimum?

f. Consider $h(x)$ and $k(x)$. Which function has the greatest average rate of change over the interval $(-2, 0)$?

2. Consider the polynomial functions $m(x) = -x^2$ and $n(x) = m(x + 4) - 3$. Which function has the greatest maximum? Explain your reasoning.

3. Consider the polynomial functions $p(x) = x^4$ and $t(x) = p(x - 1) + 7$. Which function's axis of symmetry has a greater x-value? Explain your reasoning.

Stretch

Given $f(x) = x^4 - 625$, determine all the possible polynomial functions for $g(x)$ such that $h(x) = \frac{f(x)}{g(x)}$ is a polynomial function.

Review

1. A manager conducted an 18-year study of the profits of his company. The polynomial function $p(x)$ models the company's profits from the year 1996 (when $x = 0$) to the year 2014 (when $x = 18$).

   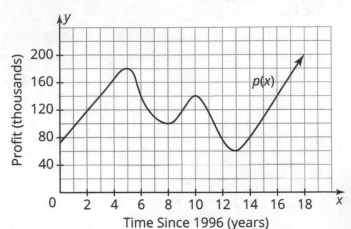

   a. Estimate when the profit was $140,000. Explain your reasoning.

   b. At what point during the 18-year study was the profit the lowest? What was the profit at that time?

   c. Estimate the average rate of change of the profit over the entire 18-year study. Explain the meaning of your answer in terms of the problem situation.

2. Determine the average rate of change for the function $f(x) = -2x^4 + x^3 - 7x^2 - 2x + 3$ over the interval (4, 8).

3. Add or subtract the expressions given.

   a. $(4x^2 - 2x + 7) + (-8x^2 + 5x - 25)$

   b. $(-9x^2 + 16x - 17) - (-12x^2 - 7x + 3)$

Characteristics of Polynomial Functions Summary

KEY TERMS

- power function
- end behavior
- symmetric about a line
- symmetric about a point
- even function
- odd function
- polynomial function

- quartic function
- quintic function
- absolute maximum
- absolute minimum
- extrema
- average rate of change

LESSON 1

So Odd, I Can't Even

A **power function** is a function of the form $P(x) = ax^n$, where n is a non-negative integer. The graph of a power function raised to an odd degree increases from left to right (or right to left if $a < 0$), flattening near the origin, as the absolute value of the power increases. The graph of a power function raised to an even degree is a concave up (or down if $a < 0$) parabola, flattening near the origin as the absolute value of the power increases.

The **end behavior** of a graph of a function is the behavior of the graph as x approaches infinity. The end behavior for even and odd degree power functions can be described as:

	Odd Degree Power Function	Even Degree Power Function
$a > 0$	As $x \to \infty$, $f(x) \to \infty$. As $x \to -\infty$, $f(x) \to -\infty$.	As $x \to \infty$, $f(x) \to \infty$. As $x \to -\infty$, $f(x) \to \infty$.
$a < 0$	As $x \to \infty$, $f(x) \to -\infty$. As $x \to -\infty$, $f(x) \to \infty$.	As $x \to \infty$, $f(x) \to -\infty$. As $x \to -\infty$, $f(x) \to -\infty$.

If a graph is **symmetric about a line**, the line divides the graph into two identical parts. Special attention is given to the line of symmetry when it is the y-axis, as it tells you that the function is even. The graph of an odd degree basic power function is symmetric about a point, in particular the origin. A function is **symmetric about a point** if each point on the graph has a point the same distance from the central point but in the opposite direction. When the point of symmetry is the origin, the graph is reflected across the x-axis and the y-axis. If you replace both (x, y) with $(-x, -y)$, the function remains the same. You can think of the point of symmetry about the origin as a double reflection.

An **even function** has a graph symmetric about the y-axis, thus $f(x) = f(-x)$. An **odd function** has a graph symmetric about the origin, thus $f(x) = -f(-x)$.

For example, consider the functions shown.

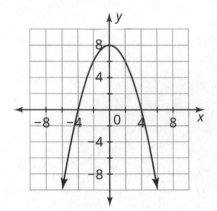

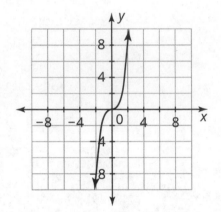

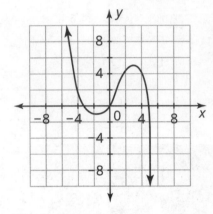

The function is even because it is symmetric about the y-axis.

The function is odd because it is symmetric about the origin.

The function is neither even nor odd because it is not symmetric.

You can use algebra to determine whether a function is even by evaluating the function at $f(-x)$. If $f(-x) = f(x)$, then the function is even. You can also evaluate the function at $-f(x)$. If $-f(-x) = f(x)$, or $-f(x) = f(-x)$, then the function is odd.

For example, consider the function $m(x) = 4x^5 - 2x^3$.

$$-m(x) = -(4x^5 - 2x^3)$$
$$= -4x^5 + 2x^3$$
$$m(x) \neq -m(x)$$

$$m(-x) = 4(-x)^5 - 2(-x)^3$$
$$= -4x^5 + 2x^3$$

$m(-x) = -m(x)$, so the function is odd.

Math Class Needs a Makeover

Linear, quadratic, and cubic functions are all examples of polynomial functions. A **polynomial function** is a function that can be written in the form

$$\blacksquare x^n + \blacksquare x^{n-1} + \dots \blacksquare x^2 + \blacksquare x + \blacksquare$$

In a polynomial function, the coefficients, represented by each $\blacksquare$, are complex numbers and the exponents are nonnegative integers.

A **quartic function** is a fourth degree polynomial function, while a **quintic function** is a fifth degree polynomial function.

Transformations performed on any polynomial function $f(x)$ to form a new function $g(x)$ can be described by the transformation function:

$$g(x) = Af(B(x - C)) + D$$

Function Form	Equation Information	Description of Transformation of Graph
$y = Af(x)$	$|A| > 1$	vertical stretch of the graph by a factor of A units
	$0 < |A| < 1$	vertical compression of the graph by a factor of A units
	$A < 0$	reflection across the x-axis
$y = f(Bx)$	$|B| > 1$	compressed horizontally by a factor of $\frac{1}{|B|}$
	$0 < |B| < 1$	stretched horizontally by a factor of $\frac{1}{|B|}$
	$B < 0$	reflection across the y-axis
$y = f(x - C)$	$C > 0$	horizontal shift right C units
	$C < 0$	horizontal shift left C units
$y = f(x) + D$	$D > 0$	vertical shift up D units
	$D < 0$	vertical shift down D units

For example, consider the function $m(x) = x^4$.

$p(x) = -m(x) + 2$

Reference Point on $m(x)$	$\rightarrow$	Corresponding Point on $p(x)$
(0, 0)	$\rightarrow$	(0, 2)
(1, 1)	$\rightarrow$	(1, 1)
(2, 16)	$\rightarrow$	(2, −14)

There is a horizontal line of reflection at $y = 1$. The function $p(x)$ is symmetric about the y-axis, so it is an even function.

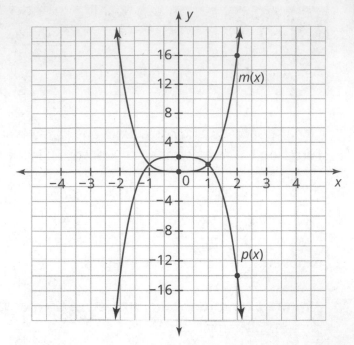

To determine multiple transformations of polynomial functions, observe how corresponding points have changed on a graph and use the data to write the new function. Or, describe the transformations based on the equation of the transformed function in terms of the original function.

For example, consider the functions $f(x) = x^3$ and $g(x) = 0.5g(x − 1) + 2$.

$A = 0.5, C = 1, D = 2$

$(x, y) \rightarrow (x + 1, 0.5y + 2)$

The graph of the function $f(x)$ has been vertically compressed by a factor of 0.5, and translated 1 unit to the right and 2 units up to produce the graph of $g(x)$.

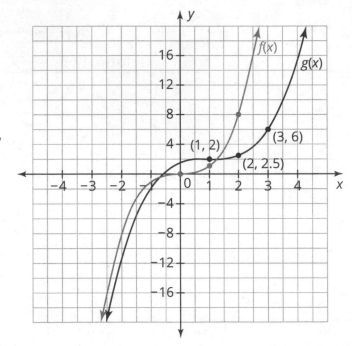

Basic power functions can be transformed and combined to create more complex polynomial functions.

For example, consider the functions $f(x) = x$ and $g(x) = x^2$.

$a(x) = 2g(x) - 3f(x)$

x	g(x)	f(x)	a(x)
−2	4	−2	14
−1	1	−1	5
0	0	0	0
1	1	1	−1
2	4	2	2

$a(x) = 2x^2 - 3x$

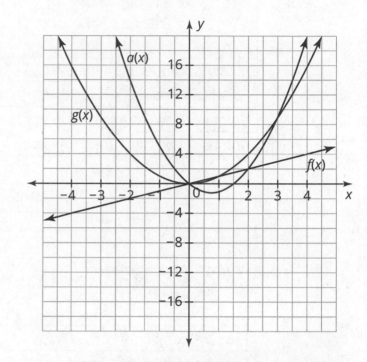

LESSON
3

Poly-Wog

The **absolute maximum** is the highest point in the entire graph, and the **absolute minimum** is the lowest point in the entire graph. The set of relative maximums, relative minimums, absolute maximums and absolute minimums, may also be referred to as **extrema**. The extrema are also called extreme points and extremum. The maximum number of extrema is one less than the degree of the polynomial. The possible number of extrema is always a difference of 2. The possible number of extrema for an odd degree polynomial is even. The possible number of extrema for an even degree polynomial is odd.

Cubics	
All possible end behavior	As $x \rightarrow \infty$, $f(x) \rightarrow \infty$
	As $x \rightarrow -\infty$, $f(x) \rightarrow -\infty$
	As $x \rightarrow \infty$, $f(x) \rightarrow -\infty$
	As $x \rightarrow -\infty$, $f(x) \rightarrow \infty$
Possible number of x-intercept(s)	3, 2, or 1
Possible number of y-intercept(s)	1
Number of possible relative extrema	2 or none
Number of possible absolute extrema	None

Quartics	
All possible end behavior	As $x \rightarrow \infty$, $f(x) \rightarrow \infty$
	As $x \rightarrow -\infty$, $f(x) \rightarrow \infty$
	As $x \rightarrow \infty$, $f(x) \rightarrow -\infty$
	As $x \rightarrow -\infty$, $f(x) \rightarrow -\infty$
Possible number of x-intercept(s)	4, 3, 2, or 1
Possible number of y-intercept(s)	1
Number of possible relative extrema	3 or 1
Number of possible absolute extrema	1

Quintics	
All possible end behavior	As $x \rightarrow \infty$, $f(x) \rightarrow \infty$
	As $x \rightarrow -\infty$, $f(x) \rightarrow -\infty$
	As $x \rightarrow \infty$, $f(x) \rightarrow -\infty$
	As $x \rightarrow -\infty$, $f(x) \rightarrow \infty$
Possible number of x-intercept(s)	5, 4, 3, 2, or 1
Possible number of y-intercept(s)	1
Number of possible relative extrema	4, 2, or none
Number of possible absolute extrema	None

The zeros of a polynomial function can either be real, imaginary, or a combination of both. The real zeros of the function may all be distinct, or can have varying degrees of multiplicity. The tables summarize all possible combinations of zeros for a linear, quadratic, and a cubic function.

Linear Function	
Zeros	Graph
1 real	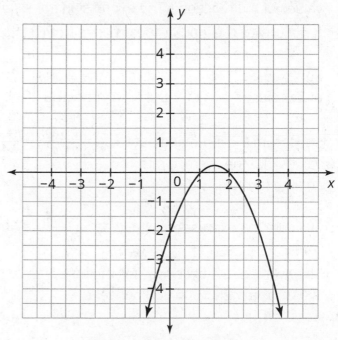

Quadratic Function	
Zeros	Graph
2 real distinct	
1 real (multiplicity 2)	
2 imaginary	

Cubic Function	
Zeros	Graph
3 real distinct	
1 real (multiplicity 3)	
1 real (multiplicity 1) 1 real (multiplicity 2)	
1 real 2 imaginary	

Key characteristics of polynomial functions, such as the number and kind of extrema, the end behavior, the a-value, degree of the function, intercepts, etc., can be used to sketch the graph of the polynomial. These characteristics can also be determined from the function and the correct polynomial function matched to the graph.

For example, consider a polynomial function with the following characteristics and a possible sketch of its graph.

- even degree polynomial
- negative a-value
- y-intercept of -2
- x-intercepts of 1 and 2

The function modeled by the graph could have the equation $f(x) = -x^2 + 3x - 2$ because it has a negative a-value, an even degree, a y-intercept of -2, and can be factored into $(-x + 1)(x - 2)$ which gives x-intercepts of 1 and 2.

LESSON 4 — Function Construction

The key characteristics of the individual functions that build a cubic function tell you about the key characteristics of the cubic function. A cubic function is built from three linear functions or a linear function and a quadratic function. A cubic function may have 0 or 2 imaginary zeros. An infinite number of cubic functions can be written from a given set of zeros.

The characteristics of a quartic function are formed by the characteristics of the functions that are its factors. A quartic function is built from four linear functions; a linear function and a cubic function; two linear functions and a quadratic function; or two quadratic functions. A quartic function may have 0, 2, or 4 imaginary zeros.

LESSON 5 — Level Up

The **average rate of change** of a function is the ratio of the change in the dependent variable to the change in the independent variable over a specific interval. The formula for average rate of change is $\frac{f(b) - f(a)}{b - a}$ for the interval (a, b). The expression $b - a$ represents the change in the input values of the function f. The expression $f(b) - f(a)$ represents the change in the output values of the function f as the input values change from a to b.

For example, you can determine the average rate of change of Zorzansa's profit for the time interval (3.25, 4.25).

Substitute the input and output values into the average rate of change formula.

$$\frac{f(b) - f(a)}{b - a} = \frac{f(4.25) - f(3.25)}{4.25 - 3.25}$$

$$= \frac{0 - (-600)}{1}$$

Evaluate the expression.

$$\frac{600}{1} = 600$$

The average rate of change for the time interval (3.25, 4.25) is approximately $600,000 per year.

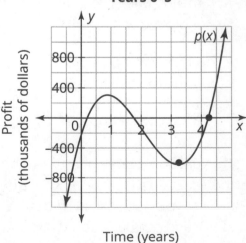

Zorzansa's Profits Over Years 0–5

Profit (thousands of dollars)

Time (years)

To a Greater or Lesser Degree

Polynomials can be represented using a graph, table of values, equation, or description of key characteristics. When comparing 2 functions in different forms, important information to look for includes the degree of each function, the shape of the graph, the number and type of zeros, transformations of a basic function, etc.

For example, consider the two functions described below. Which polynomial function has an even degree?

A polynomial function $a(x)$ with 2 absolute maximums and 1 relative minimum	$b(x) = 4(3 - 2x) + 3(x + 6)$

The function $a(x)$ has an even degree. A function with 3 turns must have a degree greater than 3. And, having absolute maximums means the end behavior of the function is to approach negative infinity as x approaches both negative and positive infinity. This indicates an even degree function. The function $b(x)$ is a linear function—the x-values are added, not multiplied.

DEVELOPING

STRUC   TURAL

SIMI   LARI   TIES

The lessons in this module build on what you already know about integers and rational numbers. You will discover that the system of polynomials is analogous to the set of integers and that the system of rational expressions is analogous to the set of rational numbers. You will extend your ability to factor quadratics to factor polynomials and use those factors to identify zeros and sketch graphs. You will use polynomial functions to solve real-world and mathematical problems. You will then use your knowledge of polynomials to represent and solve rational equations.

Relating Factors and Zeros

Polynomial functions can squiggle up and down like snakes. If this snake were a function and the log were an axis, how many zeros would it have?

Module 2: Developing Structural Similarities

TOPIC 1: RELATING FACTORS AND ZEROS

In this topic, the Factor Theorem is introduced and used to determine whether a linear expression is a factor of a polynomial function. Students then perform polynomial long division, and the Remainder Theorem is stated and used to answer questions involving polynomial division with remainders. Methods of factoring polynomials are introduced, and students solve polynomial inequalities both graphically and algebraically, given mathematical and real-world situations. Finally, students investigate the Closure Property for polynomials.

Where have we been?

Students have factored mathematical expressions since elementary school. In previous courses, they have factored degree-2 polynomial equations in order to isolate key characteristics of the functions represented by those equations. Students are also familiar with the long division algorithm from elementary school, used in this topic in a similar way to divide polynomials.

Where are we going?

Polynomial equations are used extensively in industry to track financial and inventory information, and in data science to build predictive models, and to help analyze and answer research questions. Students will use what they learned in this topic to help them build real-world polynomial models in the next topic.

Long Division with Polynomials

You can use long division with polynomials.
Polynomial long division is an algorithm for dividing one polynomial by another of equal or lesser degree. The process is similar to integer long division.

Integer Long Division	Polynomial Long Division	
$3660 \div 12$ or $\dfrac{3660}{12}$ 305 $12\overline{)3660}$ -36 $\overline{6}$ -0 $\overline{60}$ -60 $\overline{0}$	$(x^3 + 12x^2 + 41x + 72) \div (x + 8)$ $\overset{A}{x^2} + \overset{D}{4x} \overset{G}{+9}$ $x + 8\overline{)x^3 + 12x^2 + 41x + 72}$ $\underset{B}{-(x^3 +\ 8x^2)}\downarrow$ $\overset{E}{4x^2} + 41x \overset{C}{}$ $-(4x^2 + 32x)\downarrow$ $\underset{H}{9x + 72}^{F}$ $-(9x + 72)$ Remainder 0	or $\dfrac{x^3 + 12x^2 + 41x + 72}{x - 8}$ A. Divide $\frac{x^3}{x} = x^2$. B. Multiply $x^2(x + 8)$, and then subtract. C. Bring down $41x$. D. Divide $\frac{4x^2}{x} = 4x$. E. Multiply $4x(x + 8)$, and then subtract. F. Bring down $+72$. G. Divide $\frac{9x}{x} = 9$. H. Multiply $9(x + 8)$, and then subtract.

Getting Closure

The word "closure" can mean many things depending on the context. For instance, closure for a business may be caused by an organization going bankrupt. In government, closure, which is also referred to as cloture, is a procedure by which the Senate can vote to place a time limit on consideration of a bill.

Closure may also refer to humans' ability to perceive objects as wholes, even when some of the parts are missing. Your brain fills in the missing parts. For example, you perceive a white triangle on the right, even though it is not drawn there at all.

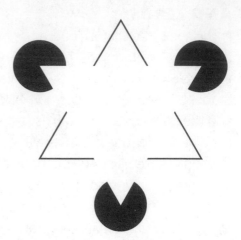

Talking Points

Polynomial division can be an important topic to know about for college admissions tests.

Here is an example of a sample question:

For what value of the constant p does $\dfrac{6x^4 + 2x^2 - 8x - p}{x + 2}$ have no remainder?

When you use long division to divide the polynomials, you see that the quotient is $6x^3 - 12x^2 + 26x - 60$ with a remainder of $-p + 120$.

Thus, only if p has a value of 120, will the division have no remainder.

Key Terms

Factor Theorem

The Factor Theorem states that a polynomial function $p(x)$ has $(x - r)$ as a factor if and only if the value of the function at r is 0, or $p(r) = 0$.

Remainder Theorem

The Remainder Theorem states that when any polynomial equation or function, $f(x)$, is divided by a linear expression of the form $(x - r)$, the remainder is $R = f(r)$, or the value of the equation or function when $x = r$.

closed under an operation

When an operation is performed on any number or expression in a set and the result is in the same set, it is said to be closed under that operation.

Satisfactory Factoring

Factoring Polynomials to Identify Zeros

Warm Up

Solve each equation for x.

1. $2x^2 - 4 = 8$

2. $(x - 1)^3 - 5 = 0$

3. $3(x - 6)^4 + 11 = 15$

4. $x^3 - 27 = 0$

Learning Goals

- Factor higher order polynomials.
- Distinguish between factoring polynomial equations over the set of real numbers and over the set of complex numbers.
- Identify zeros of polynomials when suitable factorizations are available.
- Use the zeros of a polynomial to sketch a graph of the function.

You have determined factors of degree-2 equations. How can you factor higher-degree polynomial functions?

Factor Tree Factory

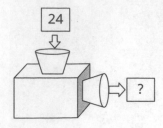

At the Factor Tree Factory, a factor machine takes any whole number as input and outputs one of its factor pairs.

1. **Suppose the number 24 is entered into the machine.**

   a. **What factor pairs might you see as the output?**

   b. **How do you know whether two numbers are a factor pair of 24?**

   c. **Can 5 be an output value? Explain your reasoning.**

2. **Cherise and Jemma each begin a factor tree for 24 using different outputs from the factor machine.**

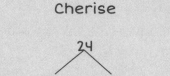

Cherise   Jemma

    24   24

2   12   3   8

   Cherise says both factor trees will show the same prime factorization when completed. Jemma says because they each started with a different factor pair, the prime factorizations will be different. Who's correct? Complete each factor tree to justify your answer.

3. Consider the expression 2 · 2 · 2 · 3.

   a. How does 2 · 2 · 2 · 3 relate to the factors determined by Cherise and Jemma?

   b. How does it relate to 24?

4. If you know a factor of a given whole number, how can you determine another factor?

5. What is the remainder when you divide a whole number by any of its factors? Explain your reasoning.

6. Create a factor tree to show the prime factorization of each number.

   a. 66   b. 210

ACTIVITY

1.1 Factoring Out a GCF

Throughout your previous mathematics courses, you have applied the idea that a whole number can be decomposed into a product of its factors to solve a variety of problems. In this lesson, you will explore different methods of decomposing a polynomial into a product of its factors. Once you have factored a polynomial, you can use the factors to identify the zeros and then use the zeros to sketch a graph.

To begin factoring any polynomial, always look for a greatest common factor (GCF). You can factor out the greatest common factor of the polynomial, and then factor what remains.

1. **Ping and Shalisha each attempt to factor $3x^3 + 12x^2 - 36x$ by factoring out the greatest common factor.**

Ping

$3x^3 + 12x^2 - 36x$

$3x(x^2 + 4x - 12)$

Shalisha

$3x^3 + 12x^2 - 36x$

$3(x^3 + 4x^2 - 12x)$

Remember:

A greatest common factor can be a variable, constant, or both.

a. **Analyze each student's work. Determine which student is correct and explain the inaccuracy in the other student's work.**

b. **Completely factor the expression that Ping and Shalisha started to factor.**

c. **Use the factors to identify the zeros of $f(x) = 3x^3 + 12x^2 - 36x$. Then sketch the graph of the polynomial.**

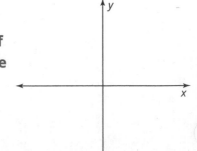

2. Factor each polynomial function and identify the zeros. Then, use the factors to sketch a graph of the function defined by the polynomial.

a. $f(x) = 3x^3 + 3x^2 - 6x$

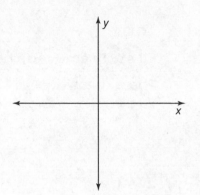

b. $f(x) = 2x^2 + 6x$

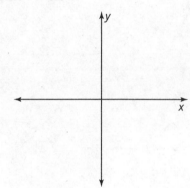

c. $f(x) = 3x^2 - 3x - 6$

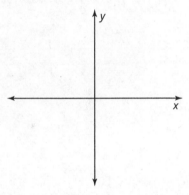

d. $f(x) = 10x^2 - 50x - 60$

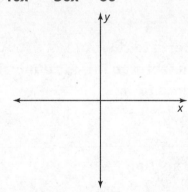

3. Analyze the factored form and the corresponding graphs in Questions 1 and 2. What do the graphs in Question 1 and Question 2, parts (a) and (b) have in common that the graphs of Question 2, parts (d) and (e) do not? Explain your reasoning.

4. Write a statement about the graphs of all polynomials that have a monomial GCF that contains a variable.

© Carnegie Learning, Inc.

5. Tony and Eva each attempt to factor $f(x) = x^3 - 2x^2 + 2x$. Analyze their work.

Tony

First, I removed the GCF, x.

The expression $x^2 - 2x + 2$ cannot be factored, so $f(x) = x(x^2 - 2x + 2)$.

Eva

$f(x) = x(x^2 - 2x + 2)$

$x^2 - 2x + 2 = 0$

$x = \dfrac{-(-2) \pm \sqrt{(-2)^2 - 4(1)(2)}}{2(1)}$

$x = \dfrac{2 \pm \sqrt{-4}}{2}$

$x = \dfrac{2 \pm 2i}{2}$

$x = 1 \pm i$

The function in factored form is
$f(x) = (x)[x - (1 + i)][x - (1 - i)]$.

a. If you consider the set of real numbers, who's correct? If you consider the set of complex numbers, who's correct? Explain your reasoning.

b. Use the Distributive Property to rewrite Eva's function to verify that the function in factored form is equivalent the original function in standard form.

c. Identify the zeros of the function $f(x)$.

Remember:

The set of complex numbers is the set of numbers that includes both real and imaginary numbers.

6. Analyze each expression.

$x^2 + 4$ $x^2 - 4$ $x^2 + 2x + 5$ $x^2 + 4x - 5$

$-x^2 + x + 12$ $x^2 + 4x - 1$ $-x^2 + 6x - 25$

a. Sort each expression based on whether it can be factored over the set of real numbers or over the set of imaginary numbers.

Complex Factors	
Real Factors	Imaginary Factors

b. Factor each expression over the set of complex numbers.

ACTIVITY 1.2

Using Structure to Factor Polynomials

Certain polynomials in quadratic form may have common factors in some of the terms, but not all terms. In this case, it may be helpful to write the terms as a product of 2 terms. You can then substitute the common term with a variable, z, and factor as you would any polynomial in quadratic form. This method of factoring is called *chunking*.

Worked Example

You can use chunking to factor $9x^2 + 21x + 10$.

Notice that the first and second terms both contain the common factor $3x$.

$9x^2 + 21x + 10 = (3x)^2 + 7(3x) + 10$	Rewrite terms as a product of common factors.
$= z^2 + 7z + 10$	Let $z = 3x$.
$= (z + 5)(z + 2)$	Factor the quadratic.
$= (3x + 5)(3x + 2)$	Substitute $3x$ for z.

The factored form of $9x^2 + 21x + 10$ is $(3x + 5)(3x + 2)$.

---

1. **Use chunking to factor and identify the zeros of**
   $f(x) = 25x^2 + 20x - 21$. **Then sketch the polynomial.**

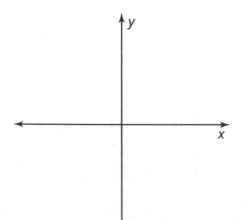

2. Given $z^2 + 2z - 15 = (z - 3)(z + 5)$, write another polynomial in general form that has a factored form of $(z - 3)(z + 5)$ with different values for z.

A special form of a polynomial is a perfect square trinomial. A perfect square trinomial has first and last terms that are perfect squares and a middle term that is equivalent to 2 times the product of the first and last term's square root.

Factoring a perfect square trinomial can occur in two forms.

$$a^2 - 2ab + b^2 = (a - b)^2$$
$$a^2 + 2ab + b^2 = (a + b)^2$$

Remember:

You can use the difference of two squares to factor a binomial of the form $a^2 - b^2$.
The binomial $a^2 - b^2 = (a + b)(a - b)$.

3. Determine which of the polynomial expression(s) is a perfect square trinomial and write it as the square of a sum or difference. If it is not a perfect square trinomial, explain why not.

a. $x^4 + 14x^2 - 49$

b. $16x^2 - 40x + 100$

c. $64x^2 - 32x + 4$

d. $9x^4 + 6x^2 + 1$

© Carnegie Learning, Inc.

In polynomials of 4 terms, you may notice that although not all terms share a common factor, pairs of terms might share a common factor. In this situation, you can factor by grouping.

4. Colt factors the polynomial expression $x^3 + 3x^2 - x - 3$.

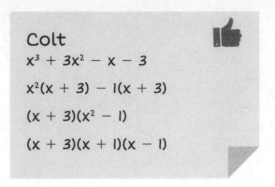

Colt

$x^3 + 3x^2 - x - 3$

$x^2(x + 3) - 1(x + 3)$

$(x + 3)(x^2 - 1)$

$(x + 3)(x + 1)(x - 1)$

a. Explain the steps Colt took to factor the polynomial expression.

$x^3 + 3x^2 - x - 3$

$x^2(x + 3) - 1(x + 3)$ Step 1: _____
_____
_____

$(x + 3)(x^2 - 1)$ Step 2: _____
_____
_____

$(x + 3)(x + 1)(x - 1)$ Step 3: _____
_____
_____

b. Use the factors to identify the zeros of $f(x) = x^3 + 3x^2 - x - 3$ and then sketch the graph.

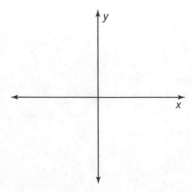

5. **Use factor by grouping to factor and identify the zeros of**
$f(x) = x^3 + 7x^2 - 4x - 28$. **Then sketch the polynomial.**

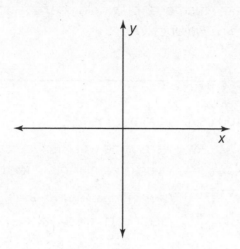

6. **Braxton and Kenny both factor the polynomial expression**
$x^3 + 2x^2 + 4x + 8$. **Analyze the set of factors in each student's work.**
Describe the set of numbers over which each student factored.

Braxton

$x^3 + 2x^2 + 4x + 8$

$x^2(x + 2) + 4(x + 2)$

$(x^2 + 4)(x + 2)$

Kenny

$x^3 + 2x^2 + 4x + 8$

$x^2(x + 2) + 4(x + 2)$

$(x^2 + 4)(x + 2)$

$(x + 2i)(x - 2i)(x + 2)$

According to the Fundamental Theorem of Algebra, any polynomial function of degree n must have exactly n complex factors:
$f(x) = (x - r_1)(x - r_2) \dots (x - r_n)$ where $r \in$ {complex numbers}.

Some degree-4 polynomials, written as a trinomial $ax^4 + bx^2 + c$, have the same structure as quadratics. When this is the case, the polynomial may be factored using the same methods you would use to factor a quadratic. This is called *factoring using quadratic form*.

> ### Worked Example
>
> Factor $x^4 - 29x^2 + 100$ using quadratic form.
>
> $x^4 - 29x^2 + 100$ Determine whether you can factor the given trinomial into 2 factors.
>
> $(x^2 - 4)(x^2 - 25)$ Determine whether you can continue to factor each binomial.
>
> $(x - 2)(x + 2)(x - 5)(x + 5)$

7. **Factor each polynomial over the set of complex numbers. Use the factors to identify the zeros and then sketch the polynomial.**

     a. $f(x) = x^4 - 4x^3 - x^2 + 4x$ b. $f(x) = x^4 - 10x^2 + 9$

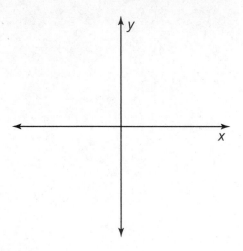
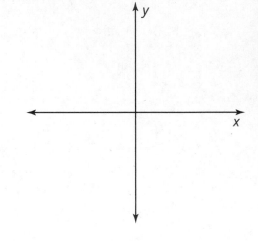

TALK the TALK

Fracture It to Factor It

You have used many different methods of factoring:

· Factoring Out the Greatest Common Factor

· Chunking

· Factoring by Grouping

· Perfect Square Trinomials

· Factoring Using Quadratic Form

Depending on the polynomial, some methods of factoring are more efficient than others.

1. **Complete the table on the next page by matching each polynomial with the method of factoring you would use from the bulleted list given. Every method from the bulleted list should be used only once. Explain why you chose the factoring method for each polynomial. Finally, write the polynomial in factored form over the set of real numbers.**

Polynomial	Method of Factoring	Reason	Factored Form
$3x^4 + 2x^2 - 8$			
$x^2 - 12x + 36$			
$x^3 + 2x^2 + 7x + 14$			
$25x^2 - 30x - 7$			
$2x^4 + 10x^3 + 12x^2$			

2. Factor each polynomial over the set of complex numbers. Explain why you chose the factoring method you used.

a. $x^4 - 7x^2 - 18$

b. $x^4 + 3x^2 - 28$

Assignment

Write

Describe the similarity between the chunking method of factoring and factoring by grouping. Discuss what the structure of a polynomial would look like in order for you to consider using each method.

Remember

You can factor out the GCF of a polynomial and then factor what remains. Analyzing the structure of a polynomial can help you decide the most efficient method for factoring. Once you have factored a polynomial, you can use the factors to identify the zeros and then use the zeros to sketch a graph.

Practice

1. Factor each polynomial over the set of real numbers. Use the factors to sketch the polynomial.

   a. $f(x) = 25x^2 - 10x - 24$

   b. $f(x) = x^3 - 4x^2 - 9x + 36$

   c. $f(x) = x^4 - 25x^2 + 144$

   d. $f(x) = 27x^3 - 18x^2 + 3x$

   e. $f(x) = 16x^3 + 54$

   f. $f(x) = 7x^4 - 56x$

Stretch

1. Sketch each piecewise function.

   a. $g(x) = \begin{cases} -x + 1, & x < 0 \\ 2x^2 - 8x & x \geq 0 \end{cases}$

   b. $f(x) = \begin{cases} x, & x < -1 \\ x^3 + x^2 - x - 1, & -1 \leq x \leq 1 \\ 4 & x > 1 \end{cases}$

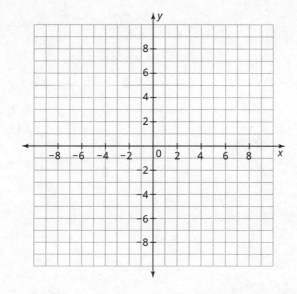

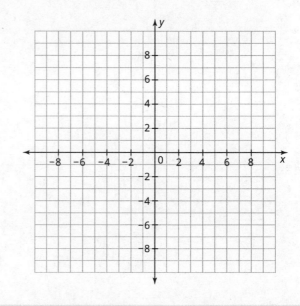

Review

1. Consider the two polynomial functions $m(x)$ and $n(x)$.

   $m(x) = -(x^2 + 2)(x^2 - 4)$

   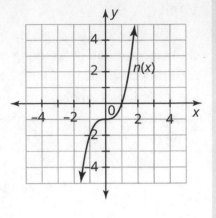

   a. Which function has the greater y-intercept?

   b. Which function has the greater output as x approaches infinity?

2. Use the factors to sketch each cubic function and label the zeros.

   a. $f(x) = x(x - 5)(x + 2)$

   b. $g(x) = (x + 4)(x - 6)(x + 1)$

3. Determine the roots of each equation. Check your solutions.

   a. $y = x^2 + 6x + 4$

   b. $y = 2x^2 + 9x - 18$

Divide and Conquer

Polynomial Division

Warm Up

Determine each quotient.

1. $9x \div 3x$

2. $4x^2 \div 2x$

3. $x^3 \div x$

Learning Goals

- Describe similarities between polynomials and integers.
- Determine factors of a polynomial using one or more roots of the polynomial.
- Compare polynomial long division to integer long division.
- Determine factors through polynomial long division.
- Use the Remainder Theorem to evaluate polynomial equations and functions.

Key Terms

- Factor Theorem
- polynomial long division
- Remainder Theorem
- synthetic division

You know how to divide integers using the long division algorithm. How can you use a similar algorithm to divide polynomials?

The *x* – *r* Factor

You have analyzed the graphs of polynomials to determine the type and location of the zeros. How can you determine the factors of a polynomial given its algebraic representation and one of its factors?

1. **Analyze the graph of the function $h(x) = x^3 + 12x^2 + 41x + 72$.**

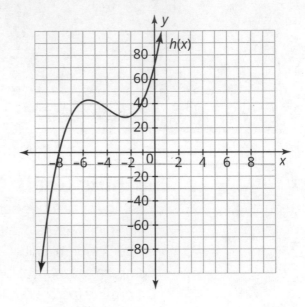

a. **Describe the key characteristics of $h(x)$.**

b. **Describe the number and types of zeros of $h(x)$.**

The **Factor Theorem** states that a polynomial function $p(x)$ has $(x - r)$ as a factor if and only if the value of the function at r is 0, or $p(r) = 0$.

You can use the Factor Theorem to show that a linear expression is a factor of a polynomial.

Worked Example

Consider the graph of the polynomial function $h(x) = x^3 + 12x^2 + 41x + 72$ in Question 1.

The graph appears to have a zero at $(-8, 0)$, so a possible linear factor of the polynomial is $(x + 8)$.

Determine the value of the polynomial at $x = -8$, or $h(-8)$.

$$h(-8) = (-8)^3 + 12(-8)^2 + 41(-8) + 72$$

$$= -512 + 768 + (-328) + 72$$

$$= 0$$

So, $(x + 8)$ is a linear factor of the polynomial function.

2. Consider that $d(x) = (x + 8)$, and $d(x) \cdot q(x) = h(x)$.

   a. What do you know about the function $q(x)$?

   b. Can you write the algebraic representation for $q(x)$?
      Explain your reasoning.

ACTIVITY 2.1 Polynomial Long Division

To solve $0 = x^3 + 12x^2 + 41x + 72$, you need to factor the polynomial and use the Zero Product Property to determine its zeros.

The Fundamental Theorem of Algebra states that every polynomial equation of degree n must have n roots. This means that every polynomial can be written as the product of n factors of the form $(ax + b)$. For example, $2x^2 - 3x - 9 = (2x + 3)(x - 3)$.

Remember:

Recall that $a \div b$ is $\frac{a}{b}$, where $b \neq 0$.

If 2 is a factor of 24, then 24 can be divided by 2 without a remainder. In the same way, the factors of a polynomial divide into that polynomial without a remainder.

Polynomial long division is an algorithm for dividing one polynomial by another of equal or lesser degree. The process is similar to integer long division.

Worked Example

Integer Long Division	Polynomial Long Division
$3660 \div 12$ or $\dfrac{3660}{12}$ $\begin{array}{r} 305 \\ 12\overline{)3660} \\ -36 \\ \hline 6 \\ -0 \\ \hline 60 \\ -60 \\ \hline 0 \end{array}$	$(x^3 + 12x^2 + 41x + 72) \div (x + 8)$ or $\dfrac{x^3 + 12x^2 + 41x + 72}{x - 8}$ Ⓐ Ⓓ Ⓖ $x + 8\overline{)x^3 + 12x^2 + 41x + 72}$ $x^2 + 4x + 9$ Ⓑ $\underline{-(x^3 + 8x^2)}$ Ⓔ $4x^2 + 41x$ Ⓒ $\underline{-(4x^2 + 32x)}$ $9x + 72$ Ⓕ Ⓗ $\underline{-(9x + 72)}$ Remainder 0 A. Divide $\frac{x^3}{x} = x^2$. B. Multiply $x^2(x + 8)$, and then subtract. C. Bring down $41x$. D. Divide $\frac{4x^2}{x} = 4x$. E. Multiply $4x(x + 8)$, and then subtract. F. Bring down $+72$. G. Divide $\frac{9x}{x} = 9$. H. Multiply $9(x + 8)$, and then subtract.

© Carnegie Learning, Inc.

1. **Analyze the worked example that shows integer long division and polynomial long division.**

   a. **In what ways are the integer and polynomial long division algorithms similar?**

   b. **Rewrite each expression as a product of its factors.**

   $3660 =$ _____ · _____ $x^3 + 12x^2 + 41x + 72 =$ _____ · _____

   c. **Is $h(x)$ completely factored? Explain your reasoning.**

   d. **Rewrite the function as a product of its linear factors.**

   e. **Determine the zeros of the function.**

2. **The expression $(x - 7)$ is a factor of $x^3 - 10x^2 + 11x + 70$. Solve $0 = x^3 - 10x^2 + 11x + 70$ over the set of complex numbers.**

Recall that you can use the difference of squares to factor a binomial of the form
$a^2 - b^2$. The binomial $a^2 - b^2 = (a + b)(a - b)$.

1. **Use the difference of squares to factor each binomial over the set of real numbers.**

   a. $x^2 - 64$

   b. $x^4 - 16$

   c. $x^8 - 1$

   d. $x^4 - y^4$

Now let's consider expressions composed of perfect cubes, such as
$f(x) = x^3 - 8$.

2. **Consider Kingston's and Toby's work.**

Kingston 👎
I can use the Properties of
Equality to determine the factors.
$x^3 - 8 = 0$
$\quad x^3 = 8$
$\quad\quad x = 2$
$f(x) = (x - 2)(x - 2)(x - 2)$
or
$f(x) = (x - 2)^3$

Toby 👍

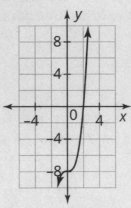

I looked at the
graph of $f(x) = x^3$
and could see that
$x = 2$ is one of
the zeros, but the
other two zeros
are imaginary.

a. **Describe Kingston's error.**

b. **Use long division to factor over the set $f(x) = x^3 - 8$ of real numbers.**

You can rewrite the expression $x^3 - 27$ as $(x)^3 - (3)^3$, and $x^3 + 27$ as $(x)^3 + (3)^3$. When you factor sums and differences of cubes, there is a special factoring formula you can use, which is similar to the difference of squares for quadratics.

To determine the formula for the difference of cubes, generalize the difference of cubes as $a^3 - b^3$.

Worked Example

To determine the factor formula for the difference of cubes, factor out $(a - b)$ by considering $(a^3 - b^3) \div (a - b)$.

$$
\begin{array}{r}
a^2 + ab + b^2 \\
a - b \overline{\smash{)}a^3 - 0a^2b + 0ab^2 - b^3} \\
\underline{-(a^3 - a^2b)} \\
a^2b + 0ab^2 \\
\underline{-(a^2b - ab^2)} \\
ab^2 - b^3 \\
\underline{-(ab^2 - b^3)} \\
0
\end{array}
$$

Therefore, the difference of cubes can be rewritten in factored form as:

$a^3 - b^3 = (a - b)(a^2 + ab + b^2)$.

When performing long division, make sure that the dividend is in descending order. If any powers are not included, use a zero to help with spacing.

---

3. **Use Properties of Equality to determine one zero. Then factor each polynomial function over the set of real numbers.**

   a. $f(x) = x^3 - 27$ b. $g(x) = x^3 + 27$

4. **Determine the formula for the sum of cubes by dividing $a^3 + b^3$ by $(a + b)$.**

5. **Use the sum or difference of cubes to factor each binomial over the set of real numbers.**

   a. $x^3 + 125$ b. $8x^3 - 1$

   c. $x^6 - 8$ d. $x^9 + y^9$

You learned that the process of dividing polynomials is similar to the process of dividing integers. Sometimes when you divide two integers there is a remainder, and sometimes there is not a remainder. What does each case mean? In this activity, you will investigate what the remainder means in terms of polynomial division.

Ask yourself:

Is the dividend in descending order? Are there any powers of x not included?

1. **Determine the quotient for each. Show all of your work.**

   a. $(x^3 + 2x^2 - 5x + 16) \div (x - 4)$

   b. $(4x^4 + 5x^2 - 7x + 9) \div (2x - 3)$

   c. $(9x^4 + 3x^3 + 4x^2 + 7x + 2) \div (3x + 2)$

2. **Consider Question 1 parts (a) through (c) to answer each.**

   a. **When there is a remainder, is the divisor a factor of the dividend? Explain your reasoning.**

   b. **Describe the remainder when you divide a polynomial by one of its factors.**

Remember from your experiences with division that:

$$\frac{\text{dividend}}{\text{divisor}} = \text{quotient} + \frac{\text{remainder}}{\text{divisor}}$$

or

dividend = (divisor) (quotient) + remainder.

It follows that any polynomial, $p(x)$, can be written in the form:

$$\frac{p(x)}{\text{linear expression}} = \text{quotient} + \frac{\text{remainder}}{\text{linear expression}}$$

or

$p(x)$ = (linear expression) (quotient) + remainder.

Generally, the linear expression is written in the form $(x - r)$, the quotient is represented by $q(x)$, and the remainder is represented by R.

$$p(x) = (x - r)\, q(x) + R$$

3. **Consider each dividend in Question 1 as a function, $p(x)$.**

    a. **In part (a), evaluate $p(x)$ for $x = 4$.**

    b. **In part (b), evaluate $p(x)$ for $x = \frac{3}{2}$.**

    c. **In part (c), evaluate $p(x)$ for $x = -\frac{2}{3}$.**

Remember:

    d. **How does the remainder relate to the divisor in each problem?**

The Factor Theorem states that a polynomial has a linear polynomial as a factor if and only if the remainder is zero. Therefore, if R = 0, then $f(r) = 0$, and $(x - r)$ is a factor of $f(x)$.

4. **What conclusion can you make about any polynomial evaluated at r?**

The **Remainder Theorem** states that when any polynomial function, $f(x)$, is divided by a linear expression of the form $(x - r)$, the remainder $R = f(r)$, or the value of the function when $x = r$.

5. Given $p(x) = x^3 + 6x^2 + 5x - 12$ and $\dfrac{p(x)}{(x - 2)} = x^2 + 8x + 21$ R 30, Rico says that $p(-2) = 30$ and Paloma says that $p(2) = 30$. Without performing any calculations, who is correct? Explain your reasoning.

6. The function $f(x) = 4x^2 + 2x + 9$ generates the same remainder when divided by $(x - r)$ and $(x - 2r)$, where r is not equal to 0. Calculate the value(s) of r.

7. **Determine the unknown in each.**

   a. $\frac{x}{7} = 18$ R 2. Determine x.

   b. $\frac{p(x)}{x+3} = 3x^2 + 14x + 15$ R 3. Determine the function $p(x)$.

   c. **Describe the similarities and differences in your solution strategies.**

Synthetic Division

Although dividing polynomials through long division is analogous to integer long division, it can still be inefficient and time consuming. **Synthetic division** is a more efficient method for dividing a polynomial by a linear expression of the form $(x - r)$. This method requires fewer calculations and less writing by representing the polynomial and the linear factor as a set of numeric values. After the values are processed, you can then use the numeric outputs to construct the quotient and the remainder.

> Notice in the form of the linear factor $(x - r)$, the x has a coefficient of 1. Also, just as in long division, when you use synthetic division, every power of the dividend must have a placeholder.

To use synthetic division to divide a polynomial $ax^2 + bx + c$ by a linear factor $x - r$, follow this pattern.

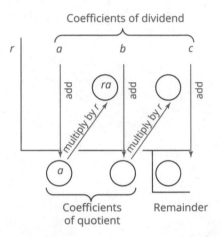

Worked Example

You can use synthetic division in place of the standard long division algorithm to determine the quotient for $(x^3 + 12x^2 + 41x + 72) \div (x + 8)$.

Long Division	Synthetic Division
$$\begin{array}{r} x^2 + \ \ 4x + 9 \\ x + 8 \overline{)\ x^3 + 12x^2 + 41x + 72} \\ -(x^3 + \ \ 8x^2) \ \ \ \ \ \ \ \ \ \ \ \ \ \ \ \ \\ 4x^2 + 41x \ \ \ \ \ \ \ \ \\ -(4x^2 + 32x) \ \ \ \ \ \ \\ 9x + 72 \\ -(9x + 72) \\ 0 \end{array}$$	$r = -8$ -8 1 12 41 72 multiply by r: -8, -32, -72; add 1 4 9 0

$$(x^3 + 12x^2 + 41x + 72) \div (x + 8) = x^2 + 4x + 9$$

1. **Analyze the worked example.**

   a. **Write the dividend as the product of its factors.**

   b. **Why does the synthetic division algorithm work?**

Think about:

When you use synthetic division, you are multiplying and adding, as opposed to multiplying and subtracting when you use long division.

2. **An example of synthetic division is provided. Perform the steps outlined for the problem.**

$$\begin{array}{r|rrrrr} 2 & 1 & 0 & -4 & -3 & 6 \\ & & 2 & 4 & 0 & -6 \\ \hline & 1 & 2 & 0 & -3 & \boxed{0} \end{array}$$

   a. **Write the dividend.**

   b. **Write the divisor.**

   c. **Write the quotient.**

   d. **Write the dividend as the product of the divisor and the quotient plus the remainder.**

Ask yourself:

How can you tell by looking at the synthetic division process whether the divisor is a factor of the polynomial?

3. **Complete the synthetic division for $(2x^4 - 4x^3 + 4x^2 - 3x + 6) \div (x + 3)$. Write the dividend as the product of the divisor and the quotient plus the remainder.**

Synthetic division works only for linear divisors in the form $(x - r)$. If the divisor has a leading coefficient other than 1, you may need to factor out a constant in order to rewrite the divisor in the form $(x - r)$.

Worked Example

You can use synthetic division to determine the quotient of $\frac{2x^3 - 6x^2 + 4x + 2}{2x - 3}$. Since the divisor is not in the form $x - r$, you must rewrite $2x - 3$ as $2\left(x - \frac{3}{2}\right)$.

The numbers in the last row become the coefficients of the quotient.

$$2x^2 - 3x - \frac{1}{2} \text{ R } \frac{5}{4}$$

You can write the dividend as the product of the divisor and the quotient plus the remainder.

$$2x^3 - 6x^2 + 4x + 2 = \left(x - \frac{3}{2}\right)\left(2x^2 - 3x - \frac{1}{2}\right) + \frac{5}{4}$$

To determine the quotient of $\frac{2x^3 - 6x^2 + 4x + 2}{2x - 3}$, you need to return to the original divisor of $(2x - 3)$. To do so, double $\left(x - \frac{3}{2}\right)$ and halve $\left(2x^2 - 3x - \frac{1}{2}\right)$.

$$2x^3 - 6x^2 + 4x + 2 = 2\left(x - \frac{3}{2}\right)\left(\frac{1}{2}\left(2x^2 - 3x - \frac{1}{2}\right)\right) + \frac{5}{4}$$

$$= (2x - 3)\left(x^2 - \frac{3}{2}x - \frac{1}{4}\right) + \frac{5}{4}$$

Therefore, $\frac{2x^3 - 6x^2 + 4x + 2}{2x - 3} = x^2 - \frac{3}{2}x - \frac{1}{4} + \frac{5}{4(2x - 3)}$.

4. **Verify $(3x - 2)(x^2 + x + 1) = 3x^3 + x^2 + x - 2$ using synthetic division. Show all work and explain your reasoning.**

5. **Determine the zeros of each function.**

a. $f(x) = x^3 + 11x^2 + 37x + 42$

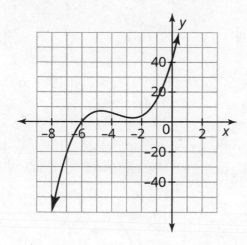

b. $f(x) = x^3 - 4.75x^2 + 3.125x - 0.50$

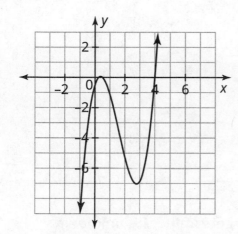

TALK the TALK 💬

A Polynomial Divided

In the Getting Started, you learned that the Factor Theorem is a way to show that a linear expression is a factor of a polynomial.

You can also use the Factor Theorem to determine unknown information about a polynomial if you know a linear factor of that polynomial.

> ### Worked Example
>
> Given the function $f(x) = x^3 - 4x^2 - ax + 10$.
>
> You can determine the unknown coefficient, a, given that $x - 5$ is a linear factor.
>
> If $(x - 5)$ is a linear factor, then, by the Factor Theorem, $f(5) = 0$.
>
> $f(5) = 5^3 - 4(5)^2 - 5a + 10$
> $ 0 = 5^3 - 4(5)^2 - 5a + 10$
> $ 0 = 125 - 100 - 5a + 10$
> $ 0 = 35 - 5a$
> $ 5a = 35$
> $ a = 7$
>
> So, the unknown coefficient, a, is equal to 7, and
> $f(x) = x^3 - 4x^2 - 7x + 10$.

1. **Use the worked example to determine the unknown coefficient, a, in each function. Then identify the zeros of the functions over the set of complex numbers.**

   a. $f(x) = x^3 - 9x^2 + ax + 60$, if $x - 5$ is a linear factor.

   b. $f(x) = x^4 + ax^2 - 3$, if $x - 1$ is a linear factor.

2. **Given the information, determine whether each statement is true or false. Explain your reasoning.**

$$p(x) = x^3 + 6x^2 + 11x + 6, \text{ and}$$
$$p(x) \div (x + 4) = x^2 + 2x + 3 \ \text{R} -6$$

a. $p(-4) = -6$

b. $p(x) = (x + 4)(x^2 + 2x + 3) - 6$

c. $(x - 3)$ is a factor of $p(x)$

d. $(x + 2)$ is a factor of $p(x)$

3. **Explain the difference between the Remainder Theorem and the Factor Theorem.**

Assignment

Write

Write an example for each term using the dividend $x^2 - 2x + 4$ and the divisor $x + 1$.

1. Factor Theorem
2. Polynomial long division
3. Remainder Theorem
4. Synthetic division

Remember

A polynomial function $p(x)$ has $(x - r)$ as a factor if and only if the value of the function at r is 0, or $p(r) = 0$. When any polynomial equation or function $f(x)$ is divided by a linear expression of the form $(x - r)$, the remainder is $R = f(r)$ or the value of the equation or function when $x = r$.

Practice

1. Use the Factor Theorem to determine whether each linear expression is a factor of the polynomial $x^4 + x^3 - 17x^2 + 15x$.

   a. $x + 3$ b. $x + 5$ c. $x - 1$

2. Factor each binomial over the set of real numbers.

   a. $4x^2 - 9y^2$ b. $x^3 + 216$

3. The Polynomial Pool Company offers 10 different pool designs numbered 1 through 10. Each pool is in the shape of a rectangular prism. The volume of water in Pool Design x can be determined using the function $V(x) = l(x) \cdot w(x) \cdot d(x) = 2x^3 + 18x^2 + 46x + 30$, where $l(x)$, $w(x)$, and $d(x)$ represent the length, width, and depth of the pool in feet.

   a. Determine the expressions for the functions $w(x)$ and $d(x)$ if $l(x) = 2x + 2$ and the width of each pool is greater than the depth. Do not use a calculator.

   b. Determine the length, width, and depth of Pool Design 9.

4. The function $m(x) = 2x^2 + 6x - 7$ generates the same remainder when divided by $(x - a)$ and $(x - 2a)$ when $a \neq 0$. Calculate the value(s) of a and determine the corresponding factors.

5. The given table of values represents the function $f(x) = x^3 + 9x^2 + 14x - 24$.

(x)	-2	-1	0	1	2
$f(x)$	-24	-30	-24	0	48

   a. Determine one of the factors of $f(x)$ without using a calculator. Explain your reasoning.
   b. Completely factor $f(x)$ without using a calculator.
   c. Determine all of the zeros of $f(x)$ without using a calculator.

Stretch

The Rational Root Theorem states that if the polynomial

$P(n) = a_nx^n + a_{1-n}x^{n-1} + \ldots + a_2x^2 + a_1x + a_0$ has any rational roots, then they must be of the

form $\pm\frac{p}{q}$, where p is factors of a_0 and q is factors of a_n.

1. Consider the function $f(x) = 3x^3 - 4x^2 - 17x + 6$.

   a. Determine the values of a_0 and a_n for this polynomial function.

   b. Determine the values of p, or the factors of a_0.

   c. Determine the values of q, or the factors of a_n.

   d. Determine the possible rational zeros of the function.

   e. Check all the possible rational zeros to determine whether any of them are
      roots of the function $f(x)$.

Review

1. Determine the zeros of each function.

   a. $f(x) = 3(x - 1)^4 - 9$

   b. $f(x) = -2(x + 2)^3 - 1$

   c. $f(x) = 5(x + 3)^3$

2. Factor each polynomial over the set of real numbers.

   a. $16x^2 - 3x - 3$ b. $x^4 - 10x^2 + 25$

3. Sketch the graph of $f(x) = x^{17}$ and describe the end behavior of the graph.

Closing Time

The Closure Property

Warm Up

Identify which of the functions are polynomials. Explain your reasoning.

1. $f(x) = 6$

2. $g(x) = \frac{1}{x}$

3. $h(x) = \sqrt{x}$

4. $m(x) = 2^x$

5. $n(x) = x^{2-9}$

Learning Goals

- Compare functions that are closed under addition, subtraction, and multiplication to functions that are not closed under these operations.
- Analyze the meaning for polynomials to be closed under an operation.
- Compare integer and polynomial operations.

Key Term

- closed under an operation

You have added, subtracted, multiplied, and divided two or more polynomial functions to build a new polynomial function. How are these operations similar to those involving integers?

Need for Closure

Throughout this course, you have added, subtracted, multiplied, and divided two or more polynomial functions to build a new polynomial function. You did this using a graph, algebra, and a table of values. When an operation is performed with any numbers or expressions in a set and the result is in the same set, it is said to be **closed under that operation**.

Are polynomials closed under addition, subtraction, multiplication, and division? In other words, when you add, subtract, multiply, or divide polynomial functions, do you always create another polynomial function?

Before answering this question, let's analyze closure within the real number system.

1. **Determine whether each set within the real number system is closed under addition, subtraction, multiplication, and division.**

   a. **Complete the table. If a set is not closed under a given operation, provide a counterexample.**

	Addition	Subtraction	Multiplication	Division
Natural Numbers {1, 2, 3, 4, . . .}				
Whole Numbers {0, 1, 2, 3, . . .}	Yes	No 2 − 3 = −1		
Integers { . . . −2, −1, 0, 1, 2 . . .}				
Rational Numbers Can be represented as the ratio of two integers				
Irrational Numbers Cannot be represented as the ratio of two integers				

   b. **What patterns do you notice?**

ACTIVITY 3.1 · The Closure Property for Polynomials

You conjectured that integers are closed under addition, subtraction, and multiplication. You also determined through counterexamples that integers are not closed under division.

1. Similarities between integer and polynomial operations are shown in the table.

	Integer Example	Polynomial Example
Addition	$400 + 30 + 7$ $+20 + 5$ $400 + 50 + 12$	$4x^2 + 3x + 7$ $+2x + 5$ $4x^2 + 5x + 12$
Subtraction	$400 + 30 + 7$ $-(20 + 5)$ $400 + 10 + 12$	$4x^2 + 3x + 7$ $-(2x + 5)$ $4x^2 + x + 2$
Multiplication	$400 +30 + 7$ $\times20 + 5$ $2000 + 150 + 35$ $8000 +600 + 140$ $8000 + 2600 + 290 + 35$	$4x^2 +3x + 7$ $\times2x + 5$ $20x^2 + 15x + 35$ $8x^3 + 6x^2 + 14x$ $8x^3 + 26x^2 + 29x + 35$
Division	$\frac{437}{25} = 17$ R12	$\frac{4x^2 + 3x + 7}{2x + 5} = (2x - 3)\text{ R}(-x + 22)$

a. Describe the similarities between polynomial and integer operations.

b. In what ways is the Distributive Property essential to performing operations with integers and polynomials?

© Carnegie Learning, Inc.

c. How does this example demonstrate that polynomials are not closed under division?

d. Verify that the polynomial division was performed correctly.

For part (d), consider the integer example. How would you verify that $\frac{437}{25} = 17$ R12?

2. Let's think about polynomials and closure in terms of graphical representations. Use technology to determine whether polynomial functions are closed under addition, subtraction, multiplication, and division.

a. Write 5 polynomials with various degrees that you will use to explore closure.

$y_1 =$ _____ $y_2 =$ _____

$y_3 =$ _____

$y_4 =$ _____ $y_5 =$ _____

b. **Determine whether the polynomials are closed under addition, subtraction, multiplication, and division. Show all work and explain your reasoning.**

Take some time to explore closure by performing operations with various polynomials. Experiment algebraically and graphically and see what happens. Then make a conjecture – that's what mathematicians do!

c. **How do you know when a polynomial is not closed under a given operation? Explain your reasoning in terms of the graph, table, and algebraic representation.**

Think
about:

Keep in mind that showing something is true using one example is not a proof. But showing just one counterexample is enough to disprove a statement.

TALK the TALK

Shut the Door and Turn Out the Lights

1. Consider the two polynomial functions $f(x)$ and $g(x)$.

$$f(x) = a_n x^n + a_{n-1} x^{n-1} + \cdots + a_1 x + a_0$$
$$g(x) = b_n x^n + b_{n-1} x^{n-1} + \cdots + b_1 x + b_0$$

a. Prove that polynomials are closed under subtraction.

b. Use the multiplication table to prove that polynomials are closed under multiplication.

$\cdot$	$a_n x^n$	$a_{n-1} x^{n-1}$	$\cdots$	$a_1 x$	a_0
$b_n x^n$					
$b_{n-1} x^{n-1}$					
$\vdots$					
$b_1 x$					
b_0					

Assignment

© Carnegie Learning, Inc.

Write

In your own words, explain what it means for a set to be closed under a certain operation.

Remember

Polynomials are closed under addition, subtraction, and multiplication.
Polynomials are not closed under division.

Practice

1. Ralph builds a function by performing one of the 4 basic operations (addition, subtraction, multiplication, or division) on 2 polynomial functions. The graph of the resulting function is shown. Which of the 4 basic operations could Ralph have used on the 2 polynomial functions to build his function? Explain your reasoning.

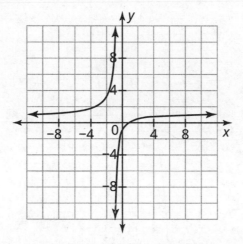

2. Write 2 polynomial functions $f(x)$ and $g(x)$ such that $h(x) = \frac{f(x)}{g(x)}$ and such that $h(x)$ is a polynomial function. Does your solution prove that polynomial functions are closed under division? Explain your reasoning.

Stretch

Given $f(x) = x^4 - 625$, determine all the possible polynomial functions for $g(x)$ such that $h(x) = \frac{f(x)}{g(x)}$ is a polynomial function.

Review

1. Determine whether $x - 2$ is a factor of $f(x) = x^4 - 8x^3 + 10x^2 + 2x - 4$.

2. Use the given information and the Remainder Theorem to sketch the graph of $g(x)$. Explain each step.

   Given: $\dfrac{g(x)}{x - 1} = x^2 + x - 15\ R - 15$

   $\dfrac{g(x)}{x + 2} = x^2 - 2x - 12\ R\ 24$

   $\dfrac{g(x)}{x - 4} = x^2 + 4x\ R\ 0$

   The function $g(x)$ is cubic and its graph is symmetric about the origin.

3. Analyze the graphs of the functions $f(x)$ and $g(x)$

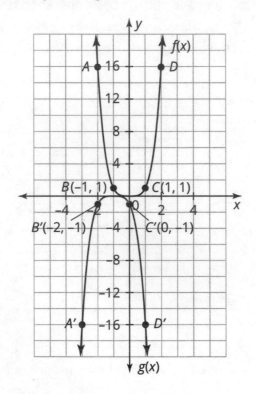

   a. Write the equation for $f(x)$.

   b. The function $g(x)$ is a transformation of the function $f(x)$. Describe the transformations performed on $f(x)$ that resulted in the function $g(x)$. Explain your reasoning.

   c. Write the equation for $g(x)$.

   d. Is the function $g(x)$ even, odd, or neither? Explain your reasoning.

4. Determine the product: $(2x - 9)(-3x^2 + 8x - 15)$.

Unequal Equals

Solving Polynomial Inequalities

Warm Up

Consider the function $f(x) = x^4 - 13x^2 + 36$. Identify the zeros and sketch a graph of the polynomial.

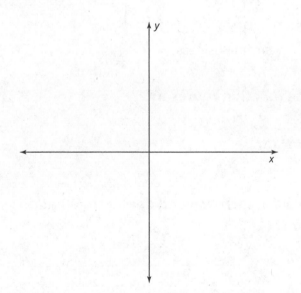

Learning Goals

- Represent problem situations using polynomial inequalities.
- Determine solutions to polynomial inequalities algebraically and graphically.

You have solved and graphed linear and quadratic inequalities. How can you graph inequalities involving polynomial expressions?

Lawn and Order

Lawn Enforcement is a small landscaping company. It has a profit model that can be represented by the function

$$p(x) = -x^4 + 19.75x^3 - 133.25x^2 + 351.25x - 280.75$$

where profit, in thousands of dollars, is a function of time, in years, the company has been in business. Let's analyze $p(x)$ represented on a graph.

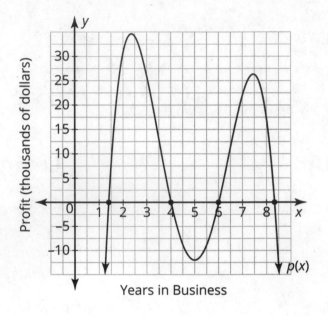

1. **What do the zeros of the function represent?**

2. **Approximate the intervals of increase and decrease. What do these intervals represent?**

The graph shown represents the change in profit as a function of the number of years that Lawn Enforcement has been in business. When did the company lose money?

Worked Example

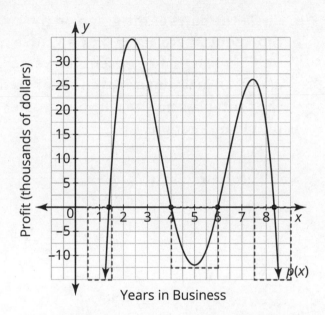

Years in Business

The points identified on the graph represent the zeros of the function where Lawn Enforcement's profit was 0.

Each point on the number line represents the years in business when Lawn Enforcement's profit was 0.

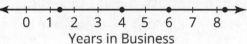

Years in Business

The function $p(x) = 0$ when $x = 1.4, 4, 6, 8.3$.

The regions on the number line enclosed in dashed boxes represent the years in business when Lawn Enforcement's profit was less than 0.

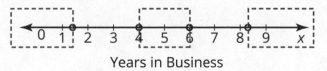

Years in Business

The function $p(x) < 0$ when $\begin{cases} x < 1.4 \\ 4 < x < 6 \\ x > 8.3 \end{cases}$.

1. Analyze the worked example.

   a. Why were the points changed to open circles on the number line to represent the years in business when $p(x) < 0$.

   b. Circle the parts of the graph on the coordinate plane that represent where $p(x) > 0$. Then circle the intervals on the number line that represent the years in business where $p(x) > 0$. Finally identify the set of x-values to complete the sentence and explain your answer in terms of this problem situation.

      The function $p(x) > 0$ when _____.

   c. Draw a solid box around the segment(s) where $p(x) > 35,000$. Then identify the set of x-values to complete the sentence. Finally, explain your answer in terms of this problem situation.

      The function $p(x) > 35,000$ when _____.

Methods for Solving Polynomial Inequalities

Solving polynomial inequalities is very similar to solving linear inequalities.

1. **Samson, Kaley, Paco, and Sal each solved the quadratic inequality** $2x^2 + 14x < -24$.

Samson 👍

I graphed both sides of the inequality.

$$y_1 = -24$$
$$y_2 = 2x^2 + 14x$$

I drew vertical dashed lines at the two points where the graphs intersect. I can then determine from the graph that the x-values of $2x^2 + 14x$ that generate values less than -24 are between -4 and -3. Therefore the solution to the inequality is $-4 < x < -3$.

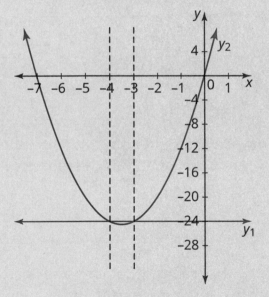

> **Remember:**
>
> The symbols $>$ or $<$ are represented with dotted lines, and $\geq$ or $\leq$ are represented with solid lines.
>
> When you are determining which region(s) to shade, look at y-values above or below the boundary line, depending on the inequality sign.

© Carnegie Learning, Inc.

Paco

I added 24 to both sides of the inequality because I wanted one side to be equal to 0. Then, I graphed that inequality.

$$y_1 = 2x^2 + 14x + 24$$

I drew vertical dashed lines where the graph crosses the x-axis.

I can then determine from the graph that the x-values of $2x^2 + 14x + 24$ that generate values less than 0 are between −4 and −3.

Therefore the solution to the inequality is $-4 < x < -3$.

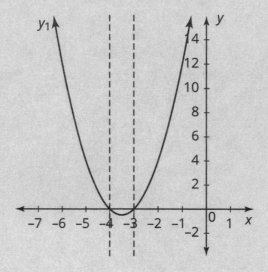

a. **Explain how Samson and Paco could have determined the zeros and axis of symmetry of the function.**

b. **Explain why the graphs of Samson and Paco are different, yet generate the same answers.**

c. **Explain the error in Sal's work.**

Kaley

I remember from solving linear inequalities that I can first treat the inequality as an equation and solve.

$0 = 2x^2 + 14x + 24$
$0 = 2(x^2 + 7x + 12)$
$0 = 2(x + 3)(x + 4)$
$x = -4, -3$

This means that the x-intercepts are -4 and -3. Breaking up the number line into 3 parts and testing each section in the original inequality $-24 > 2x^2 + 14x$, I can determine the solution.

Test x = −3.5
$-24 > 2(-3.5)^2 + 14(-3.5)$
$-24 > -24.5$
✓

Test x = −5
$-24 > 2(-5)^2 + 14(-5)$
$-24 > -20$
✗

Test x = 0
$-24 > 2(0)^2 + 14(0)$
$-24 > 0$
✗

The only section that satisfies the original inequality is when x is between -4 and -3, so the solution to the inequality is $-4 < x < -3$.

Sal

I remember from solving linear inequalities that I can treat the inequality as an equation and solve.

$2x^2 + 14x = -24$
$2x(x + 7) = -24$
$2x = -24 \quad (x + 7) = -24$
$x = -12 \qquad\qquad x = -31$

This means that the x-intercepts are -12 and -31, so the solution to the inequality is $-31 < x < -12$.

d. **Compare Samson's method to Kaley's method.**
   List advantages and disadvantages of each method.

2. Solve $18 \leq 3x^2 + x$. Show your work algebraically and graphically.

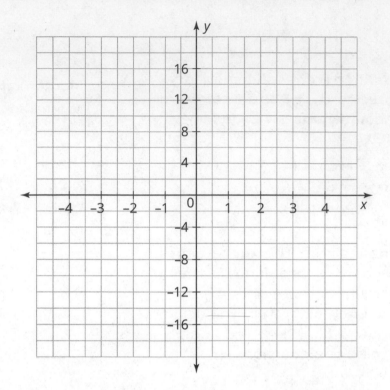

3. Solve each inequality and sketch a graph of the solution.

a. $2x^3 - 8x^2 - 8x + 32 > 0$

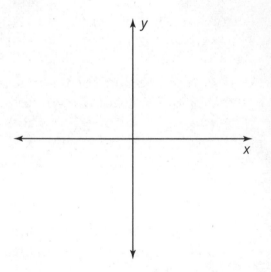

b. $6x^3 - 21x^2 - 12x > 0$

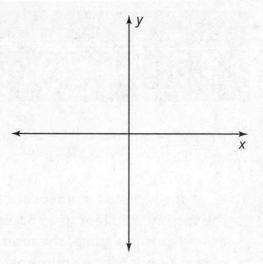

Think about:

Consider the inequality sign when graphing the polynomial. Will the graph be a dashed or solid smooth curve?

c. $x^4 - 13x^2 + 36 \leq 0$

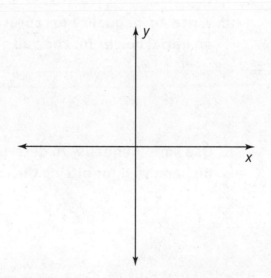

Polynomial inequalities can be used to represent everyday situations.
Write and solve each real-world inequality.

1. **Get Your Kicks is an indoor soccer complex. The roof's height at the facility is 80 feet. If a soccer ball is kicked and touches the ceiling during a game, the team that kicked the ball must have a player sit out for two minutes. Michael kicks a ball straight up in the air with an initial velocity of 73 feet per second.**

   a. **Write an inequality to represent this problem situation, given an initial height for the ball of 0 ft.**

   b. **Use your inequality to determine whether Michael's team will be penalized for hitting the ceiling. Explain your reasoning.**

Remember:

The formula for vertical motion is $h(t) = -16t^2 + V_0 t + h_0$ where v_0 represents initial velocity and h_0 represents initial height.

2. **Glen High School's student council is hosting a dance to raise money for panda bears. The dance will cost $2250. At the current ticket price of $10, the council knows that they will have 185 people attend the dance. This is not enough people to cover the cost of the dance, so they estimate that for every $0.25 decrease in ticket price, 15 more people will attend the dance.**

   a. **Write an equation that will represent the profit that the dance will make.**

   b. **Write an inequality to represent the dance making a profit.**

c. Determine the maximum price the council can charge for tickets and still make a profit.

d. Determine the price of the ticket that will maximize profit. What is the maximum profit?

3. The average blood sugar (also known as glucose) level in a person's blood should be between 70 and 100 mg/dL (milligrams per deciliter) one hour after eating. A person with Type 2 diabetes strives to keep glucose levels under 120 mg/dL with diet and exercise in order to avoid insulin injections. The glucose level of an individual over the span of 72 hours can be represented with the polynomial function

$$b(t) = 0.000139x^4 - 0.0188x^3 + 0.8379x^2 - 13.55x + 176.51$$

where glucose level is a function of the number of hours.

a. For what hours was the glucose level greater than 120 mg/dL?

b. For what hours was the glucose level less than 120 mg/dL?

TALK the TALK

Welcome Our Robot Overlords

A new robotic household assistant is now available for purchase from RoboCorp.

The robot comes in three separate packages. A cube box with unknown dimensions contains the head. A 10-inch-tall box for the two legs has the same width and length as the cube. And a third box with a 4 in. × 6 in. box bottom and the same height as the cube holds the torso.

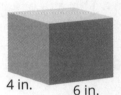

1. **What are the possible approximate volumes of the robot's head, legs, and torso if an entire shipment of one robot takes up less than half of a cubic foot?**

   Sketch a graph and show your work.

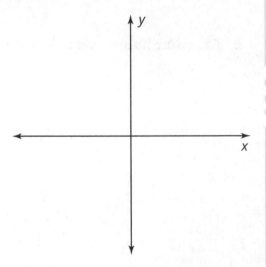

Assignment

Write

In your own words, explain how solving a polynomial inequality is similar to solving a linear inequality.

Remember

The solutions to a polynomial inequality are intervals of x-values that satisfy the inequality.

Practice

1. Emilio has been trying to regulate the pH level in his tropical fish aquarium for 5 hours. In order to make the water safe for his fish, Emilio must keep the pH level less than or equal to 9. The function $p(x) = -0.34x^3 + 2.652x^2 - 5.4638x + 11.1114$ represents the pH level in the tank x hours since Emilio began to regulate it.

   a. Write an inequality that represents the pH level in the tank being in the safe range.

   b. Solve the inequality and determine the time intervals during which the pH level in the tank safe for Emilio's fish.

2. Solve the inequality $2x^3 - 8x \leq 0$ by factoring and sketching. Use the given coordinate plane to sketch the general graph of the polynomial in order to determine which values satisfy the inequality. Label the axes.

Stretch

Solve $x^5 - 4x^3 + x^2 - 4 \leq 0$.

Review

1. Completely factor each expression over the set of real numbers.

    a. $x^3 - 4x^2 - x + 4$ 　　　　　　　　b. $x^4 - 8x^2 - 9$

2. Describe the combination of real and imaginary zeros for each graphed function. Include the multiplicity of each real zero.

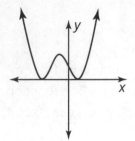 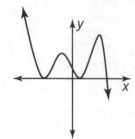

3. Describe the end behavior of each function.

    a. $f(x) = -x^4 - 4x^3 + 3x + 25$ 　　　　　　　　b. $g(x) = 2x^5 - 9x^3 + 5x^2 - 8x - 10$

Relating Factors and Zeros Summary

KEY TERMS

- Factor Theorem
- polynomial long division
- Remainder Theorem
- synthetic division
- closed under an operation

LESSON 1	Satisfactory Factoring

To begin factoring any polynomial, always look for a greatest common factor (GCF). You can factor out the greatest common factor of the polynomial, and then factor what remains. A greatest common factor can be a variable, a constant, or both.

For example, $3x^3 + 12x^2 - 36x$ has a GCF of $3x$: $3x(x^2 + 4x - 12) = 3x(x + 6)(x - 2)$.

Some functions can be factored over the set of real numbers. However, all functions can be factored over the set of complex numbers.

For example, you can you use the Quadratic Formula to determine that the zeros of the function $f(x) = x^2 + 2x + 5$ are $x = -1 + 2i$ and $x = -1 - 2i$. Therefore, the function in factored form is $(x - (-1 + 2i))(x - (-1 - 2i))$.

Some polynomials in quadratic form may have common factors in some of the terms, but not all terms. In this case, it may be helpful to write the terms as a product of 2 terms. You can then substitute the common term with a variable, z, and factor as you would any polynomial in quadratic form. This method of factoring is called *chunking*.

For example, you can use chunking to factor $9x^2 + 21x + 10$. Notice that the first and second terms both contain the common factor, $3x$.

$9x^2 + 21x + 10 = (3x)^2 + 7(3x) + 10$ Rewrite terms as a product of common factors

$= z^2 + 7z + 10$ Let $z = 3x$

$= (z + 5)(z + 2)$ Factor the quadratic

$= (3x + 5)(3x + 2)$ Substitute $3x$ for z

The factored form of $9x^2 + 21x + 10$ is $(3x + 5)(3x + 2)$.

A special form of polynomial is a perfect square trinomial. In a perfect square trinomial, the first and last terms are perfect squares and the middle term is equivalent to 2 times the product of the square root of the first term and the square root of the last term.

Factoring a perfect square trinomial can occur in two forms:

$$a^2 - 2ab + b^2 = (a - b)^2$$
$$a^2 + 2ab + b^2 = (a + b)^2$$

In polynomials with 4 terms, you may notice that although not all terms share a common factor, pairs of terms might share a common factor. In this situation, you can *factor by grouping*.

For example, consider the polynomial $x^3 + 3x^2 - x - 3$.

$(x^3 + 3x^2) + (- x - 3)$ Divide the polynomial into two groups.

$x^2(x + 3) - 1(x + 3)$ Find the common factor in each group.

$(x^2 - 1)(x + 3)$ Regroup the factors.

$(x - 1)(x + 1)(x + 3)$ Factor the first group using the difference of perfect squares.

The factored form of $x^3 + 3x^2 - x - 3$ is $(x - 1)(x + 1)(x + 3)$.

Some 4th degree polynomials, written as a trinomial, look very similar to quadratics as they have the same form, $ax^4 + bx^2 + c$. When this is the case, the polynomial may be factored using the same methods you would use to factor a quadratic. This is called *factoring by using quadratic form*.

For example, consider the trinomial $x^4 - 29x + 100$.

$x^4 - 29x + 100$ Determine whether you can factor the given trinomial into 2 factors.

$(x^2 - 4)(x^2 - 25)$ Determine whether you can continue to factor each binomial.

$(x + 2)(x - 2)(x + 5)(x - 5)$

The factored form of $x^4 - 29x + 100$ is $(x + 2)(x - 2)(x + 5)(x - 5)$.

The **Factor Theorem** states that a polynomial function $p(x)$ has $(x - r)$ as a factor if and only if the value of the function at r is 0, or $p(r) = 0$. You can use the Factor Theorem to show that a linear expression is a factor of a polynomial.

For example, consider the graph of the polynomial function $f(x) = x^3 - 3x^2$.
The graph appears to have a zero at (3, 0), so a possible linear factor of the polynomial is $x - 3$. Determine the value of the polynomial at
$$x = 3, \text{ or } f(3).$$
$$f(3) = (3)^3 - 3(3)^2$$
$$= 27 - 3(9)$$
$$= 27 - 27$$
$$= 0$$
So, $(x - 3)$ is a linear factor of the polynomial function.

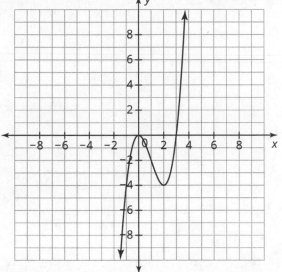

The Fundamental Theorem of Algebra states that every polynomial equation of degree n must have n roots. This means that every polynomial can be written as the product of n factors of the form $(ax + b)$. For example, $2x^2 - 3x - 9 = (2x - 3)(x - 3)$.

Just as the integers in a factor tree, the factors of a polynomial divide into that polynomial without a remainder. **Polynomial long division** is an algorithm for dividing one polynomial by another of equal or lesser degree. The process is similar to integer long division.

© Carnegie Learning, Inc.

Integer Long Division	Polynomial Long Division	Description
$3660 \div 12$ or $\dfrac{3660}{12}$ $\begin{array}{r} 305 \\ 12\overline{)3660} \\ -36 \\ \hline 6 \\ -0 \\ \hline 60 \\ -60 \\ \hline 0 \end{array}$	$(x^3 + x^2 + 3x + 3) \div (x + 1)$ or $\dfrac{x^3 + x^2 + 3x + 3}{x - 1}$ $\begin{array}{r} \textcircled{A}\quad \textcircled{D}\quad \textcircled{G} \\ x^2 + 0x + 3 \\ x + 1\overline{)x^3 + x^2 + 3x + 3} \\ \textcircled{B}(x^3 + x^2) \\ \hline \textcircled{E}\,0x^2 + 3x\,\textcircled{C} \\ -(0x^2 + 0x) \\ \hline 3x + 3\,\textcircled{F} \\ \textcircled{H}\,-(3x + 3) \\ \hline \text{Remainder } 0 \end{array}$	A. Divide $\dfrac{x^3}{x} = x^2$. B. Multiply $x^2(x + 1)$, and then subtract. C. Bring down $3x$. D. Divide $\dfrac{0x^2}{x} = 0x$. E. Multiply $0x(x + 1)$, and then subtract. F. Bring down $+3$. G. Divide $\dfrac{3x}{x} = 3$. H. Multiply $3(x + 1)$, and then subtract.

You can use the difference of squares when you have a binomial of the form $a^2 - b^2 = (a + b)(a - b)$.

The difference of cubes can be rewritten in factored form: $a^3 - b^3 = (a - b)(a^2 + ab + b^2)$.
The sum of cubes can be written in factored form: $a^3 + b^3 = (a + b)(a^2 - ab + b^2)$.

Any polynomial, $p(x)$, can be written in the form: $p(x) = $ (linear expression)(quotient) + remainder. Generally, the linear expression is written in the form $(x - r)$, the quotient is represented by $q(x)$, and the remainder is represented by R, meaning: $p(x) = (x - r)q(x) + R$.

The **Remainder Theorem** states that when any polynomial equation or function, $f(x)$, is divided by a linear expression of the form $(x - r)$, the remainder is $R = f(r)$, or the value of the equation or function when $x = r$.

You can also use the Factor Theorem to determine unknown information about a polynomial if you know a linear factor of that polynomial.

For example, given that $x - 5$ is a linear factor of $x^3 - 4x^2 - ax + 10$, you can determine the unknown coefficient, a.

If $(x - 5)$ is a linear factor, then, by the Factor Theorem, $f(5) = 0$.

$$(5)^3 - 4(5)^2 - a(5) + 10 = 0$$
$$125 - 4(25) - a(5) + 10 = 0$$
$$125 - 100 - a(5) + 10 = 0$$
$$35 - a(5) = 0$$
$$-a(5) = -35$$
$$a(5) = 35$$
$$a = 7$$

Thus, $f(x) = x^3 - 4x^2 - 7x + 10$.

Synthetic division is a shortcut method for dividing a polynomial by a linear expression of the form $(x - r)$. Notice in the form of the linear factor $(x - r)$, the x has a coefficient of 1. Also, just as in long division, when you use synthetic division, every power of the dividend must have a placeholder.

To use synthetic division to divide a polynomial $ax^2 + bx + c$ by a linear factor $(x - r)$, follow the pattern shown at right.

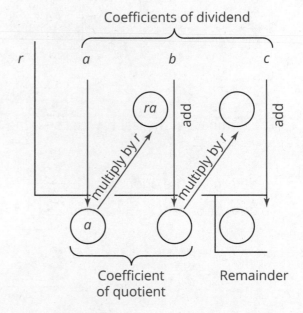

You can use synthetic division in place of the standard long division algorithm to determine the quotient for $(x^3 + x^2 + 3x + 3) \div (x + 1)$.

Long Division	Synthetic Division
$\begin{array}{r} x^2 + 0x + 3 \\ x+1\overline{)x^3 + x^2 + 3x + 3} \\ \underline{x^3 + x^2} \\ 0x^2 + 3x \\ \underline{0x^2 + 0x} \\ 3x + 3 \\ \underline{3x + 3} \\ 0 \end{array}$	$r = -1$
	$(x^3 + x^2 + 3x + 3) \div (x + 1) = (x^2 + 3)$

Synthetic division works only for linear divisors in the form $(x - r)$. If the divisor has a leading coefficient other than 1, you may need to factor out a constant in order to rewrite the divisor in the form $x - r$.

You can use synthetic division to determine the quotient of $\frac{2x^3 - 6x^2 + 4x + 2}{2x - 3}$. Since the divisor is not in the form $x - r$, you can rewrite $2x - 3$ as $2\left(x - \frac{3}{2}\right)$.

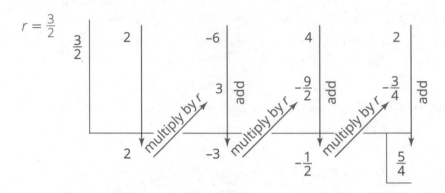

The numbers in the last row become the coefficients of the quotient.
$2x^2 - 3x - \frac{1}{2} \text{ R } \frac{5}{4}$

To determine the quotient of $\frac{2x^3 - 6x^2 + 4x + 2}{2x - 3}$, you need to return to the original divisor of $(2x - 3)$. To do so, double $\left(x - \frac{3}{2}\right)$ and halve $\left(2x^2 - 3x - \frac{1}{2}\right)$.

$$2x^3 - 6x^2 + 4x + 23 = (2x - 3)\left(x^2 - \frac{3}{2}x - \frac{1}{4}\right) + \frac{5}{4}$$

Therefore, $\frac{2x^2 - 6x^2 + 4x + 2}{2x - 3} = x^2 - \frac{3}{2}x - \frac{1}{4} + \frac{5}{4(2x - 3)}$.

LESSON 3

Closing Time

When an operation is performed with any numbers or expressions in a set and the result is in the same set, it is said to be **closed under that operation**.

Polynomials are closed under addition, subtraction, and multiplication. The sum, difference, and product is always another polynomial. They are not closed under division: the algebraic and graphical representations are not polynomials, the graph is not a smooth, continuous curve that approaches positive or negative infinity as x increases or decreases to infinity, and the algebraic representation is not in the correct form.

Unequal Equals

To determine when a polynomial function is greater than or less than 0, first determine the zeros of the function or where the function equals 0. Then use the graph to determine whether the function is greater than or less than 0 for the intervals between the zeros.

For example, consider the graphed function shown.

$f(x) < 0$ when $\begin{Bmatrix} x < -4 \\ 0 < x < 4 \end{Bmatrix}$

$f(x) > 0$ when $\begin{Bmatrix} -4 < x < 0 \\ x > 4 \end{Bmatrix}$

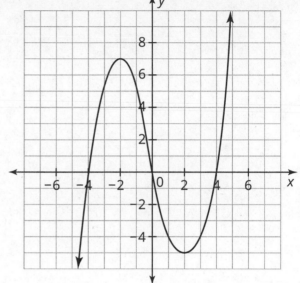

When solving polynomial inequalities treat the inequality as an equation and solve. Factor or use the Quadratic Formula to determine the x-intercepts. Then choose a test point between each interval created by the roots or graph the equation to determine which values satisfy the inequality. The section(s) that provide a true solution for the test point is the solution to the inequality.

For example, consider the inequality
$x^2 - x - 12 < 0$.
$(x + 3)(x - 4) = 0$
$x = -3, 4$
$x^2 - x - 12 < 0$ when $-3 < x < 4$

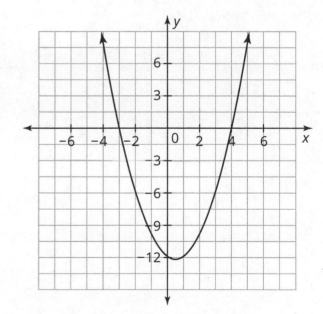

TOPIC 2
Polynomial Models

Seasonal rainfall can be modeled with a polynomial function, with various relative maxima and relative minima over the course of a year.

Module 2: Developing Structural Similarities

TOPIC 2: POLYNOMIAL MODELS

To begin this topic, Euclid's Formula is stated and used to generate Pythagorean triples. Students then analyze specific patterns in the rows of Pascal's Triangle and look for other observable patterns. The Binomial Theorem is provided and students use it to expand binomials with coefficients equal to 1 and with coefficients other than 1. They use the Binomial Theorem to determine specific terms for binomials written in the form $(x + y)^n$ and $(x - y)^n$ with the same value for n. Finally, students use polynomials to model data, such as traffic patterns, monthly precipitation, and minimum wages.

Where have we been?

The previous topic in this module has prepared students to analyze real-world data using polynomial functions. Throughout this course, pattern identification is emphasized as a key step in mathematical modeling and thinking. In previous courses, students have used linear and nonlinear regressions to analyze and make predictions about data.

Where are we going?

The Binomial Theorem is used repeatedly in combinatorial mathematics to analyze sample spaces, permutations, and combinations. Polynomial models are used throughout industry and the sciences to analyze complex phenomena and make predictions about real-world situations.

Pascal's Triangle

A large variety of different patterns can be perceived using Pascal's Triangle. The first six rows of Pascal's Triangle are shown, where $n = 0$ represents the first row, $n = 1$ represents the second row, and so on.

Even though Pascal's triangle has been around for centuries—even before the time of mathematician Blaise Pascal for whom it is named—new patterns are still being discovered.

Planes, Trains, and Automobiles

Transportation plans are an essential part of any large urban development project. Whether designing residential blocks, shopping districts, or stadiums, part of the planning process is determining how to move large groups of people in and out of an area quickly. Building new highways, bus stations, bike lanes, or railways may be necessary for some large-scale developments.

Part of urban development projects is monitoring existing conditions in a specific area. Planners must determine how well the current traffic infrastructure meets the community's needs before modeling and predicting what transportation processes may work best for a future project.

Talking Points

The Binomial Theorem can be an important topic to know about for college admissions tests.

Here is an example of a sample question:

What is the fifth term of the expansion of $(a + b)^8$?

The coefficients of the expansion given by Pascal's triangle are 1, 8, 28, 56, 70, 56, 28, 8, 1. The fifth of these is 70.

The expansion proceeds as $a^8 + 8a^7b + 28a^6b^2...$ The fifth term in the expansion, then, is $70a^4b^4$.

Key Terms

Euclid's Formula

Given positive integers r and s, where $r > s$, Euclid's Formula states that $(r^2 + s^2)^2 = (r^2 - s^2)^2 + (2rs)^2$.

Binomial Theorem

The Binomial Theorem states that it is possible to extend any power of $(a + b)$ into a sum of the form
$$(a + b)^n = \binom{n}{0}a^nb^0 + \binom{n}{1}a^{n-1}b^1 + \binom{n}{2}a^{n-2}b^2 + ... + \binom{n}{n-2}a^1b^{n-1} + \binom{n}{n}a^0b^n$$

coefficient of determination

The coefficient of determination (R^2) measures the strength of the relationship between the original data and their regression equation.

Not a Case of Mistaken Identity

Exploring Polynomial Identities

Warm Up

Expand or factor each expression.

1. $(a + 3)^2$

2. $a^2 - 25$

3. $(a - 8)^2$

Learning Goals

- Use polynomial identities to rewrite numeric expressions.
- Use polynomial identities to generate Pythagorean triples.
- Identify patterns in numbers generated from polynomial identities.
- Prove statements involving polynomials.

Key Term

- Euclid's Formula

You have explored different equivalent polynomial relationships. How can you use these relationships to perform calculations with large numbers or to prove statements involving polynomials?

Make It or Break It?

1. Choose one or more different expressions from the list that by themselves or multiplied together are equivalent to each given expression. Then write the equivalent relationship. Each expression will be used at least once.

Polynomial Expressions
$a + b$
$a - b$
$a^2 + 2ab + b^2$
$a^2 - 2ab + b^2$
$a^2 - ab + b^2$
$a^2 + ab + b^2$

a. $(a + b)^2$

b. $(a - b)^2$

c. $a^2 - b^2$

d. $(a + b)^3$

e. $(a - b)^3$

f. $a^3 + b^3$

g. $a^3 - b^3$

2. Consider the relationships you wrote in Question 1.

   a. How did you determine the expression equivalent to $(a + b)^3$ and $(a - b)^3$?

   b. How did you determine the expression equivalent to $a^3 + b^3$ and $a^3 - b^3$?

3. Zak says he can write an expression in the form $(a + b)^2$ that is equal to an expression in the form $(a - b)^2$. Meg says that isn't possible because their equivalent expressions are not equal to each other. Who's correct? Give an example to justify your reasoning.

Calculating with Polynomial Identities

You have learned about many different equivalent polynomial relationships. These relationships are also referred to as polynomial identities.

The polynomial identities you identified in the Getting Started are shown.

- $(a + b)^2 = a^2 + 2ab + b^2$
- $(a - b)^2 = a^2 - 2ab + b^2$
- $a^2 - b^2 = (a + b)(a - b)$
- $(a + b)^3 = (a + b)(a^2 + 2ab + b^2)$
- $(a - b)^3 = (a - b)(a^2 - 2ab + b^2)$
- $a^3 + b^3 = (a + b)(a^2 - ab + b^2)$
- $a^3 - b^3 = (a - b)(a^2 + ab + b^2)$

Polynomial identities can help you perform calculations. For instance, consider the expression 46^2. Without a calculator, you could calculate the value by using the standard algorithm for multiplication. You can also use a polynomial identity to write an expression that may be easier to calculate.

Worked Example

You can use the polynomial identity $(a + b)^2 = a^2 + 2ab + b^2$ to calculate 46^2.

$46^2 = (40 + 6)^2$	Write 46 as the sum of 40 and 6.
$= 40^2 + 2(40)(6) + 6^2$	Apply the polynomial identity $(a + b)^2 = a^2 + 2ab + b^2$.
$= 1600 + 2(40)(6) + 36$	Apply exponents.
$= 1600 + 480 + 36$	Perform multiplication.
$= 2116$	Perform addition.

The value of 46^2 is 2116.

1. Calculate 46^2 in a different way by writing 46 as the difference of two integers squared.

2. Use polynomial identities and number properties to perform each calculation. Show your work.

   a. 112^2

   b. 27^3

   c. 55^3

Remember that a Pythagorean triple is a set of three positive integers, a, b, and c, such that $a^2 + b^2 = c^2$.

1. **Determine whether each set of numbers is a Pythagorean triple. Explain your reasoning.**

   a. 4, 5, 9

   b. 0.4, 0.5, 0.3

   c. 89, 80, 39

You have just determined whether three given positive numbers make up a Pythagorean triple, but suppose that you want to generate integers that are Pythagorean triples.

2. **Describe a process you could use to come up with integers that are Pythagorean triples.**

© Carnegie Learning, Inc.

There is an efficient method to generate Pythagorean triples that involves a polynomial identity called *Euclid's Formula*.

Euclid's Formula is a formula used to generate Pythagorean triples given any two positive integers r and s, where $r > s$. Euclid's Formula is shown.

$$(r^2 + s^2)^2 = (r^2 - s^2)^2 + (2rs)^2$$

The expressions in Euclid's Formula represent the side lengths of a right triangle, a, b, and c, as shown.

$$
\begin{array}{ccccc}
c^2 & = & a^2 & + & b^2 \\
\downarrow & & \downarrow & & \downarrow \\
(r^2 + s^2)^2 & = & (r^2 - s^2)^2 & + & (2rs)^2
\end{array}
$$

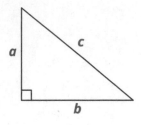

Worked Example

You can verify Euclid's Formula by transforming the right side of the equation to show that it is equal to the left side.

Given positive integers a and b, where $a > b$.

$(a^2 + b^2)^2 \stackrel{?}{=} (a^2 - b^2)^2 + (2ab)^2$	Apply Euclid's Formula.
$\stackrel{?}{=} a^4 - 2a^2b^2 + b^4 + (2ab)^2$	Square the binomial.
$\stackrel{?}{=} a^4 - 2a^2b^2 + b^4 + 4a^2b^2$	Apply Product to a Power Rule.
$\stackrel{?}{=} a^4 - 2a^2b^2 + 4a^2b^2 + b^4$	Apply the Commutative Property of Addition.
$\stackrel{?}{=} a^4 + 2a^2b^2 + b^4$	Combine like terms.
$= (a^2 + b^2)^2$	Factor perfect square trinomial.

3. **Use Euclid's Formula to generate a Pythagorean triple.**

   a. **Choose two integers and use them to generate a Pythagorean triple. Explain your choice in integers.**

b. Compare your Pythagorean triple to others in your class. Did everyone get the same triple?

4. Generate a Pythagorean triple using each pair of given integers and Euclid's Formula.

   a. 4 and 7

   b. 11 and 5

   c. 15 and 20

5. Did any of the Pythagorean triples you generated have a common factor? If so, identify them, and explain why you think this happened.

Ask yourself:

Is there only one *r*-value and only one *s*-value that will generate each Pythagorean triple?

6. The integers 5, 12, and 13 make up a fairly well known Pythagorean triple. What two integers generate this triple? Show your work.

Verify each algebraic statement by transforming one side of the equation to show that it is equivalent to the other side of the equation.

1. $v^6 - w^6 = (v^2 - w^2)(v^2 - vw + w^2)(v^2 + vw + w^2)$

2. $(p^4 + q^4)^2 = (p^4 - q^4)^2 + (2p^2q^2)^2$

3. $m^9 + n^9 = (m + n)(m^2 - mn + n^2)(m^6 - m^3n^3 + n^6)$

© Carnegie Learning, Inc.

TALK the TALK

Triple Threat

Euclid's Formula is useful in generating Pythagorean triples, but it does not generate all the Pythagorean triples.

1. Consider a triangle with sides 9, 12, and 15.

    a. Is this triangle similar to a triangle with sides 3, 4, and 5? Explain your reasoning.

    b. Are the integers 9, 12, and 15 a Pythagorean triple? Explain your reasoning.

    c. Can you use Euclid's formula to generate the integers 9, 12, and 15? Explain your reasoning.

2. **Analyze the table showing the first three Pythagorean triples generated by the smallest possible values for *r* and *s*.**

r	*s*	2*rs*	$r^2 - s^2$	$r^2 + s^2$
2	1	4	3	5
3	1	6	8	10
3	2	12	5	13
4	1			
4	2			
4	3			

a. **Complete the next three rows of the table.**

b. **Why must *r* be greater than *s* in Euclid's Formula?**

c. **Can all three numbers of a Pythagorean triple be odd? Explain your reasoning.**

Assignment

Write

Given positive integers r and s, where $r > s$, write the terms in Euclid's Formula that correspond to each side length in a right triangle, a, b, and c.

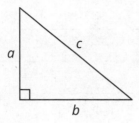

Remember

Euclid's formula is a formula used to generate Pythagorean triples given any two positive integers r and s, where $r > s$:
$(r^2 + s^2) = (r^2 - s^2) + (2rs)^2$.

Practice

1. Use polynomial identities and number properties to calculate 25^3.
2. Jordan measures the side lengths of a triangular piece of sheet metal. The side lengths are 156 cm, 133 cm, and 205 cm.
   a. Verify that the triangular piece of sheet metal is a right triangle.
   b. Use Euclid's Formula to determine the positive integers r and s, where $r > s$, that will generate these 3 side lengths.
3. Verify $(a + b)^3(a - b)^3 = (a^2 - b^2)(a^4 - 2a^2b^2 + b^4)$ by transforming one side of the equation to show that it is equivalent to the other side of the equation.

Stretch

Dave and Sandy created their own numbers. Their definitions are shown.
- The Dave numbers are any numbers that can be generated using the formula $a^3 + b^3$, where a and b are positive integers and $a > b$.
- The Sandy numbers are any numbers that can be generated using the formula $a^3 - b^3$, where a and b are positive integers and $a > b$.

The tables show the first few Dave numbers, and the first few Sandy numbers. The shaded cells with red indicate cells where a is not greater than b.

Dave Numbers: $a^3 + b^3$

		b				
		1	2	3	4	5
a	1					
	2	$2^3 + 1^3 = 9$				
	3	$3^3 + 1^3 = 28$	$3^3 + 2^3 = 35$			
	4	$4^3 + 1^3 = 65$	$4^3 + 2^3 = 72$	$4^3 + 3^3 = 91$		
	5	$5^3 + 1^3 = 126$	$5^3 + 2^3 = 133$	$5^3 + 3^3 = 152$	$5^3 + 4^3 = 189$	

Sandy's Numbers: $a^3 - b^3$

		b				
		1	2	3	4	5
a	1					
	2	$2^3 - 1^3 = 7$				
	3	$3^3 - 1^3 = 26$	$3^3 - 2^3 = 19$			
	4	$4^3 - 1^3 = 63$	$4^3 - 2^3 = 56$	$4^3 - 3^3 = 37$		
	5	$5^3 - 1^3 = 124$	$5^3 - 2^3 = 117$	$5^3 - 3^3 = 98$	$5^3 - 4^3 = 61$	

1. Determine whether each number is a Dave number, a Sandy number, both, or neither. Explain your reasoning.

   a. 35

   b. 5

Review

1. Determine which function has the greater degree. Explain your reasoning.

$f(x) = -2(x - 1)^2 + 4$	A polynomial function $p(x)$ that has 1 relative minimum and 1 relative maximum.

© Carnegie Learning, Inc.

2. Consider the polynomial functions $m(x) = x^2$ and $n(x) = m(x - 1) + 2$. Which function has the greatest minimum? Explain your reasoning.

3. Use the Factor Theorem to determine whether each linear expression is a factor of the polynomial $2x^4 + 7x^3 - 4x^2 - 27x - 18$.

a. $x + 1$

b. $x + 3$

c. $x - 1$

d. $x - 2$

4. Identify the extrema, zeros, and intercepts of the graph of the polynomial function.

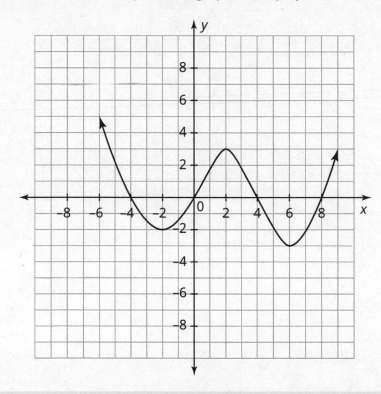

Elegant Simplicity

Pascal's Triangle and the Binomial Theorem

Warm Up

Evaluate each expression.

1. $5!$

2. $2!3!$

3. $\frac{5!}{3!}$

Learning Goals

- Identify patterns in Pascal's Triangle.
- Use Pascal's Triangle to expand powers of binomials.
- Use the Binomial Theorem to expand powers of binomials.
- Extend the Binomial Theorem to expand binomials of the form $(ax + by)^n$.

Key Term

- Binomial Theorem

You know how to expand binomials in the form $(a + b)^n$ using the Distributive Property. How can you expand binomials when n is a large number and the Distributive Property would be difficult to use?

In a Blaise of Glory

There is an interesting pattern of numbers that makes up what is referred to as Pascal's Triangle.

The first six rows of Pascal's Triangle are shown, where $n = 0$ represents the first row, $n = 1$ represents the second row, and so on.

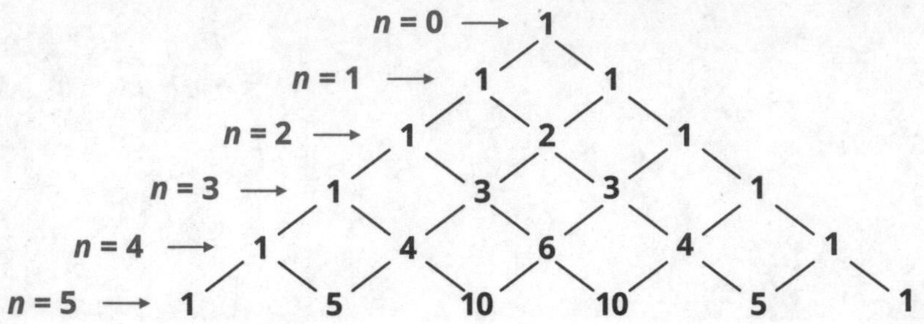

```
n = 0 →        1
n = 1 →      1   1
n = 2 →    1   2   1
n = 3 →  1   3   3   1
n = 4 →  1   4   6   4   1
n = 5 →  1   5  10  10   5   1
```

1. **Analyze the patterns in Pascal's Triangle.**

   a. **Describe all the patterns you see in Pascal's Triangle.**

   b. **Complete the rows for $n = 6$ and $n = 7$ in the diagram of Pascal's Triangle. Describe the pattern you used.**

Mathematicians have discovered countless interesting patterns and relationships within Pascal's Triangle. Despite the fact that Pascal's Triangle has been around for centuries, even before the time of mathematician Blaise Pascal, for whom it is named, new patterns are still being discovered. Because the triangle is infinite, there may yet be patterns that have not been explored.

Think

about:

What is the relationship between the numbers along the longer part of the "stick" and the lone number at the end of the shorter part of the stick?

1. **Brianna loves hockey. In fact, Brianna is so obsessed with hockey that she drew "hockey sticks" around the numbers in Pascal's Triangle. Lo and behold, she found a pattern! Her work is shown.**

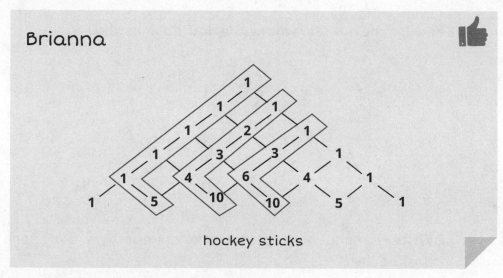

hockey sticks

a. **Describe the pattern shown by the numbers inside the hockey sticks that Brianna drew.**

b. **Sketch two more hockey sticks that include numbers that have the same pattern described in part (a).**

2. Drew and Latasha analyzed Pascal's Triangle, and each described a pattern.

Drew
The sum of the numbers in each row is equal to 2^n, where $n = 0$ represents the first row.

Latasha
If I alternate the signs of the numbers in any row after the first row and then add them together, their sum is 0.

Who's correct? Either verify or disprove each student's work.

3. Consider the numbers along the dashed lines shown.

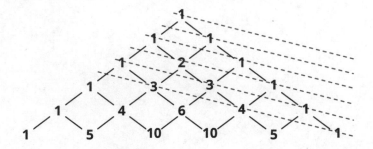

a. Write the sequence for the sum of the numbers along each dashed line.

b. Explain how the sum of numbers along the dashed lines in Pascal's Triangle can be linked to a well known sequence of numbers.

The patterns shown in Pascal's Triangle have many uses. You may have used Pascal's Triangle to calculate probabilities. Let's explore how you can use Pascal's Triangle to raise a binomial to a positive integer.

4. **Multiply to expand each binomial. Write your final answer so that the powers of a are in descending order.**

   a. $(a + b)^0 =$ b. $(a + b)^1 =$

   c. $(a + b)^2 =$ d. $(a + b)^3 =$

   e. $(a + b)^4 =$

5. **Analyze your answers to Question 4.**

   a. **Compare the coefficients of each product with the numbers shown in Pascal's Triangle. What do you notice?**

   b. **What do you notice about the exponents of the a- and b-variables in each expansion?**

   c. **What do you notice about the sum of the exponents of the a- and b-variables in each expansion?**

6. **Use Pascal's Triangle to expand each binomial.**

   a. $(a + b)^5 =$ b. $(a + b)^6 =$ c. $(a + b)^7 =$

What if you want to expand a binomial such as $(a + b)^{15}$? You could take the time to draw that many rows of Pascal's Triangle, but there is a more efficient way.

You may have seen the notation $\binom{n}{k}$ or $_nC_k$ when calculating probabilities in another course. Both notations represent the formula for a *combination*. Recall that a combination is a selection of objects from a collection in which each selection contains different objects. The formula for a combination of k objects from a set of n objects for $n \geq k$ is shown.

$$\binom{n}{k} = {_nC_k} = \frac{n!}{k!(n-k)!}$$

Remember:

Recall that the factorial of a whole number n, represented as $n!$, is the product of all numbers from 1 to n.

Mathematicians define 0! as 0! = 1.

Worked Example

Calculate $\binom{4}{2}$, or $_4C_2$.

$\binom{n}{k} = {_nC_k} = \frac{n!}{k!(n-k)!}$ Write the formula for a combination.

$n = 4$ and $k = 2$ Identify n and k.

$\binom{4}{2} = \frac{4!}{2!(4-2)!}$ Substitute the values for n and k into the formula.

$= \frac{4 \cdot 3 \cdot (2 \cdot 1)}{(2 \cdot 1)(2 \cdot 1)}$ Write each factorial as a product.

$= \frac{4 \cdot 3 \cdot \cancel{(2 \cdot 1)}}{(2 \cdot 1)\cancel{(2 \cdot 1)}}$ Divide out common factors and evaluate.

$= \frac{12}{2} = 6$

© Carnegie Learning, Inc.

1. **Explain why n must be greater than or equal to k in the formula for a combination.**

2. **Perform each calculation.**

Your graphing calculator can compute factorials and combinations.

a. $\binom{5}{1}$ =

b. $_7C_4$ =

3. **Sarah and Montel's teacher asks each student to use Pascal's Triangle to calculate $_6C_3$. Their answers and explanations are shown.**

Sarah

I can calculate $_nC_k$ by looking at the kth number (from left to right) in the nth row of Pascal's Triangle. So, $_6C_3$ is equal to 20.

Montel

I can calculate $_nC_k$ by looking at the (k + 1)th number (from left to right) in the (n + 1)th row of Pascal's Triangle. So, $_6C_3$ is equal to 35.

Who's correct? Explain your reasoning.

The **Binomial Theorem** states that it is possible to extend any power of $(a + b)$ into a sum of the form shown.

$$(a + b)^n = \binom{n}{0}a^n b^0 + \binom{n}{1}a^{n-1}b^1 + \binom{n}{2}a^{n-2}b^2 + \ldots + \binom{n}{n-1}a^1 b^{n-1} + \binom{n}{n}a^0 b^n$$

4. **Use the Binomial Theorem to expand $(a + b)^{15}$. You can use your calculator to determine the coefficients.**

Suppose you have a binomial with coefficients other than 1, such as $(2x + 3y)^5$. You can use substitution along with the Binomial Theorem to expand the binomial.

Worked Example

You can use the Binomial Theorem to expand $(a + b)^5$, as shown.

$$(a + b)^5 = \binom{5}{0}a^5b^0 + \binom{5}{1}a^4b^1 + \binom{5}{2}a^3b^2 + \binom{5}{3}a^2b^3 + \binom{5}{4}a^1b^4 + \binom{5}{5}a^0b^5$$

$$= a^5 \quad\quad + 5a^4b^1 \quad + 10a^3b^2 \quad + 10a^2b^3 \quad + 5a^1b^4 \quad + b^5$$

Now consider $(2x + 3y)^5$.

Let $2x = a$ and let $3y = b$.

You can substitute $2x$ for a and $3y$ for b into the expansion for $(a + b)^5$.

$$(2x + 3y)^5 = (2x)^5 + 5(2x)^4(3y)^1 + 10(2x)^3(3y)^2 + 10(2x)^2(3y)^3 + 5(2x)^1(3y)^4 + (3y)^5$$

$$= 32x^5 + 5(16x^4)(3y) + 10(8x^3)(9y^2) + 10(4x^2)(27y^3) + 5(2x)(81y^4) + 243y^5$$

$$= 32x^5 + 240x^4y + 720x^3y^2 + 1080x^2y^3 + 810xy^4 + 243y^5$$

Ask Yourself...

What do I substitute for a and b? Is the term positive or negative?

5. **Use the Binomial Theorem and substitution to expand each binomial.**

   a. $(3x + y)^4$

   b. $(x - 2y)^6$

TALK the TALK

Give Me a Sign

1. Consider the expressions $(x + y)^n$ and $(x - y)^n$.

   a. How many terms does the expanded form of each expression have? Explain how this number relates to Pascal's Triangle.

   b. What generalization can you make about the sign of each term in the expanded form of each expression?

   c. Aparna says that when n is an odd integer, there are $\frac{(n + 1)}{2}$ different coefficients for the terms in expanded form. Luke says that there are $n + 1$ different coefficients. Who is correct? Explain your reasoning.

2. **Use the Binomial Theorem and your generalization to determine each term.**

a. the third term of $(x + y)^{20}$

b. the third term of $(x - y)^{20}$

c. the fifth term of $(x + y)^{12}$

d. the fifth term of $(x - y)^{12}$

e. the 100th term of $(x + y)^{100}$

f. the 100th term of $(x - y)^{100}$

Assignment

Write

Describe how the Binomial Theorem is related to Pascal's Triangle.

Remember

The Binomial Theorem states that it is possible to extend any power of $(a + b)$ into a sum of the form:

$$(a + b)^n = \binom{n}{0} a^n b^0 + \binom{n}{1} a^{n-1} b^1 + \binom{n}{2} a^{n-2} b^2 + \ldots + \binom{n}{n-1} a^1 b^{n-1} + \binom{n}{n} a^0 b^n$$

The formula for a combination of k objects from a set of n objects for $n \geq k$ is:

$$\binom{n}{k} = {_n}C_k = \frac{n!}{K!(n-k)!}$$

Practice

1. Consider $(v + w)^8$.

   a. Use Pascal's Triangle to expand $(v + w)^8$.

   b. Determine the coefficient of $v^5 w^3$ in the expansion of $(v + w)^8$.

   c. Determine the coefficient of $v^5 w^3$ in the expansion of $(2v + w)^8$.

   d. Determine the coefficient of $v^4 w^4$ in the expansion of $(2v + 3w)^8$.

2. Expand $(4x + 2y)^5$.

3. Expand $(3m - n)^6$.

4. Expand $(-5x - 3y)^4$.

5. Determine the coefficient of $c^5 d^4$ in the expansion of $(2c + 3d)^9$.

6. Determine the coefficient of $j^7 k^3$ in the expansion of $(2j - k)^{10}$.

Stretch

1. Determine the coefficient of $x^{10} y^5$ in th expansion of $(-7x - 3y)^{15}$.

2. Consider the scatter plot shown.

a. The equation $y = 0.8761x - 0.2743$ represents the line that best fits the points on the graph, and the equation $y = 0.0433x^2 + 0.649x - 0.125$ represents the curve that best fits the points on the graph. Graph each equation on the scatterplot.

b. Which curve appears to fit the data the best? Explain your reasoning.

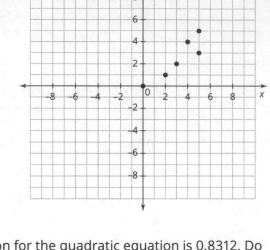

c. The coefficient of determination is a value that measures the strength of the relationship between the original data and the regression equation. The closer the value is to 1, the stronger the relationship. The coefficient of determination for the linear equation is 0.8761, and the coefficient of determination for the quadratic equation is 0.8312. Do these values match your answer from part (b)?

Review

1. Use polynomial identities and number properties to calculate 42^3.

2. Arjun measures the side lengths of a triangular piece of glass. The side lengths are 120 in., 209 in., and 241 in.

a. Verify that the triangular piece of glass is a right triangle.

b. Use Euclid's Formula to determine the positive integers r and s, where $r > s$, that will generate these three side lengths.

3. Completely factor each expression over the set of real numbers.

a. $2x^3 - 12x^2 + 16x$ b. $8x^3 - 64$

4. Use long division to determine whether $x + 4$ is a factor of $5x^4 + 16x^3 - 15x^2 + 8x + 16$. Show your work.

Modeling Gig

Modeling with Polynomial Functions and Data

Warm Up

Use technology to determine the linear regression equation for each set of data.

1. (3, 4), (7, 6), and (−2, −4)

2. (−7, 1), (3, 8), and (9, 7)

3. (−3, 6), (−2, −1), and (6, −4)

Learning Goals

· Determine the appropriate polynomial regression equation to model a problem situation.
· Predict outcomes using a polynomial regression equation.
· Sketch polynomial functions that appropriately model a problem situation.

Key Terms

· regression equation
· coefficient of determination

You have learned about linear and quadratic regressions. How can you apply polynomial regressions to analyze more complex data?

Release Your Regression

Recall that a **regression equation** is a function that models the relationship between two variables in a scatter plot. The regression equation can be used to make predictions about future events. Any degree polynomial can model a scatter plot, but data generally has one curve that best fits the data. You may also recall that the **coefficient of determination** (R^2) measures the "strength" of the relationship between the original data and their regression equation. The value ranges from 0 to 1, with a value of 1 indicating a perfect fit between the regression equation and the original data.

1. **Sketch the given polynomial. Then draw 10 data points on each coordinate plane, such that the given polynomial will model the data with a coefficient of determination close to but not equal to 1. Write the equation for the function and then use technology to determine the regression equation and R^2 for the data.**

   a. **polynomial of degree 2**

   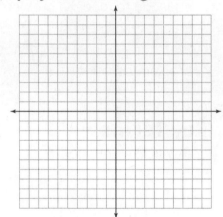

   b. **polynomial of degree 3**

   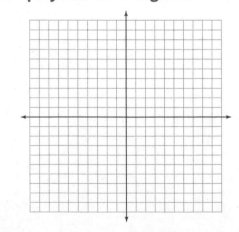

Think about:

How close is the regression equation to your function? Is this shown in the R^2 value?

ACTIVITY 3.1

Applying a Polynomial Regression

City planners consider building a new stadium on several acres of land close to the downtown of a large city. They monitored the number of vehicles entering and exiting downtown from a major highway between 1:00 PM and 7:00 PM to determine current traffic conditions.

1. **Analyze the table of values that represents the average number of vehicles entering and exiting downtown during the given hours of a typical weekday. The value for time represents the start time for the full hour over which the vehicles were monitored.**

Time (PM)	Average Number of Vehicles on a Typical Weekday (thousands)
1:00	7.0
2:00	10.8
3:00	14.5
4:00	21.1
5:00	23.9
6:00	19.0
7:00	10.0

When entering the data into your calculator, enter 1:00 as 1, 2:00 as 2, 3:00 as 3, etc.

a. **Describe any patterns you notice. Explain the patterns in the context of this problem situation.**

b. **Predict the type of polynomial that best models the data. Explain your reasoning.**

2. Create a scatter plot of the data. Be sure to label your axes.

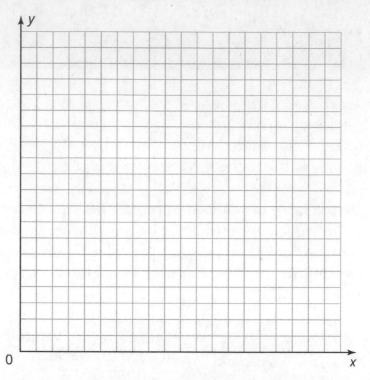

3. Use technology to determine the regression equation for the average number of vehicles entering and exiting downtown on a typical weekday. Sketch the regression equation on the coordinate plane in Question 2. How well does the regression equation model the data? Was your prediction about the type of polynomial that best fits the data correct?

4. **Use the regression equation that best models the data to make predictions.**

Use what you know about polynomials to work efficiently. Predict which degree function is the best fit first. Then check to see if it has an R^2 value close to 1.

a. **Downtown is congested when more than 20,000 vehicles are on the streets and highway. Predict when the downtown will be congested. Explain your reasoning.**

b. **Predict the hours when the number of vehicles that enter and exit downtown is less than 10,000. Explain your reasoning.**

c. **Predict the number of vehicles that enter or exit downtown during the hour starting at noon.**

d. **Predict the number of vehicles that enter or exit downtown during the hour starting at 9 PM.**

e. **Predict the number of vehicles that enter or exit downtown during the hour starting at midnight the previous evening.**

5. Consider the data and your regression equation.

a. For what intervals is the model appropriate for this problem situation? For what intervals is the model inappropriate? Explain your reasoning.

b. Sketch a curve that you believe accurately predicts the number of vehicles on the road over a 2-day period. Explain your reasoning.

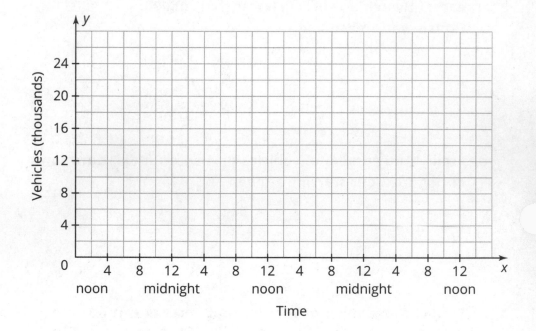

6. Do you think a polynomial function could accurately model this problem situation over the next 2 months? Explain your reasoning.

ACTIVITY 3.2 Determining a Best-Fit Polynomial

Although the minimum wage may vary from state to state, the U.S. federal government sets an absolute minimum wage for the nation every few years.

1. **Analyze the table of values that shows the absolute minimum wage, and the years it was enacted by Congress. Predict the type of polynomial that best fits this data. Explain your reasoning.**

Time Since 1950 (years)	Absolute Minimum Wage (dollars)
5	0.75
6	1.00
11	1.15
13	1.25
17	1.40
18	1.60
24	2.00
25	2.10
28	2.65
29	2.90
30	3.10
31	3.35
40	3.80
41	4.25
46	4.75
47	5.15
57	5.85
58	6.55
59	7.25

Make sure you are comfortable with the data before analyzing the problem. How would you represent 1975? 1950? 1945?

2. **Analyze the data graphically.**

   a. **Use technology to determine the best regression function $f(x)$ to model the changes in the minimum wage over the years since 1950. Sketch the regression equation on the coordinate plane. Be sure to label your axes.**

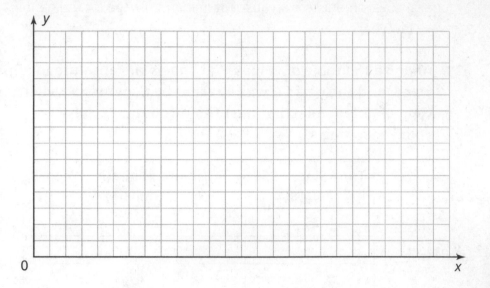

   b. **How well does the regression function model this data? Explain your reasoning.**

All of the decimal places are important in your regression equation, so don't round the coefficient when using graphing technology.

3. **Use the regression equation that best models the data to predict the minimum wage in each given year. Explain your reasoning.**

   a. **2020**   b. **1945**

4. Use the regression function to make predictions about events in the distant past and distant future. Explain your reasoning.

a. According to the regression equation, what was the minimum wage when the Civil War ended in 1865?

b. Do you think that a cubic model is appropriate to predict the minimum wage in the distant past and future?

Let's take a closer look at the minimum wage in the early part of the 20th century. A minimum wage did not exist until 1938 under the Fair Labor Standards Act. Before this time, employers could pay employees any hourly wage that employees were willing to accept. The initial hourly minimum wage in 1938 was $0.25 per hour. The wage increased steadily before reaching $0.75 in 1955.

5. Consider the minimum wage from 1900 to 1955. Sketch a graph that you believe accurately models the minimum wage for the time interval (1900, 1955). Explain your reasoning.

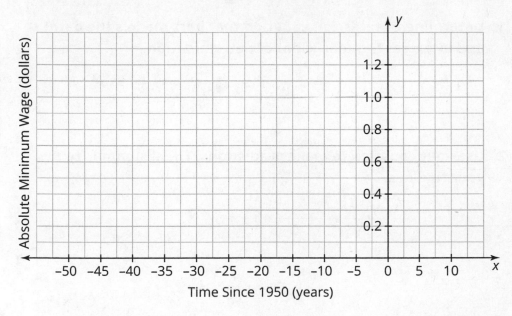

The table of values describes the average monthly precipitation in Pittsburgh, Pennsylvania, during the years 1971 through 2000.

Month	Average Monthly Precipitation (inches)
1	2.7
2	2.37
3	3.17
4	3.01
5	3.8
6	4.12
7	3.96
8	3.38
9	3.21
10	2.25
11	3.02
12	2.86

1. **Determine a regression equation that best models the data and interpret the coefficient of determination.**

2. **Use your equation to make predictions. Then, summarize your findings.**

© Carnegie Learning, Inc.

Inflation has influenced the price of a movie ticket over the years. The first movie theater opened in the year 1900, charging $0.05 per ticket. The data provided show how the average price of a movie ticket has increased over the years.

Years	Average Price of a Movie Ticket (dollars)
1900	0.05
1948	0.36
1958	0.68
1971	1.65
1983	3.15
1995	4.35
2003	6.03
2007	6.88
2009	7.50

Remember:

The function that best models the data has a coefficient of determination closest to 1.

3. **Determine a regression function that best models the data.**

4. **Use your regression equation to make predictions. Then, summarize your findings.**

TALK the TALK

Polynomial Models for $500, Please!

The Math Club sponsors an event each year to raise money for their trip to the Quiz Bowl. As the president of the Math Club, you propose having a movie night fundraiser. You survey the students to see how many students will attend. The number of students varies depending on the ticket price.

Think
about:

What information is given and how can you use this information to determine the amount of money raised for each ticket price?

Ticket Price (dollars)	Students Who Will Attend
1.25	120
1.75	105
2.25	95
2.75	83
3.25	77
3.75	64
4.25	58
4.75	40
5.25	30

1. **Write a short letter to your principal about your findings. Include details about the exact ticket price that raises the most money as well as the approximate number of students who will attend.**

© Carnegie Learning, Inc.

Assignment

Write

Explain why it is important to analyze the coefficient of determination when calculating a regression equation.

Remember

A regression equation is a function that models the relationship between two variables in a scatter plot. The coefficient of determination, or R^2, measures the strength of the relationship between the original data and their regression equation. The value ranges from 0 to 1, with a value of 1 indicating a perfect fit between the regression equation and the original data.

Practice

John Earvinson's free throw percentage has fluctuated each year since he became a professional basketball player. The table displays his free throw percentage for each year of his career. John did not play during his 7th and 12th years due to injury.

1. Create a scatter plot of the data. Predict the type of polynomial that best fits the data. Explain your reasoning.
2. Use technology to determine the regression equation for the data. Round decimals to the nearest thousandth. Sketch the scatter plot and your regression equation on a coordinate plane. How well does the regression equation model the given data? Explain your reasoning.
3. Consider the data and your regression equation. Predict John's free throw percentage if he had played in his 7th year. How accurate is this prediction? Explain your reasoning.
4. Consider the data and your regression equation. Predict John's free throw percentage in his 18th year. How accurate is this prediction? Explain your reasoning.
5. For what interval(s) is the model appropriate for this problem situation? Explain your reasoning.
6. Sketch a polynomial curve that you believe accurately predicts John's free throw percentage over a 20-year career. Explain your reasoning.
7. Predict the type of polynomial that you sketched in part (g). Explain your reasoning.

Time Since Becoming a Professional Player (years)	Free Throw Percentage
1	47.1
2	47.9
3	50.2
4	51.5
5	53.0
6	51.4
7	Did Not Play
8	54.7
9	58.3
10	61.4
11	63.3
12	Did Not Play
13	66.0
14	65.2

Stretch

The table shows the salinity levels in an estuary in North Carolina over a period of 24 days. A scatter plot of this data is also shown.

Time (days)	1	2	3	4	5	6	7	8
Salinity (parts per thousand)	27.9	27.9	28.2	30.5	29.6	28.3	27.9	27.9

Time (days)	9	10	11	12	13	14	15	16
Salinity (parts per thousand)	28.6	30.1	29.9	30	29.5	29.5	29.5	29.4

Time (days)	17	18	19	20	21	22	23	24
Salinity (parts per thousand)	29.2	29.1	29.0	29.0	28.9	28.8	28.8	28.7

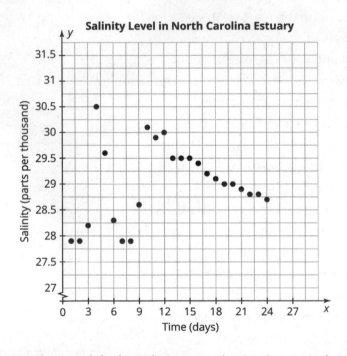

Salinity Level in North Carolina Estuary

1. Write a piecewise function that models the salinity over the 24-day period.
2. Graph the function on the scatter plot.

Review

1. Expand $(2x - y)^4$.

2. Determine the coefficient of x^3y^5 in the expansion of $(5x + 2y)^8$.

3. Determine which polynomial function has the greatest average rate of change over the interval (0, 1). Explain your reasoning.

$g(x) = -x^3 - 2x^2 + 5x - 3$	
	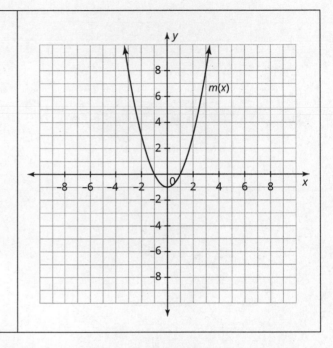

4. A manufacturer keeps records on a piece of equipment on the floor for 15 days to see whether is working properly. In order to maintain stability in the process, the amount of calibration in the piece of equipment must be less than or equal to 11.75 cm.

   The function $c(x) = 0.11x^3 - 2.07x^2 + 9.81x + 2$ represents the calibration x days since the process began.

   a. Write an inequality that represents the calibration of the machine being in the safe range.

   b. Solve the inequality and determine the time intervals during which the calibration of the machine is safe for the process.

5. Determine whether $(m - 3)$ is a factor of $m^3 - 13m^2 + 24m + 18$.

Polynomial Models Summary

KEY TERMS

- Euclid's Formula
- Binomial Theorem
- regression equation
- coefficient of determination

Not a Case of Mistaken Identity

You have explored relationships between equivalent expressions and have discovered several polynomial identities.

$$(a + b)^2 = a^2 + 2ab + b^2$$
$$(a - b)^2 = a^2 - 2ab + b^2$$
$$a^2 - b^2 = (a + b)(a - b)$$
$$(a + b)^3 = (a + b)(a^2 + 2ab + b^2)$$
$$(a - b)^3 = (a - b)(a^2 - 2ab + b^2)$$
$$a^3 + b^3 = (a + b)(a^2 - 2ab + b^2)$$
$$a^3 - b^3 = (a - b)(a^2 + 2ab + b^2)$$

Polynomial identities can be used to calculate exponential expressions. For example, you can use the polynomial identity $(a + b)^2 = a^2 + 2ab + b^2$ to calculate 46^2.

$$46^2 = (40 + 6)^2$$
$$= 40^2 + 2(40)(6) + 6^2$$
$$= 1600 + 2(40)(6) + 36$$
$$= 1600 + 480 + 36$$
$$= 2116$$

- Write 46 as the sum of 40 and 6
- Apply the polynomial identity $(a + b)^2 = a^2 + 2ab + b^2$
- Apply the exponents
- Perform Multiplication
- Perform Addition

The value of 46^2 is 2116.

A Pythagorean triple is a set of three positive integers, a, b, and c, such that $a^2 + b^2 = c^2$. **Euclid's Formula** is a formula used to generate Pythagorean triples given any two positive integers. Given positive integers r and s, where $r > s$, Euclid's Formula is $(r^2 + s^2)^2 = (r^2 - s^2)^2 + (2rs)^2$

For example, you can use Euclid's Formula to create a Pythagorean triple with the integers 2 and 1. Let $r = 2$ and $s = 1$.

$$(r^2 + s^2)^2 = (r^2 - s^2)^2 + (2rs)^2$$
$$(2^2 + 1^2)^2 = (2^2 - 1^2) + (2(2)(1))^2$$
$$(4 + 1)^2 = (4 - 1)^2 + (4)^2$$
$$(5)^2 = (3)^2 + (4)^2$$
$$25 = 9 + 16$$
$$25 = 25$$

The Pythagorean triple is 3, 4, 5.

LESSON 2

Elegant Simplicity

There is an interesting pattern of numbers that makes up what is referred to as Pascal's Triangle. The first six rows of Pascal's Triangle are shown, where $n = 0$ represents the first row, $n = 1$ represents the second row, and so on.

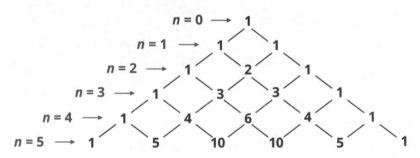

Pascal's Triangle can show the coefficients of a binomial expansion. Consider the identity $(a + b)^2 = a^2 + 2ab + b^2$. The coefficients are 1, 2, and 1, which are the elements of the third row of Pascal's Triangle.

To expand a binomial such as $(a + b)^{15}$, there is a more efficient way than listing out 15 rows of Pascal's Triangle that involves combinations.

Recall that a combination is a selection of objects from a collection in which order does not matter. The formula for a combination of k objects from a set of n objects for $n \geq k$ is shown.

$$\binom{n}{k} = {}_nC_k = \frac{n!}{k!(n-k)!}$$

Recall that the factorial of a whole number n, represented as $n!$, is the product of all counting numbers from 1 to n.

Calculate $\binom{4}{2}$, or ${}_4C_2$.

$$\binom{n}{k} = {}_nC_k = \frac{n!}{k!(n-k)!}$$ · Write the formula for a combination

$$n = 4 \text{ and } k = 2$$ · Identify n and k

$$\binom{4}{2} = \frac{4!}{2!(4-2)!}$$ · Substitute the values for n and k into the formula

$$= \frac{4 \cdot 3 \cdot 2 \cdot 1}{(2 \cdot 1)!(2 \cdot 1)!}$$ · Write each factorial as a product

$$= \frac{4 \cdot 3}{2 \cdot 1}$$ · Divide out common factors and evaluate.

$$= \frac{12}{2} = 2$$

The **Binomial Theorem** states that it is possible to rewrite any power of $(a + b)$ into a sum of the form shown.

$$(a + b)^n = \binom{n}{0}a^nb^0 + \binom{n}{1}a^{n-1}b^1 + \binom{n}{2}a^{n-2}b^2 + \ldots + \binom{n}{n-1}a^1b^{n-1} + \binom{n}{n}a^0b^0$$

You can use the Binomial Theorem to expand $(a + b)^5$, as shown.

$$(a + b)^5 = \binom{5}{0}a^5b^0 + \binom{5}{1}a^4b^1 + \binom{5}{2}a^3b^2 + \binom{5}{3}a^2b^3 + \binom{5}{4}a^1b^4 + \binom{5}{5}a^0b^5$$

$$= a^5 + 5a^4b^1 + 10a^3b^2 + 10a^2b^3 + 5a^1b^4 + b^5$$

Modeling Gig

Recall that a regression equation is a function that models the relationship between two variables in a scatter plot. The regression equation can be used to make predictions about future events. A polynomial of any degree can model a data set, but data generally has one curve that best fits the data. You may also recall that the **coefficient of determination**(R^2) measures the strength of the relationship between the original data and the regression equation. The value ranges from 0 to 1, with a value of 1 indicating a perfect fit between the regression equation and the original data.

For example, consider the situation in which city planners want to build a new stadium on several acres of land close to the downtown area of a large city. They monitor the number of cars entering and exiting downtown from a major highway between 1:00 PM and 7:00 PM to determine regular traffic conditions. The table of values represents the average number of cars entering and exiting downtown during the given hours of a typical weekday. The value for time represents the start-time for the full hour over which the vehicles are monitored.

Time (PM)	Average Number of Vehicles on a Typical Weekday (thousands)
1:00	7.0
2:00	10.8
3:00	14.5
4:00	21.1
5:00	23.9
6:00	19.0
7:00	10.0

A scatterplot of the data is shown.

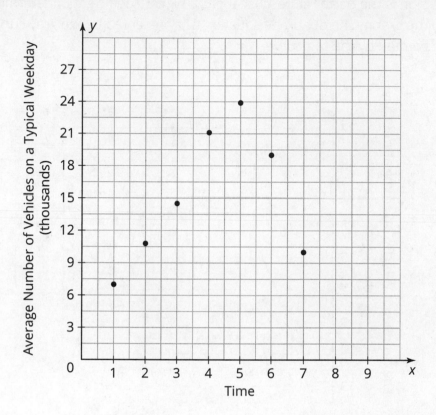

The graph appears to be quadratic. Technology can be used to determine the regression equation of best fit and the coefficient of determination.

The quadratic regression equation is approximately $y = -1.36x^2 + 12.58x - 6.16$ with a coefficient of determination of 0.83.

The cubic regression equation is approximately $y = -0.41x^3 + 3.5x^2 - 4.47x + 8.44$ with a coefficient of determination of 0.98.

The cubic regression is the better fit because it has a higher coefficient of determination. This can also be seen on the graph. The quadratic equation is represented by the gray curve and the cubic equation is represented by the red curve.

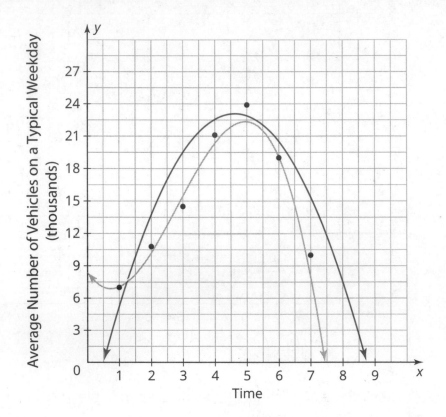

The regression equations can also be used to make predictions about the data. As time increases, the cubic function approaches negative infinity, which does not make sense in terms of this situation. The regression equation would only work for data within the range of the table. To make predictions after 7:00 PM, you would need to calculate a regression equation of a higher degree.

TOPIC 3
Rational Functions

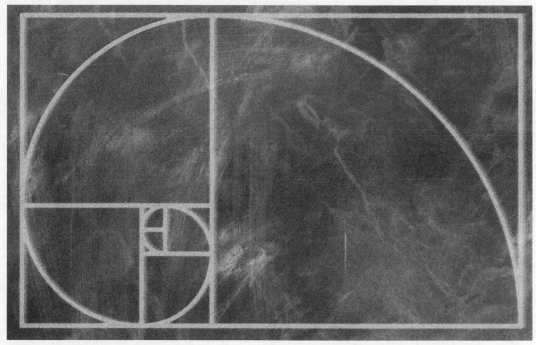

Two quantities are in the golden ratio if their ratio is the same as the ratio of their sum to the larger of the two quantities.

Module 2: Developing Structural Similarities

TOPIC 3: RATIONAL FUNCTIONS

To start this topic, students explore and compare the graphs, tables, and values of a linear function, $f(x) = x$, and its reciprocal function, $g(x) = \frac{1}{x}$. Rational functions are defined. Students then explore transformations of rational functions. The term *removable discontinuity* is defined, and students graph several rational functions with holes or asymptotes in the graph. Operations with rational expressions are next introduced followed by problem solving, during which students create proportions, write rational expressions, describe the behavior of the ratios in the proportions, identify the domain and range, and calculate average costs.

Where have we been?

Students have been working with rational numbers since elementary school. They have extensive knowledge of function behaviors and characteristics to apply to the analysis of rational functions.

Where are we going?

As students experience in the final lesson of this topic, rational functions are helpfully applied in many real-world situations involving mixtures, distances, and costs. Rational functions are used heavily in medical and econometric modeling applications for analysis and prediction. Rational functions also have applications in image resolution and acoustics.

Asymptotes of Rational Functions

The basic rational function $f(x) = \frac{1}{x}$ has a vertical asymptote at $x = 0$ and a horizontal asymptote at $y = 0$. An asymptote is a line that a function gets closer and closer to, but never intersects.

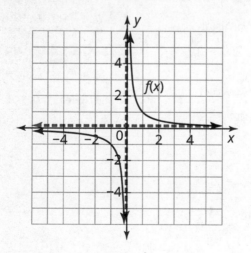

An asymptote does not represent points on the graph of the function. It represents the output value that the graph approaches but never reaches.

Undefined

Consider the following mathematical explanation that 1 is equal to 2. Start by noting that any number multiplied by 0 is equal to 0.

$$1 \times 0 = 0$$
$$2 \times 0 = 0$$

Since 1×0 and 2×0 both equal 0, then they must be equal to each other.

$$1 \times 0 = 2 \times 0$$

Dividing both sides of an equation by the same value preserves equality.

$$\frac{1 \times 0}{0} = \frac{2 \times 0}{0}$$

Anything divided by itself is 1, so $\frac{0}{0} = 1$. This leaves $1 \times 1 = 2 \times 1$, or $1 = 2$.

What is wrong with this proof?

Talking Points

Rational equations can be an important topic to know about for college admissions tests.

Here is an example of a sample question:

Add the expression $\frac{x}{2x + 4} + \frac{x}{x + 2}$.

Determine a least common denominator: $2x + 4 = 2(x + 2)$, so the LCD is $2(x + 2)$.

Multiply the second fraction by $\frac{2}{2}$, which is the same as multiplying it by 1, and rewrite the sum as:

$$\frac{x}{2(x + 2)} + \frac{2x}{2(x + 2)} = \frac{3x}{2(x + 2)}$$

The given expression is equal to $\frac{3x}{2x + 4}$.

Key Terms

rational function

A rational function is any function that can be written as the ratio of two polynomials.

removable discontinuity

A removable discontinuity is a single point at which a function is not defined.

rational equation

A rational equation is an equation that contains one or more rational expressions. Rational equations are proportions.

There's a Fine Line Between a Numerator and a Denominator

Introduction to Rational Functions

Warm Up

Rewrite each fraction in lowest terms.

1. $\frac{12}{3}$

2. $\frac{3}{12}$

3. $\frac{0}{3}$

4. $\frac{3}{0}$

Learning Goals

- Graph rational functions.
- Compare rational functions in multiple representations.
- Compare the basic rational function to various basic polynomial functions.
- Analyze the key characteristics of rational functions.

Key Terms

- rational function
- vertical asymptote

You have learned that polynomials are related to the integers. What functions relate to the set of rational numbers?

Two Integers, Both Alike in Dignity

You have learned about rational numbers in previous courses, and you have used rational numbers throughout this course. Let's review what you know.

1. List some properties of rational numbers, along with examples.

Remember:

The reciprocal of any number x is $\frac{1}{x}$. For example, the reciprocal of 5 is $\frac{1}{5}$ and the reciprocal of 0.5 is $\frac{1}{0.5}$, or 2.

2. Determine the reciprocals of the rational numbers you wrote in Question 1. Explain why these numbers are reciprocals.

3. Explain what happens when the denominator of a rational number is zero.

4. Write a definition of *rational number*.

Throughout this course you have studied many connections between polynomial functions and real numbers. It follows then that polynomial functions also have reciprocals. Is the reciprocal also a polynomial? Is it a function? How does $\frac{1}{f(x)}$ compare to the original function $f(x)$?

To begin answering these questions, consider the reciprocal of the basic linear function $f(x) = x$. The reciprocal can be defined as $g(x) = \frac{1}{f(x)}$, or simply $g(x) = \frac{1}{x}$.

Remember:

Polynomials are not closed under division.

1. **Consider the graph and table of values for $f(x) = x$. The domain of $f(x)$ is $(-\infty, \infty)$. The points $(-1, -1)$ and $(1, 1)$ are shown and used to create three intervals for analysis.**

−6	−5	−4	−3	−2	−1	x
−6	−5	−4	−3	−2	−1	$f(x) = x$
						$g(x) = \frac{1}{x}$

x	1	2	3	4	5	6
$f(x) = x$	1	2	3	4	5	6
$g(x) = \frac{1}{x}$						

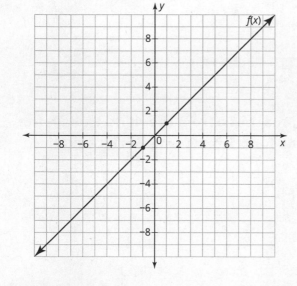

a. **Complete the tables of values for $g(x) = \frac{1}{x}$. Then plot the points and draw a smooth curve to graph $g(x)$ on the coordinate plane.**

x	−1	$-\frac{1}{2}$	$-\frac{1}{10}$	$-\frac{1}{100}$	0	$\frac{1}{100}$	$\frac{1}{10}$	$\frac{1}{2}$	1
$f(x) = x$	−1	$-\frac{1}{2}$	$-\frac{1}{10}$	$-\frac{1}{100}$	0	$\frac{1}{100}$	$\frac{1}{10}$	$\frac{1}{2}$	1
$g(x) = \frac{1}{x}$									

© Carnegie Learning, Inc.

b. Describe the graph of $g(x)$. How is it similar to the graphs of other functions that you've studied? How is it different?

The point at $g(0)$ is said to be undefined because it is impossible to divide by 0.

c. Describe the end behavior of $g(x)$. Explain your reasoning in terms of the graph, equation, and table of values.

d. Describe $g(x)$ as x approaches 0 from the left. Explain the output behavior of the function in terms of the equation.

e. Describe $g(x)$ as x approaches 0 from the right. Explain the output behavior of the function in terms of the equation.

2. Henry and Rosie disagree about $g(x) = \frac{1}{x}$.

Henry
The graph and table both clearly show that it is a function.

Rosie
It is not a function. Every input doesn't have an output.

Who is correct? Explain your reasoning.

3. Analyze the key characteristics of $g(x) = \frac{1}{x}$.

a. Does the graph ever intersect the horizontal line $y = 0$? Explain your reasoning in terms of the graph, table, and equation.

b. Does the graph ever intersect the vertical line $x = 0$? Explain your reasoning in terms of the graph, table, and equation.

c. Describe the domain and range of $g(x)$.

Previously, you have represented the domain and range of functions using words, inequalities, or interval notation. You can also use set notation to represent these characteristics of functions.

Worked Example

Suppose that both the domain and range of a rational function, $g(x)$, are represented verbally as "all real numbers except for 4." You can use inequalities, interval notation, and set notation to represent this verbal statement.

	Domain	Range
Inequalities	$x > 4$ or $x < 4$	$g(x) > 4$ or $g(x) < 4$
Interval notation	$(-\infty, 4) \cup (4, \infty)$	$(-\infty, 4) \cup (4, \infty)$
Set notation	$\{x \mid x \neq 4\}$	$\{g(x) \mid g(x) \neq 4\}$

d. Write your answer to Question 3, part (c), using each notation shown.

All polynomials are rational functions. Remember $Q(x)$ can be equal to 1.

The function $g(x) = \frac{1}{x}$ is an example of a *rational function*. A **rational function** is any function that can be written as the ratio of two polynomials. It can be written in the form $f(x) = \frac{P(x)}{Q(x)}$ where $P(x)$ and $Q(x)$ are polynomial functions and $Q(x) \neq 0$. You have already seen some specific types of rational functions. Linear, quadratic, cubic, and higher-order polynomial functions are types of rational functions.

Recall from your study of exponential functions that a horizontal asymptote is a horizontal line that a function gets closer and closer to. In most cases, a graph never intersects a horizontal asymptote, but in some cases it does. In this problem, the function $g(x)$ has a horizontal asymptote at $y = 0$.

Given the horizontal asymptote, the range of the rational function $g(x) = \frac{1}{x}$ can be expressed:

- verbally: all real numbers except for 0.
- as a compound inequality: $g(x) > 0$ or $g(x) < 0$.
- in interval notation: $(-\infty, 0) \cup (0, \infty)$.
- in set notation: $\{g(x) \mid g(x) \neq 0\}$.

The function $g(x) = \frac{1}{x}$ has a *vertical asymptote* at $x = 0$. A **vertical asymptote** is a vertical line that a function gets closer and closer to, but never intersects. The asymptote does not represent points on the graph of the function. It represents the output value that the graph approaches. An asymptote occurs for input values that result in a denominator of 0.

A graph cannot cross its vertical asymptote because the function is undefined at that value.

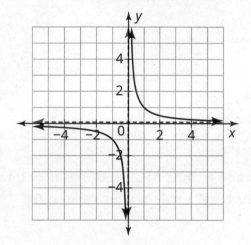

The vertical asymptote is often represented in textbooks and graphing calculators as a dashed or solid line. The convention used in this textbook is to represent asymptotes as dashed lines.

Changing the mode to "dot" on many calculators removes the asymptote from the screen. Asymptotes are often more easily viewed with a smaller viewing window.

Given the vertical asymptote, the domain of the rational function $g(x) = \frac{1}{x}$ can be expressed:

- verbally: all real numbers except for 0
- as a compound inequality: $x > 0$ or $x < 0$.
- in interval notation: $(-\infty, 0) \cup (0, \infty)$.
- in set notation: $\{x \mid x \neq 0\}$.

4. **Analyze each function.**

$$f(x) = x \qquad\qquad g(x) = \frac{3x}{2} \qquad\qquad h(x) = \frac{\sqrt{x}}{2x}$$

$$p(x) = \frac{3}{x} + 2 \qquad\qquad k(x) = 12 \qquad\qquad n(x) = \frac{2^x}{5}$$

$$j(x) = \frac{4x^2 + 3x + 2}{6x^3 + 10} \qquad\qquad m(x) = \frac{1}{(x + 2)(x - 3)}$$

a. **Circle the rational functions.**

b. **Explain why the remaining functions are not rational.**

c. **Do you think the graphs of all rational functions will have a vertical asymptote? Explain your reasoning.**

Graphing Reciprocals of Power Functions

In the previous activity, you discovered that the graph of the function $g(x) = \frac{1}{x}$ looks very different than the linear function $f(x) = x$. How do the graphs of the other power functions compare to their reciprocals? Do they all have the same shape? Do they all have asymptotes?

Remember:

Power functions are any functions of the form $y = x^n$ for $n \geq 1$.

1. **Analyze the graph of the quadratic power function $q(x) = x^2$.**

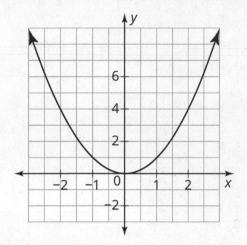

Predict the graph of $r(x) = \frac{1}{x^2}$. Sketch it on the coordinate plane. Explain your reasoning.

2. Consider the graph and table of values for $q(x) = x^2$.
   The domain of $q(x)$ is $(-\infty, \infty)$. The tables represent three intervals of the domain.

−5	−4	−3	−2	−1	x
		9	4	1	$q(x) = x^2$
					$r(x) = \frac{1}{x^2}$

x	1	2	3	4	5
$q(x) = x^2$	1	4	9		
$r(x) = \frac{1}{x^2}$					

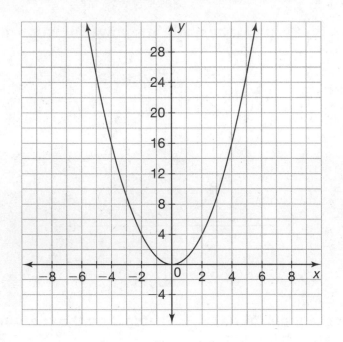

x	−1	−$\frac{1}{2}$	−$\frac{1}{10}$	−$\frac{1}{100}$	0	$\frac{1}{100}$	$\frac{1}{10}$	$\frac{1}{2}$	1
$q(x) = x^2$									
$r(x) = \frac{1}{x^2}$									

a. Complete the table of values for $r(x) = \frac{1}{x^2}$.

b. Plot the points and sketch the reciprocal function $r(x)$ on the coordinate plane.

c. Describe the shape of the graph of $r(x) = \frac{1}{x^2}$. How is it similar to $g(x) = \frac{1}{x}$? How is it different?

3. Analyze the key characteristics of $r(x)$.

   a. Describe the domain and range of $r(x)$. Use interval notation.

   b. Describe the end behavior of $r(x)$.

   c. Describe the horizontal and vertical asymptotes of $r(x)$. How can you determine the asymptotes from the graph, table, and equation?

4. Use graphing technology to explore the key characteristics of the reciprocals of all power functions. Consider the general shape of the graphs, domain, range, end behavior, horizontal asymptotes, and vertical asymptotes.

   a. List your conjectures about the reciprocals of the even-powered functions $\left\{\frac{1}{x^2}, \frac{1}{x^4}, \frac{1}{x^6}, \ldots\right\}$. Justify your conjectures.

   b. List your conjectures about the reciprocals of the odd-powered functions $\left\{\frac{1}{x^3}, \frac{1}{x^5}, \frac{1}{x^7}, \ldots\right\}$. Justify your conjectures.

ACTIVITY 1.3 Modeling a Situation with a Rational Function

Suppose you want to purchase a new laptop which will cost $2200.

1. **Complete the table to show the amount of time it would take to save $2200 for different weekly savings amounts.**

Weekly Savings (dollars)	Time (weeks)
10	
20	
40	
50	
100	

2. **Use the information in the table to construct a graph of the problem situation. Be sure to label the axes.**

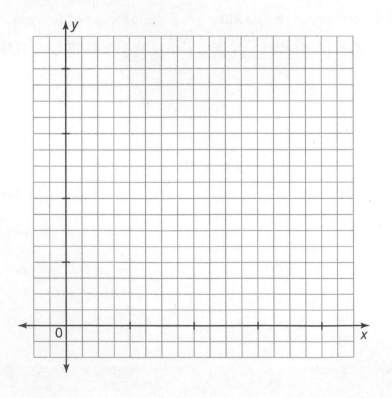

3. Can this problem situation be modeled by a function?
   Explain your reasoning.

4. Write an algebraic equation to model this problem situation.

5. Describe the asymptotic behavior of the graph in this situation.

   a. What happens to the graph as *x* approaches zero?

   b. What happens to the graph as *x* approaches infinity?

TALK the TALK

Now and Venn

1. Use the Venn diagram to summarize the similarities and differences between the groups of reciprocal power functions. Characteristics that are shared should go in the overlapping space.

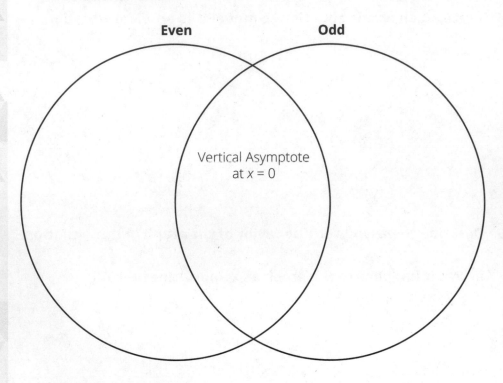

Even   **Odd**

Vertical Asymptote
at $x = 0$

An example is provided. What other characteristics are shared? Which ones are different? How would you describe them?

2. How does a vertical asymptote affect the domain of a rational function?

Assignment

Write

Describe why a rational function never crosses its vertical asymptote.

Remember

A rational function is any function that can be written as the ratio of two polynomials. It can be written in the form $f(x) = \frac{P(x)}{Q(x)}$ where $P(x)$ and $Q(x)$ are polynomial functions and $Q(x) \neq 0$.

Practice

1. Consider the function $f(x) = \frac{4}{x}$.

   a. Complete the table.

x	−8	−4	−2	−1	$-\frac{1}{2}$	0	$\frac{1}{2}$	1	2	4	8
f(x)											

   b. Use the table to graph the function.

   c. Analyze the function and the corresponding table and graph. Describe the domain, range, and end behavior of the function. Determine all of the asymptotes of the function. Explain your reasoning.

2. Consider the function $h(x) = \frac{8}{x^2}$.

   a. Complete the table.

x	−8	−4	−2	−1	$-\frac{1}{2}$	0	$\frac{1}{2}$	1	2	4	8
h(x)											

   b. Use the table to graph the function.

   c. Analyze the function and the corresponding table and graph. Describe the domain, range, and end behavior of the function. Determine all of the asymptotes of the function. Explain your reasoning.

Stretch

1. Consider the function $f(x) = \frac{2}{x^{-2}}$.

   a. Complete the table.

x	−2	0	$\frac{1}{2}$	1	$\frac{3}{2}$	2	$\frac{5}{2}$	3	$\frac{7}{2}$	4	6
f(x)											

   b. Use the table to graph the function.

   c. Analyze the function and the corresponding table and graph. Describe the domain, range, and end behavior of the function. Determine all of the asymptotes of the function. Explain your reasoning.

Review

1. The table shows the amount of money road repairs have cost (in thousands of dollars) during a six-year period. Use technology to determine a quartic regression equation for the data. Sketch the data and the regression equation on the coordinate plane with the scatter plot. How well does the regression equation model the given data? Explain your reasoning.

2. Use polynomial identities and number properties to calculate 54^3.

3. Identify the extrema, zeros, and intercepts of the graph of the polynomial function $p(x)$.

Year	Repair Costs (thousands of $)
2005	60
2006	70
2007	59
2008	40
2009	50
2010	39
2011	35

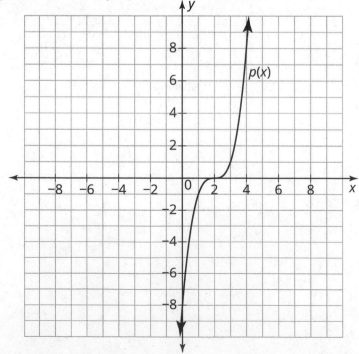

Approaching Infinity

Transformations of Rational Functions

Warm Up

Write each expression as a product of linear factors.

1. $x^2 + \frac{1}{2}x$

2. $x^2 + 2x - 3$

3. $(2x - 3)^2$

4. $x^3 + 2x^2 - 19x - 20$

Learning Goals

- Determine the graphical behavior of rational functions from the structure of the equation.
- Analyze transformations of rational functions, including translations and dilations.

You have explored transformations of linear, quadratic, and other polynomial functions. How can you transform rational functions on the coordinate plane?

That Graph Looks a Little Shifty

You know that transformations performed on any function $f(x)$ to form a new function $g(x)$ can be described by the transformation function form.

$$g(x) = Af(B(x - C)) + D$$

Recall that this transformational function generalizes to any function. Changes to the A-or D-values dilate, translate, or reflect a function vertically. Changes to the B-or C-values dilate, translate, or reflect a function horizontally.

For a rational function, consider the form shown.

$$r(x) = A\left(\frac{1}{B(x - C)}\right) + D$$

1. **Cut out the graphs and equations located at the end of the lesson. Match each equation representing a rational function with its graph. If an equation does not match a graph, create the graph of the equation. If a graph does not match an equation, write the equation that matches the graph. Explain how you sorted the equations and graphs.**

2. **Identify the vertical and horizontal asymptotes of each function.**

3. **Identify the domain and range of each function.**

You have studied only a small subset of all rational functions. Let's consider the structure of the rational functions that you have explored so far.

Remember:

Rational functions are any functions of the form $f(x) - \frac{P(x)}{Q(x)}$ where $P(x)$ and $Q(x)$ are polynomial functions, and $Q(x) \neq 0$.

1. **Describe the effects of changes to the *C*-value and *D*-value on each characteristic given.**

   a. **Domain**

   b. **Range**

   c. **End behavior**

2. **What determines a vertical asymptote? When does a rational function have more than one vertical asymptote?**

3. **Given $f(x) = \frac{1}{x}$, sketch each transformation and explain your process.**

   a. $g(x) = f(x) + 5$

   b. $h(x) = f(x + 5)$

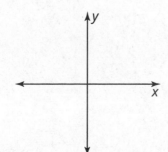

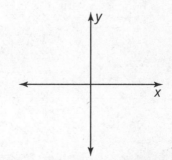

4. Write a rational function $g(x)$ that matches the given characteristics. Then sketch the function.

a. Vertical asymptote at $x = 2$
   Horizontal asymptote at $y = 1$

b. Vertical asymptote
   at $x = 1$, $x = -5$
   Horizontal asymptote
   at $y = -3$

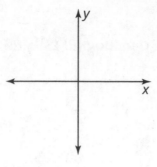

$g(x) =$

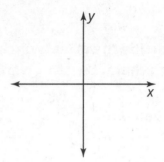

$g(x) =$

c. For $f(x) = \frac{1}{x}$, $g(x) = f(x - 2) - 4$

d. For $f(x) = \frac{1}{x}$, $g(x)$ shifts $f(x)$ up and to the left.

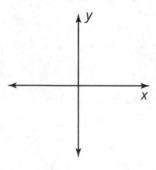

$g(x) =$

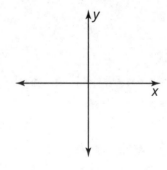

$g(x) =$

ACTIVITY 2.2
Sketching Transformations of Rational Functions

You have analyzed equations and sketched many graphs in this course. Let's consider how you can apply your prior knowledge to sketch graphs of more complex rational functions.

1. **Analyze the methods Jodi and Theresa each used to graph the rational function $j(x) = \frac{1}{x^2 - 4}$.**

Jodi

I created a table and plotted the points.

−6	−5	−4	−3	−2	−1	0	1	2	3	4	5	6
$\frac{1}{32}$	$\frac{1}{21}$	$\frac{1}{12}$	$\frac{1}{5}$	undefined	$-\frac{1}{3}$	$-\frac{1}{4}$	$-\frac{1}{3}$	undefined	$\frac{1}{5}$	$\frac{1}{12}$	$\frac{1}{21}$	$\frac{1}{32}$

I see that vertical asymptotes occur at x = −2 and x = 2, where the denominator is 0 and the output is undefined.

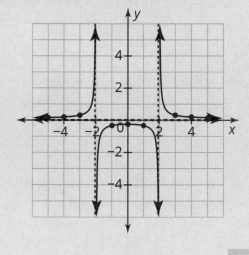

Theresa

I graphed the function $f(x) = x^2 - 4$. The function $j(x)$ is the reciprocal of $f(x)$, so I took the reciprocal of several key points and sketched the graph.

$f(x) = x^2 - 4$

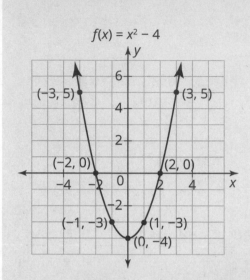

$j(x) = \dfrac{1}{x^2 - 4}$

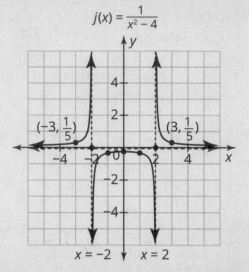

The zeros of the function $f(x) = x^2 - 4$ are $(-2, 0)$ and $(2, 0)$ that become asymptotes at $x = -2$ and $x = 2$ in the function $j(x) = \dfrac{1}{x^2 - 4}$. The y-intercept shifts from $(0, -4)$ in $f(x)$ to $\left(0, \dfrac{-1}{4}\right)$ in $j(x)$. By plotting a couple key points and recognizing that a horizontal asymptote is at $y = 0$, I can sketch the function.

a. **Which method do you think is most efficient? Explain your reasoning.**

b. **Which method do you think is the most accurate? Explain your reasoning.**

c. **How does a vertical asymptote affect the domain of a function?**

2. Without technology, sketch each function and then identify the key characteristics.

a. $g(x) = \dfrac{1}{(x-2)(x+4)}$

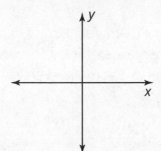

Domain:

Range:

Asymptote(s):

y-intercept:

b. $g(x) = \dfrac{2}{x^2 - 2x - 8}$

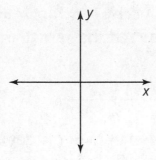

Domain:

Range:

Asymptote(s):

y-intercept:

c. $h(x) = \dfrac{1}{x^2 + 3x - 10}$

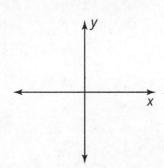

Domain:

Range:

Asymptote(s):

y-intercept:

Recall from the Fundamental Theorem of Algebra that a function of degree n has n zeros. Some of the zeros may be imaginary. Therefore, it follows that the reciprocal of a function of degree n can have at most n vertical asymptotes.

1. Sarah determines the vertical asymptotes for the function $f(x) = \dfrac{1}{2x^2 - 14x - 16}$.

Sarah

The terms in the denominator have a common factor of 2, so I factored it out first. Then I factored the remaining quadratic.

$$f(x) = \frac{1}{2(x^2 - 7x - 8)} = \frac{1}{2(x - 8)(x + 1)}$$

Vertical asymptotes occur when the denominator is zero. So, the asymptotes will occur when $x - 8 = 0$ and when $x + 1 = 0$. Therefore, the asymptotes occur at $x = 8$ and $x = -1$.

Is Sarah correct? Explain your reasoning.

2. **Analyze each rational function. Use algebra to determine the vertical asymptote(s).**

   a. $f(x) = \dfrac{5}{7x - 35}$

   b. $g(x) = \dfrac{1}{x(x - 2)(2x + 3)}$

   c. $h(x) = \dfrac{10}{x^2 - 3x - 10}$

   d. $h(x) = \dfrac{x}{2x^2 + 9x + 4}$

   Think

   About:

   Something interesting is going on with the function in part (g). We'll explore this concept later in the topic, but for now consider why their asymptotic behavior might be different.

   e. $h(x) = \dfrac{7}{x^4 - 1}$

   f. $f(x) = \dfrac{2}{x^2 + 2}$

   g. $g(x) = \dfrac{x + 2}{(x + 2)(x - 5)}$

   h. **Use technology to check your answers by graphing and then by analyzing the corresponding table of values.**

TALK the TALK

Whatever Floats Your Asymptote

1. Abby and Natasha disagree about functions of the form $p(x) = \frac{a}{x}$ where a is a constant.

Abby
The horizontal asymptote will vary depending on the a-value.

Natasha
All rational functions of this form will have a horizontal asymptote at $y = 0$.

Who is correct? Explain your reasoning.

2. Determine a rational function with the characteristics given.

   a. Vertical asymptotes at $x = 3$, $x = -1$, and $x = 0$

   b. Vertical asymptotes at $x = -7$, $x = 12$

   c. No vertical asymptotes

   d. A vertical asymptote at $x = 5$ and a horizontal asymptote at $y = 0$

Function Graph Cutouts

A

B

C

D

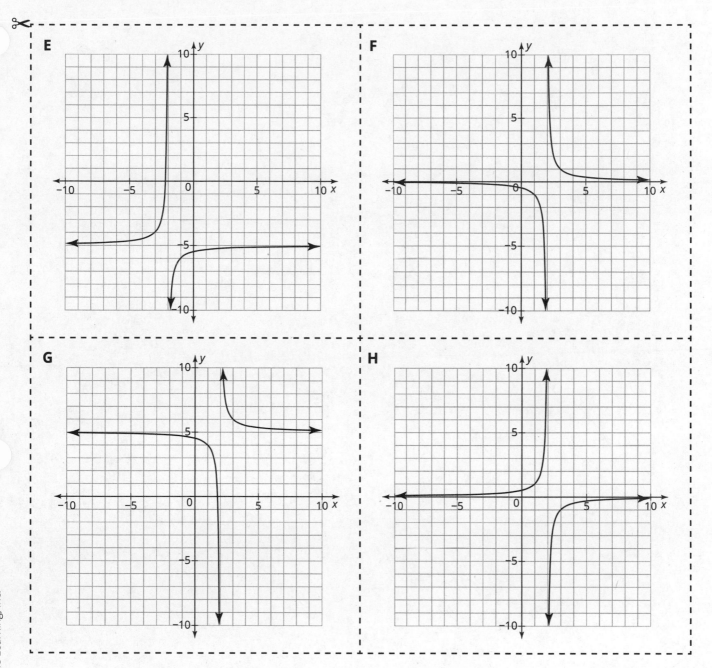

E

F

G

H

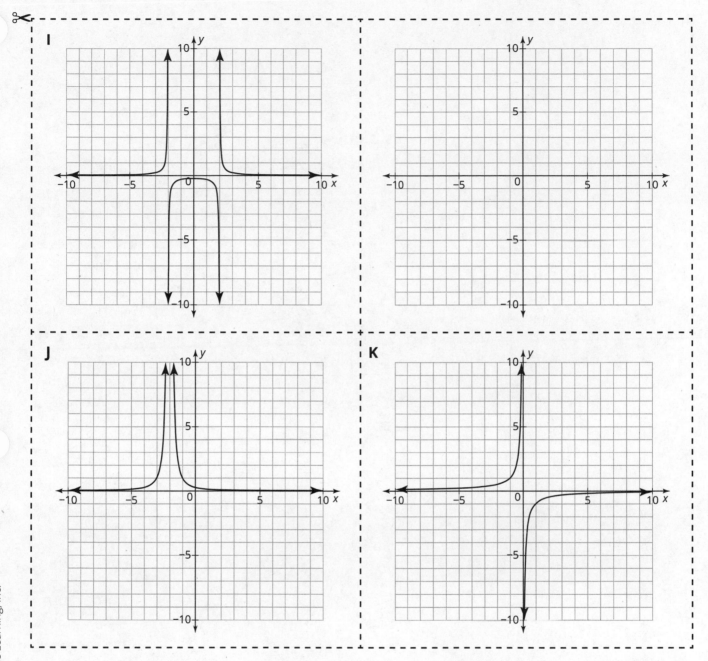

L

M

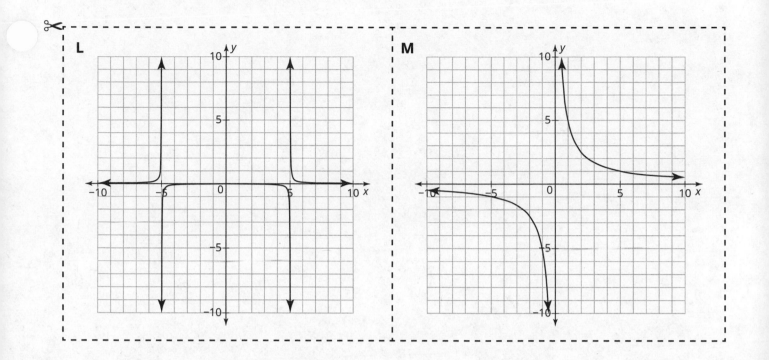

Function Equation Cutouts

$f(x) = \dfrac{1}{(x-2)^2}$

$f(x) = \dfrac{1}{x^2} + 5$

$f(x) = \dfrac{1}{x-2} - 5$

$f(x) = -\dfrac{1}{x+2} - 5$

$f(x) = \dfrac{1}{x-2} + 5$

$f(x) = \dfrac{1}{(x+2)(x-2)}$

$f(x) = \dfrac{5}{x}$

$f(x) = -\dfrac{1}{x}$

$f(x) = -\dfrac{1}{x-2}$

$f(x) = \dfrac{1}{x-2}$

$f(x) = \dfrac{1}{x+2} + 5$

$f(x) = \dfrac{1}{x+2}$

Assignment

Write

Explain how the A-, B-, C-, and D-values of the transformation of the rational function $f(x) = \frac{1}{x}$ affect the horizontal and vertical asymptotes of the function.

Remember

Translations of a rational function $f(x)$ are given in the form $g(x) = Af(B(x - C)) + D$, where the D-value translates $f(x)$ vertically, and the C-value translates $f(x)$ horizontally.

Dilations of a rational function $f(x)$ are given in the form $g(x) = Af(B(x - C)) + D$, where the A-value vertically stretches $f(x)$ and the B-value horizontally stretches $f(x)$.

Practice

1. Consider the functions $f(x) = x^2 + x - 6$ and $g(x) = \frac{1}{x^2 + x - 6}$.
   a. Graph and label the function $f(x) = x^2 + x - 6$ on the given coordinate plane.
   b. Graph and label the function $g(x) = \frac{1}{x^2 + x - 6}$ on the same coordinate plane.
   c. Determine the domain, range, vertical asymptote(s), horizontal asymptote(s), and y-intercept of $g(x)$.
   d. How do the output values of $f(x)$ and $g(x)$ compare for any given input value?

2. Write a rational function with vertical asymptotes $x = 0$ and $x = 6$ and a horizontal asymptote $y = -2$. Sketch the function on the given coordinate plane.

3. Consider the basic rational function $f(x) = \frac{1}{x}$. Explain how the graph of each new function compares to the graph of $f(x)$.
   a. $g(x) = f(x + 5) - 9$
   b. $h(x) = \frac{10}{x} + 8$
   c. $m(x) = \frac{4}{x - 7} - 1$

Stretch

1. Consider the functions $f(x) = x^2 - x - 12$ and $g(x) = x - 4$.

   a. Create the rational function $h(x) = \frac{f(x)}{g(x)}$. Complete the table of values for the function $h(x)$ and then sketch the function.

x	−6	−4	0	4	6
h(x)					

   b. Does the sketch include any vertical asymptotes? Why or why not? Use algebra to explain.

c. Create the rational function $m(x) = \frac{g(x)}{f(x)}$. Complete the table of values for the function $h(x)$ and then sketch the function.

x	−5	−4	−3	−2	4	6
m(x)						

d. Does the sketch include any vertical asymptotes? Why or why not? Use algebra to explain.

e. If $f(x)$ and $g(x)$ are polynomials, are the vertical asymptotes of the rational function
$R(x) = \frac{f(x)}{g(x)}$ always going to be the zeros of the function $g(x)$? Explain.

Review

1. Consider the function $f(x) = \frac{2}{x}$.

   a. Graph the function.

   b. Analyze the function and the corresponding table and graph. Describe the domain, range, and end behavior of the function. Determine all of the asymptotes of the function. Explain your reasoning.

2. The graph shows the amount of money spent by a town on road repairs over a 6 year period. The dots represent the actual data and the curve represents the quartic regression equation that best fits the data. Would you use the regression equation to make a prediction about how much the town spent in 2012? Explain your reasoning.

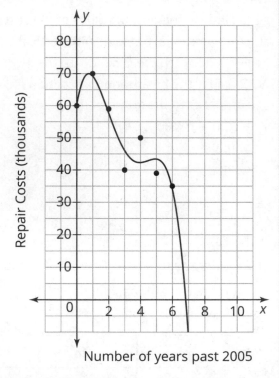

Number of years past 2005

3. Macy measures the side lengths of a triangular piece of metal. The side lengths are 44 cm, 117 cm, and 125 cm.

   a. Verify that the triangular piece of metal is a right triangle.

   b. Use Euclid's Formula to determine the positive integers r and s, where $r > s$, that will generate these three side lengths.

There's a Hole in My Function!

Graphical Discontinuities

Warm Up

Rewrite each expression in lowest terms.

1. $\dfrac{45x}{25x^2}$

2. $\dfrac{b^2 + b - 30}{3b^2 + 18b}$

3. $\dfrac{56v - 72}{32v}$

4. $\dfrac{a + 7}{a^2 + 6a - 7}$

Learning Goals

- Identify domain restrictions of continuous and discontinuous rational functions.
- Compare removable discontinuities to vertical asymptotes.
- Rewrite rational expressions.
- Sketch discontinuous rational functions with asymptotes and removable discontinuities.

Key Terms

- discontinuous function
- removable discontinuity

You have sketched and analyzed rational functions with discontinuities in the form of asymptotes. What other discontinuities are possible when graphing rational functions?

Mend Your Function

1. **Without using technology, select a rational equation to represent each graph.**

$$y = \frac{1}{x - 2} \qquad y = \frac{1}{x} \qquad y = \frac{x^2}{x} \qquad y = \frac{x - 2}{x - 2}$$

$$y = \frac{x^3}{x} \qquad y = \frac{(x - 2)^2}{x - 2} \qquad y = \frac{x}{x} \qquad y = \frac{(x - 2)^3}{x - 2}$$

You may want to match the ones you know first. Consider the exponent rules and how the functions may be rewritten in to a simpler form.

a.

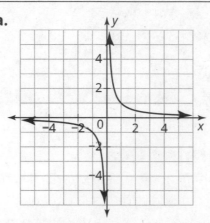

b.

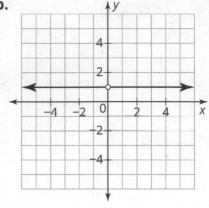

c.

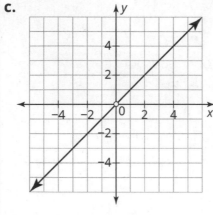

d.

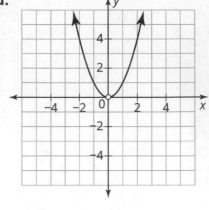

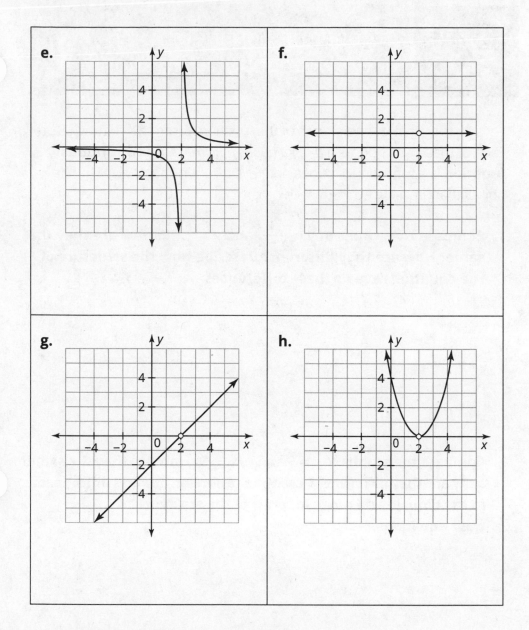

e.

f.

g.

h.

2. **Which functions have asymptotes and which functions have "holes" in their graphs? Describe how the structure of the equation determines whether the function will have an asymptote or a "hole".**

ACTIVITY
3.1

Comparing Continuous and Discontinuous Functions

Let's further analyze the graphs of the functions from the Getting Started. Each of these functions is a *discontinuous function*. A **discontinuous function** is a function that does not have a continuous curve—it has points that are isolated from each other.

When comparing the graphs, consider the general shape of the graph, domain, range, asymptotes, end behavior, etc.

1. **Compare the graphs of $y = \frac{1}{x-2}$ and $y = \frac{x-2}{x-2}$. How are they the same? How are they different? Describe how the structure of the equation reveals these differences.**

2. **Compare the graphs of $y = \frac{x}{x}$ and $y = \frac{x-2}{x-2}$. How are they the same? How are they different? Describe the similarities and differences in the domain and range in terms of the structure of their equations.**

3. **Without using technology, describe the similarities and differences between the graphs of $y = \frac{x^3}{x^2}$ and $y = x$. Explain your reasoning in terms of the structure of the equations.**

Many rational functions have holes, or breaks, in the graphs instead of asymptotes. Let's analyze the structure of the function $y = \frac{x}{x}$ to determine why this function has a hole in the graph rather than a vertical asymptote at $x = 0$.

The function $y = \frac{x}{x}$ can be rewritten as the product of two factors: $y = (x)\left(\frac{1}{x}\right)$. Looking at these reciprocal factors as separate functions reveals important characteristics.

x	-4	-3	-2	-1	0	1	2	3
$y = (x)\left(\frac{1}{x}\right)$	$(-4)\left(-\frac{1}{4}\right)$ 1	$(-3)\left(-\frac{1}{3}\right)$ 1	$(-2)\left(-\frac{1}{2}\right)$ 1	$(-1)\left(-\frac{1}{1}\right)$ 1	$(0)\left(\frac{1}{0}\right)$ und	$(1)\left(\frac{1}{1}\right)$ 1	$(2)\left(\frac{1}{2}\right)$ 1	$(3)\left(\frac{1}{3}\right)$ 1

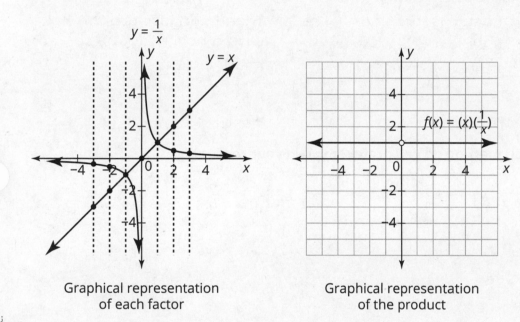

Graphical representation of each factor

Graphical representation of the product

Multiplying the outputs for each input reveals that $(x)\left(\frac{1}{x}\right) = 1$. This graph is a horizontal line that is undefined at $x = 0$. It is undefined at $x = 0$ because this is the value for which an asymptote exists for the factor $\frac{1}{x}$. Similar reasoning can be used to show that for any function $f(x)$, $f(x) \cdot \frac{1}{f(x)} = 1$, with breaks in the graph for all undefined values where $f(x) = 0$. These breaks in the graph are called *removable discontinuities*. A **removable discontinuity** is a single point at which the graph is not defined. Vertical asymptotes and removable discontinuities must be listed as domain restrictions.

This shows graphically why common factors divide to 1. This is why it is not mathematically correct to say that terms "cancel."

4. Henry and Liza each describe a different way to graph $y = \frac{x^3}{x^2}$.

Henry

I know any function multiplied by its reciprocal is 1. I can rewrite the function as $y = \frac{x^3}{x^2} = x \cdot \left(\frac{x^2}{x^2}\right)$. This means that the output of $y = x$ is multiplied by $y = 1$ with a discontinuity at $x = 0$. The result is the line $y = x$ with a removable discontinuity at $(0, 0)$, so $x \neq 0$.

Liza

A removable discontinuity exists anywhere that the denominator is 0 for the original function. In this case, it is $(0, 0)$. I can rewrite the function using the Quotient Rule of Powers.
$y = \frac{x^3}{x^2}$
$\quad = x^{3-2}$
$\quad = x^1$
Then I can just graph $y = x$ with a hole at $(0, 0)$, so $x \neq 0$.

Which method do you prefer? Explain your reasoning.

5. **Sketch the graph of each function. Be sure to note any asymptotes or holes in the graph.**

a. $y = \frac{2x^2}{x^2}$

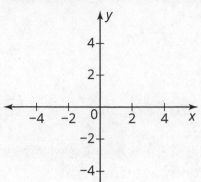

b. $y = \frac{x^2}{x^3}$

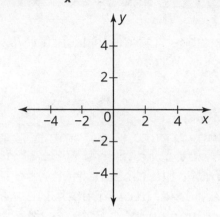

c. $y = \frac{x^4}{x^1}$

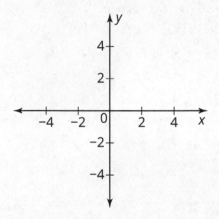

d. $y = \frac{-x^2}{x^4}$

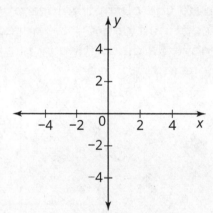

Henry graphed the rational function $f(x) = \frac{x^2 + x - 6}{x - 2}$.
Analyze his work.

Think about:

The common factors do not "cancel." Many people use this term incorrectly to describe when factors divide to equal 1.

Henry

I know there is a domain restriction, so $x \neq 2$. I'm not sure if this is a vertical asymptote or a removable discontinuity, so I'm going to factor the numerator, if possible, to see if a common factor exists.

$$f(x) = \frac{x^2 + x - 6}{x - 2} = \frac{(x - 2)(x + 3)}{x - 2}$$

$$= \frac{1(x + 3)}{1} = x + 3$$

I know the output values of $\frac{(x - 2)}{(x - 2)} = 1$ with a discontinuity at $x = 2$. Therefore, $f(x) = x + 3$. The removable discontinuity is at $(2, 5)$ and appears as a hole in the graph.

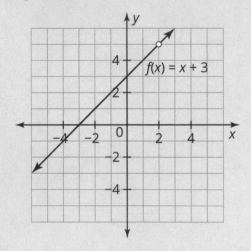

$f(x) = x + 3$

1. **Why did Henry include an open circle at (2, 5) and *not* a vertical asymptote at $x = 2$?**

The graphs of rational functions will have either a removable discontinuity or a vertical asymptote for all domain values that result in division by 0. Simplifying rational expressions is similar to simplifying rational numbers; common factors divide to 1.

2. **Analyze the table of examples that shows similarities between rational numbers and rational expressions.**

	Rational Numbers	Rational Expressions
A common numerator and denominator divide to equal 1	$\frac{5}{5} = 1$	$\frac{x}{x} = 1$
	$\frac{10.7}{10.7} = 1$	$\frac{5x}{5x} = 1$
	$\frac{0.025 + 0.016}{0.025 + 0.016} = 1$	$\frac{x + 5}{x + 5} = 1$
Common monomial factors divide to equal 1.	$\frac{5 \cdot 3}{5} = \frac{1 \cdot 3}{1} = 3$	$\frac{5x}{5} = \frac{1 \cdot x}{1} = x$
	$\frac{4}{4 \cdot 6} = \frac{1}{1 \cdot 6} = \frac{1}{6}$	$\frac{x}{xz} = \frac{1}{1 \cdot z} = \frac{1}{z}$
Common binomial factors divide to equal 1.	$\frac{(5 + 3)(16 - 7)}{(5 + 3)} = \frac{1 \cdot (16 - 7)}{1}$ $= 16 - 7$	$\frac{(x + 5)(x - 4)}{(x + 5)} = \frac{1(x - 4)}{1}$ $= (x - 4)$
	$\frac{(9 - 4)}{(9 - 4)(9 + 5)} = \frac{1}{(9 + 5)}$	$\frac{(x - 4)}{(x - 4)(x + 5)} = \frac{1}{(x + 5)}$

a. **Describe how rewriting rational numbers in lowest terms is similar to rewriting rational expressions.**

b. **Why is there a 1 in the numerator after rewriting $\frac{x}{xz} = \frac{1}{z}$?**

c. **For each example in the rational expressions column, list any restrictions on the domain.**

3. **Liza rewrites the rational expression as shown. Describe the error in Liza's reasoning.**

Liza

$$\frac{x^2 + 4x + 3}{4x + 3} = x^2$$

I divided out the common factors. The numerator and denominator each have a 4x and a 3, so I am left with the squared term.

4. **Rewrite each rational function by dividing out common factors. List any restrictions on the domain.**

a. $f(x) = \frac{2x^2 - 8}{x - 2}$

b. $f(x) = \frac{3xy - 3y}{x^2 - 1}$

c. $f(x) = \frac{x^2 - 5x + 6}{3x - 9}$

d. $f(x) = \frac{x^3 - 7x^2 - 18x}{3x^2 - 9x}$

e. $f(x) = \frac{25x^2 - 9}{5x^2 - 12x - 9}$

f. $f(x) = \frac{x^3 - 5x^2 - x + 5}{x^2 - 6x + 5}$

5. **Consider how Forrest rewrote the expression $\frac{x - 2}{x - 1}$. Describe the error in Forrest's reasoning.**

Forrest

I divided out the in the numerator x-1 and denominator.

$$\frac{\cancel{x} - 2}{\cancel{x} - 1} = \frac{-2}{-1} = 2$$

You have analyzed rational functions with asymptotes, and you have analyzed rational functions with discontinuities. Now let's consider functions that may have both.

1. **Determine whether the graph of the rational function has a vertical asymptote, a removable discontinuity, both, or neither. List the discontinuities and justify your reasoning.**

   a. $j(x) = \dfrac{x + 2}{x(x + 2)}$

   b. $h(x) = \dfrac{x}{x + 5}$

   c. $k(x) = \dfrac{5}{5(x + 2)}$

   d. $m(x) = \dfrac{x + 2}{x^2 - 2x - 15}$

2. **Write two examples of rational functions with one or more removable discontinuities. Explain your reasoning.**

3. **Write a unique function that has a vertical asymptote and a removable discontinuity. Explain your reasoning.**

4. Liza graphed the rational function $h(x) = \frac{x-1}{x^2+x-2}$.
   Analyze her work.

Liza

I'm not sure where the asymptotes are, so I'm going to start by factoring the denominator.

$$h(x) = \frac{x-1}{x^2+x-2} = \frac{x-1}{(x-1)(x+2)} = \frac{1}{x+2}$$

I know there are domain restrictions at $x = 1$ and $x = -2$. The common factor $(x-1)$ is in the numerator so $\frac{x-1}{x-1} = 1$. Therefore, $x = 1$ is a removable discontinuity, while $x = -2$ is a vertical asymptote. I can sketch $h(x) = \frac{1}{x+2}$ as a horizontal shift of $h(x) = \frac{1}{x}$ two units to the left. I know a discontinuity exists at $\left(1, \frac{1}{3}\right)$. A horizontal asymptote is at $y = 0$, and the y-intercept is $\left(0, \frac{1}{2}\right)$.

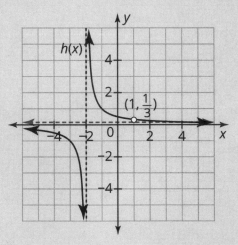

a. Summarize why $x = -2$ is a vertical asymptote while $x = 1$ appears as a hole in the graph.

b. Explain why the graph has a horizontal asymptote at $y = 0$.

5. Sketch each function without the use of technology. Identify any restrictions.

a. $f(x) = \dfrac{x + 2}{x^2 + 4x + 4}$

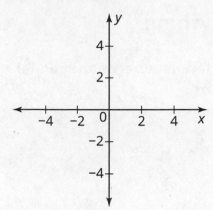

b. $g(x) = \dfrac{x}{x^2 + 3x}$

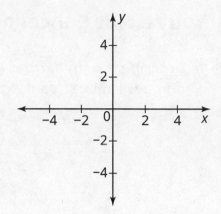

c. $h(x) = \dfrac{x}{x^3 - x}$

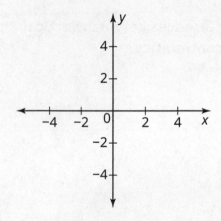

d. $m(x) = \dfrac{x^2 + 5x + 6}{x^2 + 5x + 6}$

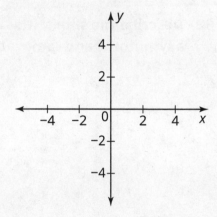

e. $k(x) = \dfrac{x^2 - 2x - 15}{x - 5}$

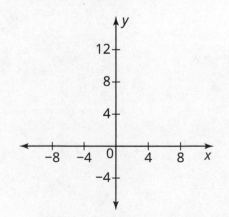

f. $k(x) = \dfrac{x^3 + x^2 + 2x + 2}{x + 1}$

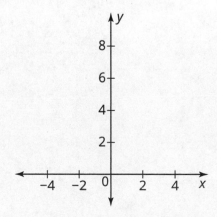

TALK the TALK 💬

You're Not Canceling Anything

1. Describe the similarities and differences between rational numbers and rational expressions.

2. Describe the similarities and differences between vertical asymptotes and removable discontinuities.

3. Why is it incorrect to describe division by a common factor as *canceling out*?

4. Four hints necessary to write a rational function are given. Read each hint one at a time. Attempt to write the function after each hint before proceeding to the next hint. You may need to readjust your function after each hint.

a. First hint: It is a rational function.

b. Second hint: It is a rational function with a horizontal asymptote at $y = 0$.

c. Third hint: It is a rational function with a horizontal asymptote at $y = 0$ and it has removable discontinuities at 4 and -4.

d. Fourth hint: It is a rational function with a horizontal asymptote at $y = 0$, it has removable discontinuities at 4 and -4, and it has a vertical dilation factor of 3.

Write

1. Write a definition for each term.
   a. discontinuous function
   b. removable discontinuity

Remember

The graphs of rational functions have either a removable discontinuity or a vertical asymptote for all domain values that result in division by 0.

Holes are created in the graphs of rational functions when a common factor divides out of the numerator and denominator of the function.

Practice

1. Consider the rational function $f(x) = \frac{x - 4}{x^2 - 4x}$.
   a. Determine any vertical and horizontal asymptotes and any removable discontinuities of the graph of $f(x)$. Explain your reasoning.
   b. Sketch the graph of $f(x)$ without a calculator. Explain your reasoning.
2. Write a function $g(x)$ with a vertical asymptote $x = -5$ and removable discontinuities at $x = 0$ and $x = -3$. Explain your reasoning. Explain how to sketch the graph of the function $g(x)$ without using a calculator.
3. Write a function $h(x)$ with no vertical asymptotes and with removable discontinuities at $x = -2$ and $x = 6$. Explain your reasoning. Explain how to sketch the graph of the function $h(x)$ without using a calculator.
4. Explain how to sketch the graph of $m(x) = \frac{-x^2 + 2x + 35}{x^2 - 2x - 35}$ without using a calculator.

Stretch

1. Consider the rational function $f(x) = \frac{4x^3 + 8x^2 - 20x - 24}{x^4 - 2x^3 - 13x^2 + 14x + 24}$.
   a. Determine any vertical and horizontal asymptotes and any removable discontinuities of the graph of $f(x)$. Explain your reasoning.
   b. Sketch the graph of $f(x)$ without a calculator. Explain your reasoning.

Review

1. Write a rational function with vertical asymptotes $x = -2$ and 2 and a horizontal asymptote $y = 4$. Sketch the function on the given coordinate plane.
2. Consider the basic rational function $f(x) = \frac{1}{x}$. Explain how the graph of $h(x) = \frac{1}{x - 2} - 6$ compares to the graph of $f(x)$.
3. Expand $(-3x + 4y)^5$.
4. Determine the coefficient of a^7b^5 in the expansion of $(2a - 3b)^{12}$.

Must Be a Rational Explanation

Operations with Rational Expressions

Warm Up

1. $\frac{1}{2} + \frac{1}{3}$

2. $\frac{1}{2} - \frac{1}{3}$

3. $\frac{1}{2} \cdot \frac{1}{3}$

4. $\frac{1}{2} \div \frac{1}{3}$

Learning Goals

- Add and subtract rational expressions.
- Factor rational expressions to determine a least common denominator.
- Multiply and divide rational expressions.

You know how to add, subtract, multiply, and divide rational numbers. How can these processes be extended to include rational expressions?

Light the Corners of My Mind

In elementary school, you divided rational numbers using long division. You wrote the quotient first with a remainder and then as a mixed number.

For example, $13 \div 3 = 4$ R1, and $13 \div 3 = 4\frac{1}{3}$.

1. **How are the quotients of rational expressions connected to those you determined in elementary school?**

   a. **Write the quotient of $x^2 + 2x - 3 \div (x - 2)$ in two ways. Show your work.**

   b. **How do you know that $x \neq 2$ is a restriction for the quotient?**

Calculating Sums and Differences of Rational Expressions

You learned that operating with polynomials is similar to operating with integers. Likewise, operating with rational expressions is similar to operating with rational numbers. Consider the table shown.

	Rational Numbers	Rational Expressions Involving Variables in the Numerator
Example 1	$\dfrac{1}{6} + \dfrac{5}{6} - \dfrac{1}{6} = \dfrac{5}{6}$	$\dfrac{1x}{6} + \dfrac{5x}{6} - \dfrac{1x}{6} = \dfrac{5x}{6}$
Example 2	$\dfrac{3}{2} + \dfrac{2}{5} - \dfrac{3}{4} = \dfrac{3(10)}{2(10)} + \dfrac{2(4)}{5(4)} - \dfrac{3(5)}{4(5)}$ $= \dfrac{30}{20} + \dfrac{8}{20} - \dfrac{15}{20}$ $= \dfrac{23}{20}$	$\dfrac{3x}{2} + \dfrac{2y}{5} - \dfrac{3x}{4} = \dfrac{3(10)x}{2(10)} + \dfrac{2(4)y}{5(4)} - \dfrac{3(5)x}{4(5)}$ $= \dfrac{30x}{20} + \dfrac{8y}{20} - \dfrac{15x}{20}$ $= \dfrac{15x + 8y}{20}$
Example 3	$\dfrac{3}{5} + \dfrac{2}{3} - \dfrac{2}{15} = \dfrac{3(3)}{5(3)} + \dfrac{2(5)}{3(5)} - \dfrac{2}{15}$ $= \dfrac{9}{15} + \dfrac{10}{15} - \dfrac{2}{15}$ $= \dfrac{17}{15}$	$\dfrac{3x}{5} + \dfrac{2y}{3} - \dfrac{2}{15} - \dfrac{2x + 3y}{5} = \dfrac{3(3)x}{5(3)} + \dfrac{2(5)y}{3(5)} - \dfrac{2}{15} - \dfrac{(2x + 3y)(3)}{5(3)}$ $= \dfrac{9x}{15} + \dfrac{10y}{15} - \dfrac{2}{15} - \dfrac{6x + 9y}{15}$ $= \dfrac{9x + 10y - 2 - (6x + 9y)}{15}$ $= \dfrac{9x + 10y - 2 - 6x - 9y}{15}$ $= \dfrac{3x + y - 2}{15}$

1. **Analyze the examples.**

   a. **Explain the process used to add and subtract each expression.**

   b. **In Example 2, why is $\dfrac{3}{2} = \dfrac{3(10)}{2(10)}$ and why is $\dfrac{3x}{2} = \dfrac{3(10)x}{2(10)}$?**

2. **Analyze Noelle's work. Explain how Noelle could have been more efficient in her work.**

Noelle

$$\frac{3x}{3} + \frac{2x}{8} - \frac{1}{2}$$

To add and subtract fractions, I need a common denominator. To determine one, I multiply all the denominators together: $3 \cdot 8 \cdot 2 = 48$

$$\frac{3x(16)}{3(16)} + \frac{2x(6)}{8(6)} - \frac{1(24)}{2(24)} = \frac{48x}{48} + \frac{12x}{48} - \frac{24}{48}$$
$$= \frac{60x - 24}{48}$$
$$= \frac{5x - 2}{4}$$

3. **Calculate each sum and difference.**

   a. $\frac{3}{6} + \frac{5x}{4} - \frac{y}{8}$

   b. $\frac{x - 2y}{3} + \frac{x}{12} - \frac{z}{4}$

   c. $\frac{4x}{6} - \frac{2x}{9} - \frac{x}{18}$

4. **Notice that all the variables in the right column of the table on the previous page are in the numerator. If there were variables in the denominator, do you think the process of adding and subtracting the expressions would change? Explain your reasoning.**

Determining the LCD
of Rational Expressions

When rational expressions contain variables in the denominator, the process remains the same—you still need to determine the least common denominator (LCD) before adding and subtracting.

1. **Consider Method A compared to Method B in both columns of the table.**

	Rational Numbers	Rational Expressions Involving Variables in the Denominator
Method A	$\frac{1}{3} + \frac{1}{3^2} = \frac{1(3^2)}{3(3^2)} + \frac{1(3)}{3^2(3)}$ $= \frac{3^2}{3^3} + \frac{3}{3^3}$ $= \frac{3^2 + 3}{3^3}$ $= \frac{3(3 + 1)}{3(3^2)}$ $= \frac{4}{3^2}$	$\frac{1}{x} + \frac{1}{x^2} = \frac{1(x^2)}{x(x^2)} + \frac{1(x)}{x^2(x)}$ $= \frac{x^2}{x^3} + \frac{x}{x^3}$ $= \frac{x^2 + x}{x^3}$ $= \frac{x(x + 1)}{x(x^2)}$ $= \frac{x + 1}{x^2}$ $\frac{1}{x} + \frac{1}{x^2} = \frac{x + 1}{x^2}$ for $x \neq 0$
Method B	$\frac{1}{3} + \frac{1}{3^2} = \frac{1(3)}{3(3)} + \frac{1}{3^2} = \frac{4}{3^2}$	$\frac{1}{x} + \frac{1}{x^2} = \frac{1(x)}{x(x)} + \frac{1}{x^2}$ $= \frac{x + 1}{x^2}$ $\frac{1}{x} + \frac{1}{x^2} = \frac{x + 1}{x^2}$ for $x \neq 0$

a. **Explain the difference in the methods.**

b. **Explain why the statement $\frac{1}{x} + \frac{1}{x^2} = \frac{x + 1}{x^2}$ has the restriction $x \neq 0$.**

c. **How would these methods change if the examples involved subtracting the rational expressions: $\frac{1}{3} - \frac{1}{3^2}$ and $\frac{1}{x} - \frac{1}{x^2}$? Explain your reasoning.**

2. Ruth and Samir determine the LCD for the expression
$$\frac{1}{x^2 - 1} + \frac{1}{x + 1}.$$

Ruth

$\frac{1}{x^2 - 1} + \frac{1}{x + 1}$

$(x^2 - 1)(x + 1)$

LCD: $x^3 + x^2 - x - 1$

Samir

$\frac{1}{x^2 - 1} + \frac{1}{x + 1}$

$\frac{1}{(x - 1)(x + 1)} + \frac{1}{x + 1}$

$(x - 1)(x + 1)$

LCD: $x^2 - 1$

Who is correct? Explain your reasoning.

| Make sure to list the restrictions for the variable. |

3. Determine the least common denominator for each set of rational expressions.

a. $\dfrac{3}{x + 4}, \dfrac{7x}{x - 4}$

b. $\dfrac{-2}{3x - 2}, \dfrac{4x}{3x^2 + 7x - 6}$

c. $\dfrac{-11}{x}, \dfrac{7}{x - 4}, \dfrac{x}{x^2 - 16}$

d. $\dfrac{2x}{x^2 - 5x + 6}, \dfrac{7x + 11}{x^2 - 6x + 9}$

Notice that even when there are binomials in the denominator, adding two rational expressions is similar to adding two rational numbers. The example shows a difference of two rational expressions of degree 2.

> **Worked Example**
>
> You can determine the difference of two rational expressions with binomials in the denominator.
>
> $$\frac{1}{x^2 - 1} - \frac{1}{x^2 + 2x + 1} = \frac{1}{(x + 1)(x - 1)} - \frac{1}{(x + 1)(x + 1)}$$
>
> $$= \frac{1(x + 1)}{(x + 1)(x - 1)(x + 1)} - \frac{1(x - 1)}{(x + 1)(x + 1)(x - 1)}$$
>
> $$= \frac{(x + 1) - (x - 1)}{(x + 1)(x + 1)(x - 1)}$$
>
> $$= \frac{2}{(x + 1)(x + 1)(x - 1)}, x \neq -1, 1$$

4. **How would the method change if the example shown involved adding the rational expressions? Explain your reasoning.**

5. **Anthony and Marissa add $\frac{2x + 2}{x} + \frac{1}{x}$.**

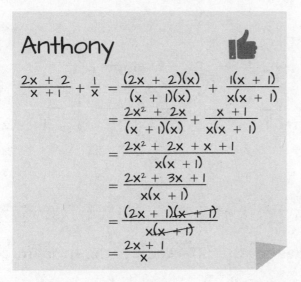

Anthony 👍

$$\frac{2x + 2}{x + 1} + \frac{1}{x} = \frac{(2x + 2)(x)}{(x + 1)(x)} + \frac{1(x + 1)}{x(x + 1)}$$

$$= \frac{2x^2 + 2x}{(x + 1)(x)} + \frac{x + 1}{x(x + 1)}$$

$$= \frac{2x^2 + 2x + x + 1}{x(x + 1)}$$

$$= \frac{2x^2 + 3x + 1}{x(x + 1)}$$

$$= \frac{(2x + 1)(x + 1)}{x(x + 1)}$$

$$= \frac{2x + 1}{x}$$

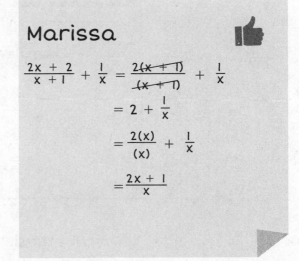

Marissa 👍

$$\frac{2x + 2}{x + 1} + \frac{1}{x} = \frac{2(x + 1)}{(x + 1)} + \frac{1}{x}$$

$$= 2 + \frac{1}{x}$$

$$= \frac{2(x)}{(x)} + \frac{1}{x}$$

$$= \frac{2x + 1}{x}$$

a. **Explain the difference in the methods used.**

b. **Joyce says the only restriction on the variable x in Anthony and Marissa's problem is $x \neq 0$. Alaina says $x \neq 0, -1$.**

Who is correct? Explain your reasoning.

Consider the worked examples.

> **Worked Example**
>
> Determine each difference.
>
> | **Example 1** | **Example 2** |
> |---|---|
> | $\dfrac{3}{x-1} - \dfrac{3}{x+1}$ | $\dfrac{1}{x-1} - \dfrac{1}{x+1}$ |
> | $\dfrac{3(x+1)}{(x-1)(x+1)} - \dfrac{3(x-1)}{(x+1)(x-1)}$ | $\dfrac{1(x+1)}{(x-1)(x+1)} - \dfrac{1(x-1)}{(x+1)(x-1)}$ |
> | $\dfrac{3x+3-3x+3}{(x-1)(x+1)}$ | $\dfrac{x+1-x+1}{(x-1)(x+1)}$ |
> | $\dfrac{6}{(x-1)(x+1)}$ | $\dfrac{2}{(x-1)(x+1)}$ |

1. **Describe the similarities and the differences in the structure of each example.**

2. **Consider the given expression and the resulting difference. What pattern do you notice?**

3. **If the numerators in Example 1 of the worked example were doubled, what would be the new answer?**

4. **Can you use this pattern to determine $\dfrac{4}{x-2} - \dfrac{4}{x+2}$? Explain your reasoning.**

5. How would the pattern in the worked example change if you added the terms together?

6. Calculate each sum or difference. Make sure to list the restrictions for the variable, and rewrite in lowest terms.

a. $\dfrac{5x - 6}{x^2 - 9} - \dfrac{4}{x - 3}$

b. $\dfrac{x - 7}{x^2 - 3x + 2} + \dfrac{4}{x^2 - 7x + 10}$

c. $\dfrac{2x - 5}{x} - \dfrac{4}{5x} - 4$

d. $\dfrac{3x - 5}{4x^2 + 12x + 9} + \dfrac{4}{2x + 3} - \dfrac{2x}{3}$

e. $\dfrac{x + 2}{x - 4} + \dfrac{2}{x} + \dfrac{5}{3x - 1}$

Remember:

When you multiply rational numbers, you can divide out factors at the beginning or the end, and the product is the same. However, dividing out factors earlier saves time and keeps the expressions simpler.

Previously, you learned that adding and subtracting rational expressions involved the same process as adding and subtracting rational numbers. Now, you will see that multiplying rational expressions involves the same steps as multiplying rational numbers.

1. **Consider Method A compared to Method B in both columns of the table.**

	Rational Numbers	Rational Expressions Involving Variables	
Method A	$\frac{2}{15} \cdot \frac{5}{8} = \frac{10}{120}$ $= \frac{1}{12}$	$\frac{2x}{15x} \cdot \frac{5x}{8} = \frac{10x^2}{120x}$ $= \frac{x}{12}$	$\frac{2x}{15x^2} \cdot \frac{5x^2}{8} = \frac{10x^3}{120x^2}$ $= \frac{x}{12}$
Method B	$\frac{\overset{1}{\cancel{2}}}{\underset{3}{\cancel{15}}} \cdot \frac{\overset{1}{\cancel{5}}}{\underset{4}{\cancel{8}}} = \frac{1}{12}$	$\frac{\overset{x}{\cancel{2x}}}{\underset{3}{\cancel{15x}}} \cdot \frac{\overset{1}{\cancel{5x}}}{\underset{4}{\cancel{8}}} = \frac{x}{12}$	$\frac{\overset{1}{\cancel{2x}}}{\underset{3}{\cancel{15x^2}}} \cdot \frac{\overset{1}{\cancel{5x^2}}}{\underset{4}{\cancel{8}}} = \frac{x}{12}$

a. **Explain the difference in the methods.**

b. **Which method do you prefer?**

2. Given the equation $\frac{2x}{15x^2} \cdot \frac{5x^2}{8} = \frac{x}{12}$, Brody says that $x \neq 0$. Damiere says that there are no restrictions because the answer is $\frac{x}{12}$ and there are no variables in the denominator. Who is correct? Explain your reasoning.

3. Analyze Isha's work. Explain how Isha could have multiplied the rational expressions more efficiently.

Isha

$$\frac{12xyz^2}{11} \cdot \frac{33x}{8z} = \frac{\overset{9}{\cancel{396}}x^2y\overset{z}{\cancel{z^2}}}{\underset{2}{\cancel{88z}}}$$

$$= \frac{9x^2yz}{2}$$

4. Shaheen multiplies $\frac{5x^2}{3x^2 - 75} \cdot \frac{3x - 15}{4x^2}$ without dividing out factors first. Complete the same problem as Shaheen, by dividing out common factors first, and then list the restrictions.

Shaheen

$$\frac{5x^2}{3x^2 - 75} \cdot \frac{3x - 15}{4x^2} = \frac{15x^3 - 75x^2}{12x^4 - 300x^2}$$

$$= \frac{15x^2(x - 5)}{3x^2(4x^2 - 100)}$$

$$= \frac{\overset{5}{\cancel{15}}x^{\cancel{2}}(x - 5)}{\underset{1}{\cancel{3}}x^{\cancel{2}}(4x^2 - 100)}$$

$$= \frac{5(x - 5)}{4(x^2 - 25)}$$

$$= \frac{5\cancel{(x - 5)}}{4\cancel{(x - 5)}(x + 5)}$$

$$= \frac{5}{4(x + 5)}$$

5. **Multiply each expression. List the restrictions for the variables.**

a. $\dfrac{3ab^2}{4c} \cdot \dfrac{2c^2}{27\,ab}$

b. $\dfrac{3x}{5x - 15} \cdot \dfrac{x - 3}{9x^2}$

c. $\dfrac{x + 5}{x^2 - 4x + 3} \cdot \dfrac{x - 3}{4x + 20}$

d. $\dfrac{7x - 7}{3x^2} \cdot \dfrac{x + 5}{9x^2 - 9} \cdot \dfrac{x^2 - 5x - 6}{x^3 + 6x^2 + 5x}$

Patterns in Rational Expression Quotients

Dividing rational expressions is similar to the process you use when dividing rational numbers.

You may recall that, to divide fractions, you multiply the dividend by the multiplicative inverse of the divisor.

	Rational Numbers	Rational Expressions Involving Variables	
Example 1	$\frac{1}{5} \div \frac{3}{10} = \frac{1}{\cancel{5}_1} \cdot \frac{\cancel{10}^{2}}{3}$ $= \frac{2}{3}$	$\frac{xy}{5z} \div \frac{3xy}{10z} = \frac{\cancel{xy}^{1}}{\cancel{5z}} \cdot \frac{\cancel{10z}^{2}}{\cancel{3xy}}$ $= \frac{2}{3}$	$\frac{xy^2}{5z} \div \frac{3xy}{10z^2} = \frac{\cancel{xy^2}^{y}}{\cancel{5z}} \cdot \frac{\cancel{10z^2}^{2z}}{\cancel{3xy}_{1}}$ $= \frac{2yz}{3}; x, y, z \neq 0$
Example 2	$\frac{6}{7} \div 4 = \frac{\cancel{6}^{3}}{7} \cdot \frac{1}{\cancel{4}_2}$ $= \frac{3}{14}$	$\frac{6a}{7b} \div 4a = \frac{\cancel{6a}^{3}}{7b} \cdot \frac{1}{\cancel{4a}_2}$ $= \frac{3}{14b}$	$\frac{6a^3}{7b} \div 4a = \frac{\cancel{6a^3}^{3a^2}}{7b} \cdot \frac{1}{\cancel{4a}_2}$ $= \frac{3a^2}{14b}; a, b, \neq 0$

1. **Analyze the examples shown in the table.**

   a. **Explain the process for dividing rational expressions.**

   b. **In Example 2, explain why $\frac{1}{4a}$ is the multiplicative inverse of $4a$.**

2. **Determine the quotients of each expression.**

   a. $\dfrac{9ab^2}{4c} \div \dfrac{18c^2}{5ab}$

   b. $\dfrac{7x^2}{3x^2 - 27} \div \dfrac{4x^2}{3x - 9}$

   c. $\dfrac{3x^2 + 15x}{x^2 - 3x - 40} \div \dfrac{5x^2}{x^2 - 64}$

TALK the TALK

Closure: Wherever You Go, There You Are

You have compared operating with rational expressions to operating with rational numbers.

1. **Determine each sum, difference, product, or quotient.**

   a. $\frac{1}{x} + \frac{1}{y}$

   b. $\frac{1}{x} - \frac{1}{y}$

   c. $\frac{1}{x} \cdot \frac{1}{y}$

   d. $\frac{1}{x} \div \frac{1}{y}$

   e. $\frac{1}{x^2} + \frac{1}{y}$

   f. $\frac{1}{x^2} + \frac{1}{y^2}$

   g. $\frac{1}{x^2} - \frac{1}{y}$

   h. $\frac{1}{x^2} - \frac{1}{y^2}$

   i. $\frac{1}{x^2} \cdot \frac{1}{y}$

   j. $\frac{1}{x^2} \cdot \frac{1}{y^2}$

   k. $\frac{1}{x^2} \div \frac{1}{y}$

   l. $\frac{1}{x^2} \div \frac{1}{y^2}$

2. **What similarities and differences are there in the methods you used to determine your answers?**

3. **Determine whether the set of rational expressions is closed under each operation.**

   a. **Addition**

   b. **Subtraction**

   c. **Multiplication**

   d. **Division**

Assignment

Write

In your own words, explain how operating with rational expressions is similar to operating with rational numbers. Use examples to illustrate your reasoning.

Remember

The process for adding and subtracting rational expressions is similar to the process for adding and subtracting rational numbers, and the process for multiplying and dividing rational expressions is similar to the process for multiplying and dividing rational numbers.

Practice

1. Add or subtract each expression. List any restrictions on the variables.

   a. $\dfrac{3y}{4} - \dfrac{x}{3} + \dfrac{5y}{6}$

   b. $\dfrac{2}{2x - 4} - \dfrac{5}{x^2 - 4}$

   c. $\dfrac{60 - 3x}{x^2 + x - 20} + \dfrac{3x + 9}{x + 3}$

   d. $\dfrac{2}{2x^2 + 7x + 3} - \dfrac{x}{x^2 - 2x - 15} + 1$

2. Alicia multiplied $\dfrac{3x - 6}{8x - 16} \cdot \dfrac{4x}{9}$. Her work is shown.

   Alicia

   $$\dfrac{3x - 6}{8x - 16} \cdot \dfrac{4x}{9} = \dfrac{\overset{1}{\cancel{3x}} - 6}{\underset{2}{\cancel{8x}} - 16} \cdot \dfrac{\overset{1}{\cancel{4x}}}{\underset{3}{\cancel{9}}}$$

   $$= \dfrac{x - 6}{-14} \cdot \dfrac{1}{3}$$

   $$= \dfrac{x - 6}{-42}; \; x \neq 2$$

   Identify the error(s) in Alicia's work. Then correctly perform the multiplication.

3. Multiply or divide each. List any restrictions on the variables.

   a. $\dfrac{2x^2 - 32}{x^2 - 10x + 24} \cdot \dfrac{x^2 - 4x - 12}{10x + 20}$

   b. $\dfrac{6x}{x - 9} \cdot \dfrac{x^2 - 10x + 9}{2x + 12} \cdot \dfrac{x + 6}{x^4 + x^3 - 2x^2}$

   c. $\dfrac{8a^3b}{5c} \div \dfrac{10ab^2}{3c}$

   d. $\dfrac{14x^2}{4x + 20} \div \dfrac{7x^2 - 21x}{x^2 - 25}$

   e. $\dfrac{xy^2 - 6y^2}{2x + 18} \div \dfrac{2xy + y}{8x + 24} \div \dfrac{x^2 - 3x - 18}{2x^2 - 3x - 2}$

Stretch

1. Perform the operations.

$$\frac{12x}{3x^2 - 10x + 3} - \frac{x - 2}{x^2 - 9} + 2$$

Review

1. Consider the rational function $\frac{x + 1}{x^2 - 4x - 5}$. Determine any vertical and horizontal asymptotes and any removable discontinuities of the graph of $f(x)$. Explain your reasoning.

2. Write a function $f(x)$ with a vertical asymptote $x = -2$ and removable discontinuities at $x = 1$ and $x = -4$. Explain your reasoning. Explain how to sketch the graph of the function $g(x)$ without using technology.

3. Determine the domain points of discontinuity for the rational function. Explain your reasoning.
$$f(x) = \frac{x^2 + 5x + 4}{x^3 + 64}$$

4. Data is collected to determine levels of a medication in a patient's bloodstream. The level of medication in milligrams, y, in a patient's bloodstream x hours after the medication is taken can be modeled by the equation $y = 0.03x^4 + 0.41x^3 - 7.2x^2 + 22.9x$.

   a. Sketch the regression equation on the given coordinate plane.

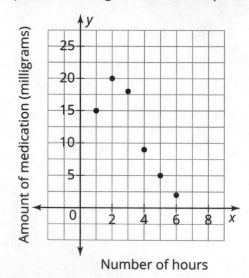

Number of hours

   b. For what interval(s) is the model appropriate for the problem situation? Explain your reasoning.

5

Thunder. Thun-Thun- Thunder.

Solving Problems with Rational Equations

© Carnegie Learning, Inc.

Warm Up

Solve each proportion.

1. $\frac{x}{12} = \frac{5}{3}$

2. $\frac{x + 2}{8} = \frac{6}{3}$

Learning Goals

- Model situations with rational functions.
- Use rational expressions to solve real-world problems.
- Solve rational equations in one variable.

Key Term

- rational equation

You have analyzed and performed operations with rational expressions. How can you solve equations composed of rational expressions?

The Golden Ratio

The ancient Greeks thought certain rectangles in art and architecture were much more pleasing to the eye than others. When the ratio of the sum of the length and width to the length is approximately 1.618, they felt the rectangle was perfectly proportionate. This ratio came to be known as the Golden Ratio.

1. **Draw and describe the length and width of several rectangles with dimensions that are in the Golden Ratio.**

Writing Equations to Solve Problems

A door-to-door salesperson for TV Bonanza Cable Company offers cable television for only $55.95 per month. However, there is a one-time installation cost of $180.

1. **Determine the total cost of cable for the first two months. What is the average cost per month over the first two months?**

2. **Determine the total cost of cable for the first year. What is the average cost per month over the first year?**

3. **Write an equation to represent the total cost of cable for *x* months.**

4. **Write an equation to represent the average monthly cost of cable for *x* months. Use technology to graph your equation and sketch it on the coordinate plane.**

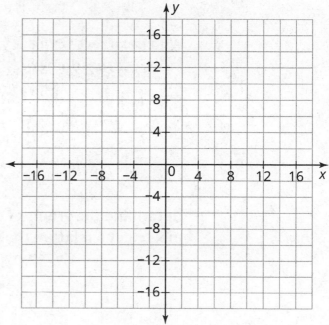

5. **A competitor offers a similar product for $65 per month and no installation charges. Who is offering the better deal? Use your graph to approximate the solution and then verify algebraically. Show all work and explain your reasoning.**

Crunchy College Kid Snack Company manufactures a new brand of trail mix containing peanuts, almonds, and chocolate. Each package contains 400 grams of trail mix, with 50% peanuts, 35% almonds, and 15% chocolate. Herbert loves chocolate. When he gets home, he wants to add enough chocolate so that the mixture is 50% chocolate. How many grams of chocolate should he add?

6. Tracy and Adrian model the given scenario with a rational function.

Tracy

I must first determine the amount of chocolate in the bag.

$(0.15) \cdot (400) = 60g$

The ratio of chocolate to total trail mix must increase to 50%. Adding chocolate increases the total amount of trail mix, so the new ratio is $\frac{60 + x}{400 + x}$. I can set up the proportion $\frac{60 + x}{400 + x} = 0.50$. The x-value represents the amount of additional chocolate.

Adrian

The current chocolate to trail mix ratio is $\frac{15}{100}$. Adding chocolate to get a mixture with 50% chocolate, add x to the percent chocolate as well as the total, so the rational equation becomes $\frac{15 + x}{100 + x} = 0.50$. The x-value of the intersection point represents the amount of chocolate Herbert must add.

a. **Who is correct? Explain your reasoning. Describe the incorrect reasoning.**

b. **Determine the grams of chocolate that Herbert must add to the trail mix to get a mixture that is 50% chocolate.**

A common misconception is that you can determine how far away a storm is by measuring the time between thunder and lightning. In reality, though, the time between seeing lightning and hearing thunder is a function of both distance and temperature. The time between seeing lightning and hearing thunder is represented by the function Time $= \frac{d}{1.09t + 1050}$, where d is the distance (feet) between the observer and the lightning, and t is the temperature (Fahrenheit).

7. **If the temperature outside is 70° and you count 3 seconds between the thunder and the lightning, approximately how far away is the storm? Show all of your work and explain your reasoning.**

8. **If the temperature is 80° and you estimate half a second between thunder and lightning, how far away is the storm? Show all of your work and explain your reasoning.**

9. **On a 60° day, what is the time between thunder and lightning when the storm is directly overhead? Show all work and explain your reasoning.**

In an electrical circuit, when resistors are connected in parallel, the total resistance R_T of the circuit in ohms is given by:

$$\frac{1}{R_T} = \frac{1}{R_1} + \frac{1}{R_2} + \ldots + \frac{1}{R_n}$$

where n is the number of resistors and R_1 through R_n are the resistances of each resistor in ohms.

10. **Determine the total resistance of an electrical circuit having two resistors connected in parallel if their resistances are 5 ohms and 8 ohms.**

11. **Three resistors connected in parallel have resistances of 4 ohms, 6 ohms, and 10 ohms. What is the total resistance in this electric circuit?**

12. **The total resistance in a parallel wiring circuit with two resistors is 12 ohms. If the resistance of one branch is 30 ohms, what is the resistance in the other branch?**

13. **A three-resistor parallel wiring circuit has a total resistance of 10 ohms. If two of the branches of the circuit have resistances of 20 ohms and 30 ohms, what is the resistance in the third branch?**

14. Scott is taking a test that has two different parts to it. His goal is to get a 90%. He finished Part 1, and a quick scan by the teacher reveals that he got 18 out of the 23 questions correct. He begins Part 2. If he answers each consecutive question correctly, how many must he answer correctly for his grade to be higher than a 90%? Show all of your work and explain your reasoning.

15. Manuel is considering joining a local gym. Joining the gym costs $30 each month, plus $2 per hour for using the basketball courts. They also allow people who are not members of the club to use the courts for $7 per hour. If he joins the gym, how many hours would he have to play before the average cost is less than $7 per hour? Show all work and explain your reasoning.

Methods for Solving Rational Equations

A **rational equation** is an equation that contains one or more rational expressions. There are multiple methods you can use to solve rational equations. Depending on the structure of the equation, some methods will be more efficient than others.

1. **Sully used proportional reasoning to solve the equation $\frac{x+5}{x+2} = \frac{x+1}{x-5}$. Explain how he solved it.**

Sully

$$\frac{x+5}{x+2} = \frac{x+1}{x-5}$$

Restrictions: $x \neq -2, 5$

$$(x+5)(x-5) = (x+2)(x+1)$$
$$x^2 - 25 = x^2 + 3x + 2$$
$$-25 = 3x + 2$$
$$-27 = 3x$$
$$x = -9$$

2. **Three students each solved a slightly different equation: $\frac{x+5}{(x-5)(x+2)} = \frac{x+1}{x-5}$. They first recognized the restrictions as $x \neq -2, 5$. Consider their work.**

Jermaine

$$(x+5)(x-5) = (x-5)(x+2)(x+1)$$
$$x + 5 = x^2 + 3x + 2$$
$$0 = x^2 + 2x - 3$$
$$0 = (x+3)(x-1)$$
$$-3, 1 = x$$

Dona

$$\frac{x + 5}{x + 1} = \frac{(x - 5)(x + 2)}{x - 5} \quad \leftarrow \text{Rewrite the proportion.}$$

$$\frac{x + 5}{x + 1} = x + 2$$

$$(x + 5) = (x + 1)(x + 2)$$

$$x^2 + 3x + 2 = x + 5$$

$$x^2 + 2x - 3 = 0$$

$$(x + 3)(x - 1) = 0$$

$$x = -3, 1$$

Quentin

$$\frac{(x + 1)(x + 2)}{(x - 5)(x + 2)} = \frac{x + 5}{(x - 5)(x + 2)} \quad \leftarrow \text{Write with common denominator.}$$

$$(x + 1)(x + 2) = (x + 5)$$

$$x + 5 = x^2 + 3x + 2$$

$$0 = x^2 + 2x - 3$$

$$0 = (x + 3)(x - 1)$$

$$-3, 1 = x$$

a. **What is different about the structure of this equation compared to the equation in Question 1?**

b. **Explain how Dona rewrote the proportion to solve the equation.**

c. How did Quentin determine the common denominator?

d. Which method do you think is more efficient based on the structure of the equation?

3. Consider how Jake begins to solve $\dfrac{2x + 4}{x^2 - 2x - 8} = \dfrac{x + 1}{x - 4}$.
    Finish solving the equation and describe your strategy.
    Be sure to list the restrictions.

Jake

$$\frac{2x + 4}{x^2 - 2x - 8} = \frac{x + 1}{x - 4}$$

$$\frac{2(x + 2)}{(x - 4)(x + 2)} = \frac{x + 1}{x - 4}$$

$$x \neq 4, -2$$

$$\frac{2(x + 2)}{(x - 4)(x + 2)} = \frac{x + 1}{x - 4}$$

4. Describe the methods Seth and Sidonie each used to solve the rational equation.

Seth 👍

$$\frac{6}{x^2 - 4x} + \frac{4}{x} = \frac{2}{x - 4}$$

$$\frac{6}{x(x-4)} + \frac{4}{x} \cdot \frac{(x-4)}{(x-4)} = \frac{2}{x-4} \cdot \frac{x}{x}$$

$$x \neq 0, 4$$

$$\frac{6}{x(x-4)} + \frac{4x - 16}{x(x-4)} = \frac{2x}{x(x-4)}$$

$$\frac{6 + 4x - 16}{x(x-4)} = \frac{2x}{x(x-4)}$$

$$\cancel{x(x-4)} \left[\frac{6 - 16 = -10}{\cancel{x(x-4)}} = \frac{2x}{\cancel{x(x-4)}} \right]$$

$$6 + 4x - 16 = 2x$$

$$4x - 10 = 2x$$

$$2x = 10$$

$$x = 5$$

Sidonie 👍

$$\frac{6}{x^2 - 4x} + \frac{4}{x} = \frac{2}{x - 4}$$

$$\frac{6}{x(x-4)} + \frac{4}{x} = \frac{2}{x-4}$$

$$x \neq 0, 4$$

$$(x(x-4)) \cdot \left[\frac{6}{x(x-4)} + \frac{4}{x} = \frac{2}{x-4} \right]$$

$$6 + 4(x-4) = 2x$$

$$6 + 4x - 16 = 2x$$

$$4x - 10 = 2x$$

$$2x = 10$$

$$x = 5$$

5. Solve the equation $\frac{10}{x^2 - 2x} + \frac{1}{x} = \frac{3}{x - 2}$. Explain why you chose your solution method.

Think about:

How does the structure of this equation inform your strategy?

TALK the TALK

Structure. Stru- Stru- Structure.

1. Cut out the equations located at the end of the lesson. Sort the equations based on the solution method you intend to use. Finally, solve each equation. Be sure to list any domain restrictions.

2. Did you solve the equations using the method you first intended?

a. $\frac{12}{x + 5} = -2$

b. $\frac{x - 5}{3} = \frac{x - 38}{12} - \frac{x}{4}$

c. $\frac{x^2 - 5x}{4} = \frac{8x}{2}$

d. $\frac{1}{x - 5} = \frac{5}{x^2 + 2x - 35}$

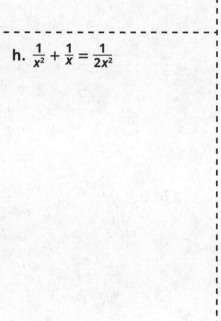

e. $\dfrac{3}{x-1} + \dfrac{2}{5x+5} = \dfrac{-3}{x^2-1}$

f. $\dfrac{x-5}{x-2} = \dfrac{8}{9}$

g. $\dfrac{5}{x} = 25 + \dfrac{5}{x}$

h. $\dfrac{1}{x^2} + \dfrac{1}{x} = \dfrac{1}{2x^2}$

i. $\dfrac{-2}{x+3} + \dfrac{3}{x-2} = \dfrac{5}{x^2+x-6}$

j. $\dfrac{7}{x+3} = \dfrac{8}{x-2}$

k. $\dfrac{x+3}{x^2-1} + \dfrac{-2x}{x-1} = 1$

l. $\dfrac{3}{x^2+2x} = \dfrac{6}{x^2}$

Assignment

Write

1. In your own words, define a rational equation. Use examples to illustrate your reasoning.

Remember

Rational expressions and equations are used to solve problems that involve comparing two quantities of the same unit of measure.

Practice

1. In football, a quarterback's completion percentage is the ratio of the number of complete passes to the total number of pass attempts. The current record holder for highest completion percentage is Chad Pennington who completed 66% of his passes over the course of his career in the National Football League. The quarterback in second place completed 3843 passes out of 5853 attempts. Estimate the number of consecutive completed passes the second place quarterback must throw in order to break the record. Show all of your work and explain your reasoning.

2. Josie compares two different refrigerators at the local hardware store. The sales tags are shown. Josie does some research online and learns that a kilowatt hour costs approximately $0.06. She also learns that the average refrigerator lasts about 10 years.

ICY COLD	COOL AS A CUCUMBER
• Crushed Ice Dispenser	• Gold Star EPA efficiency rating
• Price $699.00	• Price $825
• Uses 75 Kilowatt hours of electricity per month	• Uses 30 Kilowatt hours of electricity per month

   a. Write a function to represent the average cost of each refrigerator per month.
   b. Which refrigerator will have a lower average monthly cost over the next ten years? Show all of your work and explain your reasoning.

Stretch

1. Blaise is running in a ten mile race. Blaise runs the first 4 miles of the race at a pace that averages 0.5 miles an hour faster than the last 6 miles of the race. It takes Blaise one hour and 45 minutes to run the 10 miles. Write and solve an equation to determine Blaise's average speed for the first 4 miles and the last 6 miles of the race. Show your work.

Review

1. Perform each operation. List any restrictions on the variables.

   a. $\dfrac{3}{3x^2 - 11x - 4} + \dfrac{2x}{x^2 - 3x - 4}$

   b. $\dfrac{2x - 4}{3x^3} \cdot \dfrac{9x}{x - 2}$

2. The graph shows the the level of medication in milligrams, y, in a patient's bloodstream x hours after the medication is taken. The dots represent the actual data and the curve represents the quartic regression equation that best fits the data, $y = 0.03x^4 + 0.41x^3 - 7.2x^2 + 22.9x$. Consider the data and the regression equation. Predict the patients level of medication 2.5 hours after taking the medicine. How accurate is this prediction? Explain your reasoning.

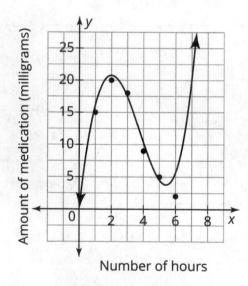

Number of hours

16 Tons and What Do You Get?

Solving Work, Mixture, Distance, and Cost Problems

Warm Up

Solve for x.

1. $32 = \dfrac{x}{2}$

2. $\dfrac{3}{4} + \dfrac{4}{x} = 1$

3. $\dfrac{x}{10} + \dfrac{x}{20} = 1$

Learning Goals

- Use rational equations to model and solve work problems, mixture problems, distance problems, and cost problems.
- Model real-world and mathematical situations using rational equations.

You have solved rational equations. How can you model real-world situations using rational equations?

© Carnegie Learning, Inc.

Mixing It Up

You have two containers—one holds cranberry juice and one holds ginger ale. The volume of liquid is the same in each container.

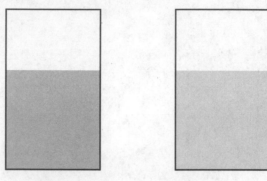

Suppose you do the following:

- Take exactly one cup of cranberry juice and pour it into the ginger ale container. Assume that the cranberry juice mixes perfectly into the ginger ale.
- Take exactly one cup from the cranberry juice and ginger ale mixture and pour it back into the cranberry juice container.

Think

about:

Suppose the containers were full of marbles–100 red for cranberry juice and 100 yellow for ginger ale.

This can help you solve the original problem.

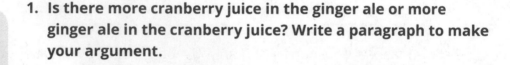

1. **Is there more cranberry juice in the ginger ale or more ginger ale in the cranberry juice? Write a paragraph to make your argument.**

Solving Work Problems

A work problem involves the rates of several workers and the time it takes to complete a job. For example, the rate at which each of two painters works the total time it takes them to paint a house while working together is an example of a work problem.

Anita and Martin are the assistant managers for the marketing department of the Snarky Larks Hockey Team. This hockey season is fast-approaching, and the rink board ads need to be mounted to the rink boards before the season begins.

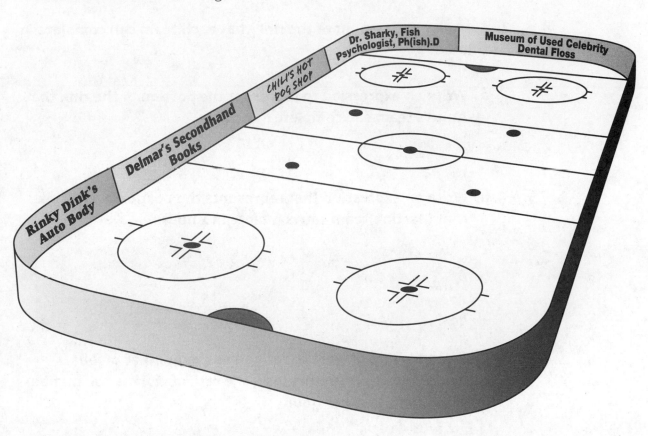

Each ad is like a giant vinyl sticker that is stuck to each rink board along the inside of the hockey rink. It takes a team of three people to attach each ad: two people hold the ad while a third person presses it to the rink board, being careful that it does not wrinkle.

Up until last year, Anita's team and Martin's team have taken turns doing this job—Anita's team attached the rink boards for the first season, Martin's team attached them for the next season, the following season Anita's team attached them, and so on.

It takes Anita's team 20 hours to attach all of the rink boards, and it takes Martin's team 30 hours to attach all of the rink boards. This year, however, their boss has asked them to work together to get the job done faster.

1. **Determine the portion of the rink each team completes in the given number of hours.**

Anita's Team	Martin's Team
1 hour:	**1 hour:**
5 hours:	**5 hours:**
10 hours:	**10 hours:**

2. **Consider the amount of the rink that each team can complete in *x* hours.**

   a. **Write an expression to represent the portion of the rink that Anita's team can complete in *x* hours.**

   b. **Write an expression that represents the portion of the rink that Martin's team can complete in *x* hours.**

3. **Each team's rate of work is defined as the number of jobs completed per hour. In this case, the rate of work is the number of rinks completed per hour.**

   a. **Determine Anita's team's rate of work.**

   b. **Determine Martin's team's rate of work.**

© Carnegie Learning, Inc.

4. Complete the table.

	Portion of the Rink Completed	Time Spent Working	Rate of Work
	Rinks	Hours	$\dfrac{\text{Rinks}}{\text{Hour}}$
Anita's Team		x	
Martin's Team		x	
Entire Job, or 1 Rink		x	

5. Consider the expression from the table that represents the portion of the rink that Anita's and Martin's teams can complete when working together. If you want to determine the total time it takes the two teams to complete one rink while working together, what should you set this expression equal to?

6. Write and solve an equation to determine the total time it takes the two teams to complete the rink.

Make sure you are using the appropriate units of measure.

7. Suppose that the two teams work together attaching rink board ads for 4 hours each day. How many days will it take them to complete the job?

Maureen is a community volunteer. She volunteers by watering the large vegetable garden in her neighborhood. Sometimes, Maureen's friend Sandra Jane also volunteers.

8. **It takes Maureen 90 minutes to water the garden. When Maureen and Sandra Jane work together, they can complete the job in 40 minutes.**

   a. **Complete the table. Let *x* represent the time it takes Sandra to water the garden if she works alone.**

	Portion of the Garden Watered	Time Spent Watering	Rate of Watering
	Gardens	Minutes	$\dfrac{\text{Gardens}}{\text{Minute}}$
Maureen		40	
Sandra Jane		40	
Entire Job, or 1 Garden		40	

   b. **Write and solve an equation to determine the total time it would take Sandra Jane to water the garden if she were working alone.**

Solving Mixture and Density Problems

A mixture problem involves the combination of two or more substances and the concentration, or density, of one substance relative to the other.

Manuel is a taking a college chemistry course, and some of his time is spent in the chemistry lab. He is conducting an experiment for which he needs a 2% salt solution. However, all he can find in the lab is 120 milliliters (mL) of 10% salt solution.

1. **How many milliliters of salt and how many milliliters of water are in 120 mL of 10% salt solution?**

2. **What would the concentration of the salt solution be if Manuel added 80 mL of water? 180 mL of water?**

3. **Write and solve an equation to calculate the amount of water Manuel needs to add to the 120 mL of 10% salt solution to make a 2% salt solution. Let *x* represent the amount of water Manuel needs to add.**

Toni is working on a chemistry experiment. She has 20 mL of a 20% sulfuric acid solution that she is mixing with a 5% sulfuric acid solution.

4. **Describe the range of possible concentrations for the new solution.**

5. **Suppose that the 20 mL of 20% sulfuric acid solution is mixed with 10 mL of the 5% sulfuric acid solution. What is the concentration of the resulting solution? Explain your reasoning.**

6. **Write and solve an equation to calculate the amount of 5% sulfuric acid solution Toni added if the resulting solution is a 12% sulfuric acid solution. Let *x* represent the amount of 5% sulfuric acid that Toni added.**

The density of a substance is its mass divided by the volume of space it occupies at that mass. Water has a density of 1 g per cubic centimeter, and frozen water has a density of 0.934 g per cubic centimeter.

7. **If you place a bottle of water in the freezer long enough, it may explode. How could this happen if the density of frozen water is less than the density of water? Model an example to explain your thinking.**

© Carnegie Learning, Inc.

Solving Distance Problems

A distance problem involves distance, rate, and time.

A river barge travels 140 miles from a loading dock to a warehouse to deliver supplies. Then the barge returns to the loading dock. The barge travels with the current to the warehouse and against the current from the warehouse. The barge's total travel time is 20 hours, and it travels in still water at an average speed of 15 miles per hour.

1. **Use the given information to complete the table. Let x represent the average speed of the current.**

	Distance Traveled	Time Traveled	Average Speed
	Miles	Hours	$\dfrac{\text{Miles}}{\text{Hours}}$
With the Current			$15 + x$
Against the Current	140		
Round Trip		20	

2. **You are given that the barge's total travel time is 20 hours. Write an algebraic expression, in terms of the number of hours the barge travels with the current and the number of hours it travels against the current, that is equivalent to 20 hours.**

3. **Write and solve an equation to calculate the average speed of the current.**

4. Calculate each value.

   a. What is the barge's average speed during its trip to the warehouse?

   b. What is the barge's average speed during its trip back to the loading dock?

   c. How long does it take the barge to get from the loading dock to the warehouse?

   d. How long does it take the barge to return to the loading dock from the warehouse?

   e. Use your answers to parts (a) and (b) to calculate the average speed of the barge in still water. Verify that your answer matches the given information.

   f. Use your answers to parts (c) and (d) to calculate the barge's total travel time. Verify that your answer matches the given information.

Solving Cost Problems

A cost problem involves the cost of ownership of an item over time.

Melinda has decided that it is time to replace her old refrigerator. She purchases a new Energy Star certified refrigerator. Energy Star certified refrigerators use less electricity than those that are not certified. In the long run, the Energy Star refrigerator should cost Melinda less to operate.

Melinda purchases a new Energy Star refrigerator for $2000. The refrigerator costs $46 per year to operate. Assume that the refrigerator is reliable and its only costs of ownership are the purchase price and the cost of operation.

1. **Determine Melinda's average annual cost of owning the new refrigerator for the given number of years.**

   a. **1 year**

   b. **5 years**

   c. **10 years**

2. **Write an expression to represent Melinda's average annual cost of owning the new refrigerator for *x* years.**

3. **When Melinda's average annual cost of owning the refrigerator is less than $400, she plans to shop for a new television. When can Melinda shop for a new television?**

Melinda is curious to know how much money the Energy Star certified refrigerator will save her, compared to one that is not certified. A comparable non-certified model costs $1900 to purchase and $60 per year to operate. Assume that this non-certified refrigerator's only costs of ownership are the purchase price and the operation cost.

4. **Determine the average annual cost of owning this refrigerator in the given number of years.**

   a. **1 year**

   b. **5 years**

   c. **10 years**

5. **Write an expression to represent the average annual cost of owning the non-certified refrigerator for *x* years.**

6. **In how many years will the average annual cost of owning the Energy Star certified refrigerator be less than the average annual cost of owning the non-certified refrigerator? Show all of your work.**

TALK the TALK

Why You Salty?

Use a rational expression to solve this problem situation.

1. **A saline or salt solution of 120 ml contains 10% salt. How much water should be added to the solution for it to contain only 2% salt?**

Describe and correct the error in each problem.

2. $\frac{2}{3} + \frac{4}{x} = 1$

    $3x\left(\frac{2}{3} + \frac{4}{x}\right) = 1$

    $2x + 12 = 1$

    $2x = -11$

    $x = -\frac{11}{2}$

3. $\frac{\frac{10}{100+x}}{} = 5\%$

    $\frac{10}{100+x} = \frac{5}{100}$

    $1000 = 500 + x$

    $500 = x$

Assignment

Write

In your own words, explain how you use rational expressions to solve work, mixture, distance, and/or cost problems.

Remember

A work problem is a type of problem that involves the rates of several workers and the time it takes to complete a job.

A mixture problem is a type of problem that involves the combination of two or more liquids and the concentrations of those liquids.

A distance problem is a type of problem that involves distance, rate, and time.

A cost problem is a type of problem that involves the cost of ownership of an item over time.

Practice

1. Moe and Curly have been hired to paint the interior of a school during summer break. Moe can paint the entire school in 80 hours by himself. Working together, it takes Moe and Curly 50 hours to paint the entire school. Write and solve an equation to determine how long it would take Curly to paint the interior of the school by himself. Show your work.
2. Trey buys a 500 mL bottle of rubbing alcohol. The bottle contains a solution of 70% alcohol and 30% water. The instructions for his toy train set say he should use a solution of 40% alcohol and 60% water to clean the tracks. Write and solve an equation to determine how much water Trey must add to the solution he purchased to have the correct solution for cleaning the tracks. Show your work.
3. Matthew is an aerial photographer. He photographs a 200-mile long oil pipeline that runs straight from east to west. He flies the 200 miles from west to east with an eastward tailwind. He returns over the same route and flies 200 miles against an eastward headwind. The total time of the 400-mile flight is 180 minutes. The plane travels at a speed of 150 miles per hour without a tailwind or headwind. Assume the wind speed is constant during the entire flight. Write and solve an equation to determine the wind speed during Matthew's flight. Show your work.
4. Ramona is trying to decide between 2 satellite Internet providers. ProSat Internet charges a $250 installation fee and a monthly fee of $50. SuperSat Internet charges a $90 installation fee and a monthly fee of $58. Write and solve an equation to determine when the average monthly cost (including installation and monthly fees) of each service would be the same. Show your work.
5. To balance a lever (seesaw), the weight must vary inversely with the distance of the object from the fulcrum.
   a. Write an inverse variation equation relating weight w and distance d. Use the variable k for the constant of variation.

b. Juanita, who weighs 60 pounds, is 6 feet from the fulcrum on a seesaw. Use her weight and distance from the fulcrum in the inverse variation equation to find the value of k.

c. Write an inverse variation equation relating weight and distance using the value of k found in part (b).

d. Determine how far Maria should sit from the fulcrum in order to balance the seesaw with Juanita. Maria weighs 80 pounds.

e. Determine how far Carlos, who weighs 50 pounds, should sit from the fulcrum to balance the seesaw with Juanita.

f. Write a general statement about how weight relates to where a person should sit on the seesaw to balance it with Juanita.

Stretch

Three friends own a lawnscape service. One of their biggest clients is a museum. When Kayden, Jaylen, and Zion work together they can mow the museum lawn in 3 hours. When Kayden works alone, he can mow the lawn in 6 hours. It takes Jaylen an hour more than Zion to mow the lawn. Write and solve an equation to determine how long it would take Jaylen and Zion to mow the lawn on their own. Show your work.

Review

1. Krish plays chess online. So far, Krish has won 325 out of 464 games. In order to move up to the next skill level his winning percent must be 75%. Estimate the number of consecutive games Krish will need to win to move up to the next skill level. Show all of your work and explain your reasoning.

2. Claudina is going to join a yoga studio. The Peaceful Zen studio costs $480 for the year and $5 for each class that she takes. The Ohm Tree studio cost $375 for the year and $7 for each class that she takes.

   a. Write a function to represent the average cost of each class per year for the two studios.

   b. Which studio will have a lower average cost per class over the next year if she takes two classes a week? Show all of your work and explain your reasoning.

3. DeMarcus has 340 out of 400 points possible in his biology class. He needs an 80% in the class in order to be on the Dean's List for the semester. The only remaining graded items will be class participation points worth 1 point each. Estimate the number of consecutive class participation points DeMarcus can miss and have his grade be an 80%. Show all of your work and explain your reasoning.

4. Write a function $h(x)$ with a vertical asymptote $x = 0$ and with a removable discontinuity at $x = -1$. Explain your reasoning. Explain how to sketch the graph of the function $h(x)$ without using technology.

Rational Functions Summary

KEY TERMS

- rational function
- vertical asymptote
- discontinuous function
- removable discontinuity
- rational equation

LESSON 1

There's a Fine Line Between a Numerator and a Denominator

The function $g(x) = \frac{1}{x}$ is an example of a *rational function*. A **rational function** is any function that can be written as the ratio of two polynomials. It can be written in the form $f(x) = \frac{P(x)}{Q(x)}$ where $P(x)$ and $Q(x)$ are polynomial functions, and $Q(x) \neq 0$. Linear, quadratic, cubic, and higher-order polynomial functions are types of rational functions.

Given the horizontal asymptote, the range of the rational function $g(x) = \frac{1}{x}$ can be expressed:

- Verbally: all numbers except for 0
- As a compound inequality: $g(x) > 0$ or $g(x) < 0$
- In interval notation: $(-\infty, 0) \cup (0, \infty)$
- In set notation: $\{g(x) \mid g(x) \neq 0\}$

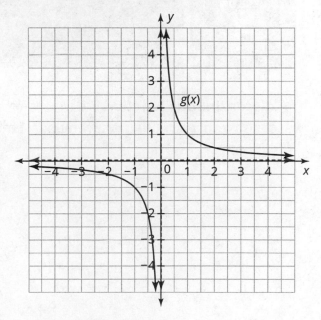

The function $g(x) = \frac{1}{x}$ has a *vertical asymptote* at $x = 0$. A **vertical asymptote** is a vertical line that a function gets closer and closer to, but never intersects. The asymptote does not represent points on the graph of the function. It represents the output value that the graph approaches. An asymptote occurs for input values that result in a denominator of 0.

The vertical asymptote is often represented in textbooks and graphing calculators as a dashed or solid line.

© Carnegie Learning, Inc.

For a rational function, the transformation function form can be written as:

$$r(x) = A\left(\frac{1}{B(x - C)}\right) + D$$

Vertical asymptotes are determined by input values for which the denominator is 0. If a rational function has more than one value that makes the denominator zero, then the rational function will have more than one vertical asymptote. The vertical asymptotes will limit the domain of a function. Factoring a function will make it easier to determine the zeros and thus the vertical asymptotes.

For example, consider the function, $f(x) = \frac{1}{x^2 - 2x - 15}$. It's factored form is $f(x) = \frac{1}{(x - 5)(x + 3)}$.

There are two values that make the denominator zero, $x = 5$ or $x = -3$. These are the vertical asymptotes of the function and are not included in the domain.

Recall from the Fundamental Theorem of Algebra that a function of degree n has n zeros. Some of the zeros may be imaginary. Therefore, it follows that the reciprocal of a function of degree n can have at most n vertical asymptotes.

A **discontinuous function** is a function that is not a continuous curve. It has points that are isolated from each other. Many rational functions have "holes," or breaks, in the graphs instead of asymptotes.

For any function $f(x)$, $f(x) \cdot \frac{1}{f(x)} = 1$, with breaks in the graph for all undefined values where $f(x) = 0$. These breaks, or "holes," in the graph are called *removable discontinuities*. A **removable discontinuity** is a single point at which the graph is not defined. Vertical asymptotes and removable discontinuities must be listed as domain restrictions. The graphs of rational functions will have either a removable discontinuity or a vertical asymptote for all domain values that result in division by 0.

Rewriting rational expressions is similar to rewriting rational numbers: common factors divide to 1.

For example, consider the function $g(x) = \frac{x + 5}{x^2 + 9x + 20}$. In factored form: $g(x) = \frac{x + 5}{(x + 5)(x + 4)}$. The factors $\frac{x + 5}{x + 5} = 1$, so an equivalent form of the function is $g(x) = \frac{1}{x + 4}$. There will be a removable discontinuity at $x = -5$ as this value would have made the denominator of the original function to equal zero. There will also be an asymptote at $x = -4$. The domain will not include either of these values.

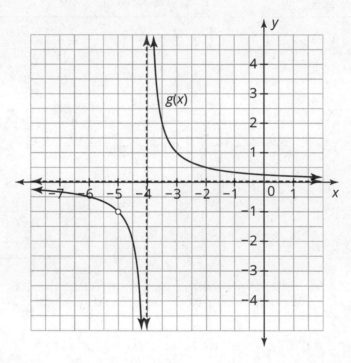

Recall that rational numbers are numbers that can be written as the ratio of two integers, $\frac{a}{b}$, such that the denominator b is not 0.

Performing operations on rational expressions involving variables is just like performing operations on rational numbers. Consider the table shown.

	Rational Numbers	**Rational Expressions Involving Variables in the Numerator**
Example 1	$\frac{1}{6} + \frac{5}{6} - \frac{1}{6} = \frac{5}{6}$	$\frac{1x}{6} + \frac{5x}{6} - \frac{1x}{6} = \frac{5x}{6}$
Example 2	$\frac{3}{2} + \frac{2}{5} - \frac{3}{4} = \frac{3(10)}{2(10)} + \frac{2(4)}{5(4)} - \frac{3(5)}{4(5)}$ $= \frac{30}{20} + \frac{8}{20} - \frac{15}{20}$ $= \frac{23}{20}$	$\frac{3x}{2} + \frac{2y}{5} - \frac{3x}{4} = \frac{3(10)^x}{2(10)} + \frac{2(4)y}{5(4)} - \frac{3(5)x}{4(5)}$ $= \frac{30x}{20} + \frac{8y}{20} - \frac{15x}{20}$ $= \frac{15x + 8y}{20}$
Example 3	$\frac{3}{5} + \frac{2}{3} - \frac{2}{15} = \frac{3(3)}{5(3)} + \frac{2(5)}{3(5)} - \frac{2}{15}$ $= \frac{9}{15} + \frac{10}{15} - \frac{2}{15}$ $= \frac{17}{15}$	$\frac{3x}{5} + \frac{2y}{3} - \frac{2}{15} - \frac{2x + 3y}{5} = \frac{3(3)x}{5(3)} + \frac{2(5)y}{3(5)} - \frac{2}{15} - \frac{(2x + 3y)(3)}{5(3)}$ $= \frac{9x}{15} + \frac{10y}{15} - \frac{2}{15} - \frac{6x + 9y}{15}$ $= \frac{9x + 10y - 2 - 6x - 9y}{15}$ $= \frac{3x + y - 2}{15}$

When rational expressions contain variables in the denominator, the process remains the same—you still need to determine the least common denominator (LCD) before adding and subtracting.

For example, consider the difference of two rational expressions of degree 2.

$$\frac{1}{x^2 - 1} - \frac{1}{x^2 + 2x + 1} = \frac{1}{(x + 1)(x - 1)} - \frac{1}{(x + 1)(x + 1)}$$

$$= \frac{1(x + 1)}{(x + 1)(x - 1)(x + 1)} - \frac{1(x - 1)}{(x + 1)(x + 1)(x - 1)}$$

$$= \frac{(x + 1) - (x - 1)}{(x + 1)(x + 1)(x - 1)}$$

$$= \frac{2}{(x + 1)(x + 1)(x - 1)}, x \neq -1, 1$$

Multiplying rational expressions involves the same steps as multiplying rational numbers. Remember that when you multiply rational numbers, you can divide out factors at the beginning or the end, and the product is the same; however, dividing out earlier saves time and will keep the expressions simpler.

For example, consider both methods. In Method A, the process is to multiply and then divide out common factors. In Method B, common factors are divided out first.

	Rational Numbers	Rational Expressions Involving Variables	
Method A	$\frac{2}{15} \cdot \frac{5}{8} = \frac{10}{120} = \frac{1}{12}$	$\frac{2x}{15x} \cdot \frac{5x}{8} = \frac{10x^2}{120x} = \frac{x}{12}$	$\frac{2x}{15x^2} \cdot \frac{5x^2}{8} = \frac{10x^3}{120x^2} = \frac{x}{12}$
Method B	$\frac{2}{15} \cdot \frac{5}{8} = \frac{1}{3} \cdot \frac{1}{4} = \frac{1}{12}$	$\frac{2x}{15x} \cdot \frac{5x}{8} = \frac{1}{3} \cdot \frac{1x}{4} = \frac{x}{12}$	$\frac{2x}{15x^2} \cdot \frac{5x^2}{8} = \frac{1x}{3} \cdot \frac{1}{4} = \frac{x}{12}$

Dividing rational expressions is similar to the process you use when dividing rational numbers.

Notice that when you multiply $\frac{4}{5}$ by a form of 1, in this case $\frac{3}{3}$, you maintain equivalent fractions;

$$\frac{4}{5} \cdot \frac{3}{3} = \frac{12}{15}$$
$$\frac{4}{5} = \frac{12}{15}$$

This same process works when the numerator and denominator are fractions. Consider $\frac{\frac{4}{5}}{\frac{3}{7}}$. When you multiply by a form of 1, in this case $\frac{\frac{7}{3}}{\frac{7}{3}}$, you maintain equivalent fractions;

$$\frac{\frac{4}{5}}{\frac{3}{7}} \cdot \frac{\frac{7}{3}}{\frac{7}{3}} = \frac{\frac{28}{15}}{\frac{21}{21}} = \frac{\frac{28}{15}}{1} = \frac{28}{15}$$

$$\frac{\frac{4}{5}}{\frac{3}{7}} = \frac{28}{15}$$

You may recall that, to divide fractions, you multiply the dividend by the multiplicative inverse of the divisor.

	Rational Numbers	Rational Expressions Involving Variables	
Example 1	$\frac{1}{5} \div \frac{3}{10} = \frac{1}{\cancel{5}_1} \cdot \frac{\cancel{10}^2}{3}$ $= \frac{2}{3}$	$\frac{xy}{5z} \div \frac{3xy}{10z} = \frac{\cancel{xy}^1}{\cancel{5z}} \cdot \frac{\cancel{10z}^2}{\cancel{3xy}}$ $= \frac{2}{3}$	$\frac{xy^2}{5z} \div \frac{3xy}{10z^2} = \frac{\cancel{xy^2}^y}{5z} \cdot \frac{\cancel{10z^2}^{2z}}{\cancel{3xy}_1}$ $= \frac{2yz}{3}; x, y, z \neq 0$
Example 2	$\frac{6}{7} \div 4 = \frac{\cancel{6}^3}{7} \cdot \frac{1}{\cancel{4}_2}$ $= \frac{3}{14}$	$\frac{6a}{7b} \div 4a = \frac{\cancel{6a}^3}{7b} \cdot \frac{1}{\cancel{4a}_2}$ $= \frac{3}{14b}$	$\frac{6a^3}{7b} \div 4a = \frac{\cancel{6a^3}^{3a^2}}{7b} \cdot \frac{1}{\cancel{4a}_2}$ $= \frac{3a^2}{14b}; a, b, \neq 0$

A **rational equation** is an equation that contains one or more rational expressions. Rational equations are proportions. There are multiple methods you can use to solve rational equations. Depending on the structure of the equation, some methods will be more efficient than others.

For example, consider the equation:

$$\frac{x+5}{x+2} = \frac{x+1}{x-5}$$

This equation is already set up as a proportion, so rewriting the equation as the product of the means equal to the product of the extremes is the most efficient method to solve.

$$(x-5)(x+5) = (x+1)(x+2)$$
$$x^2 - 25 = x^2 + 3x + 2$$
$$-25 = 3x + 2$$
$$-27 = 3x$$
$$x = -9$$

It is more efficient to solve equations that have been factored.

For example, consider the equation:

$$\frac{2x+4}{x^2-2x-8} = \frac{x+1}{x-4}$$

$$\frac{2(x+2)}{(x-4)(x+2)} = \frac{x+1}{x-4}$$

$$\frac{2}{x-4} = \frac{x+1}{x-4}$$

$$2(x-4) = (x+1)(x-4)$$

$$2 = x+1$$

$$x = 1$$

A work problem is a type of problem that involves the rates of several workers and the time it takes to complete a job.

For example, consider the work problem.

Maureen is a community volunteer. She volunteers by watering the large vegetable garden in her neighborhood. Sometimes, Maureen's friend Sandra Jane also volunteers. It takes Maureen 90 minutes to water the garden. When Maureen and Sandra work together, they can complete the job in 40 minutes.

	Portion of the Garden Watered	Time Spent Watering	Rate of Watering
	Gardens	Minutes	Gardens/Minute
Maureen	$40\left(\frac{1}{90}\right) = \frac{4}{9}$	40	$\frac{1}{90}$
Sandra Jane	$40\left(\frac{1}{x}\right) = \frac{40}{x}$	40	$\frac{1}{x}$
Entire Job, or 1 Garden	$\frac{4}{9} + \frac{40}{x}$	40	

A mixture problem is a type of problem that involves the combination of two or more liquids and the concentrations of those liquids.

For example, consider the mixture problem.

Manuel is a taking a college chemistry course, and some of his time is spent in the chemistry lab. He is conducting an experiment for which he needs a 2% salt solution. However, all he can find in the lab is 120 milliliters (mL) of 10% salt solution.

Calculate the amount of water Manuel would need to add to the 120 mL of 10% salt solution to make a 2% salt solution.

	Liquid	% Salt	Amount of Salt
Water	x	0	0
10% Solution	120	10	$0.10(120) = 12$
2% Solution	$120 + x$	2	$0.02(120 + x)$

$$12 = 0.02(120 + x)$$
$$12 = 2.4 + 0.02x$$
$$9.6 = 0.02x$$
$$x = 480$$

Manuel would need to add 480 mL of water to make a 2% salt solution.

A distance problem is a type of problem that involves distance, rate, and time.

For example, consider the distance problem.

A river barge travels 140 miles from a loading dock to a warehouse to deliver supplies. Then the barge returns to the loading dock. The barge travels with the current to the warehouse and against the current from the warehouse. The barge's total travel time is 20 hours, and it travels in still water at an average speed of 15 miles per hour.

	Distance Traveled	Time Traveled	Average Speed
	Miles	Hours	Miles/Hours
With the Current	140	$\frac{140}{15 + x}$	$15 + x$
Against the Current	140	$\frac{140}{15 - x}$	$15 - x$
Round Trip	280	20	$\frac{280}{20} = 14$

If the total time the barge travels is 20 hours then the equation to represent the total time traveled is $\frac{140}{15 + x} + \frac{140}{15 - x}$.

A cost problem is a type of problem that involves the cost of ownership of an item over time.

For example, consider the cost problem.

Melinda has decided that it is time to replace her old refrigerator. She purchases a new Energy Star certified refrigerator. Energy Star certified refrigerators use less electricity than those that are not certified. In the long run, the Energy Star refrigerator should cost Melinda less to operate.

Melinda purchases a new Energy Star refrigerator for $2000. The refrigerator costs $46 per year to operate. Assume that the refrigerator is reliable and its only costs of ownership are the purchase price and the cost of operation. Then Melinda's average annual cost of ownership for 1 year would be $2046. The average annual cost of operating the refrigerator over x years would be $\frac{2000 + 46x}{x}$.

Glossary

A
---

absolute maximum

A function has an absolute maximum if there is a point that has a y-coordinate that is greater than the y-coordinates of every other point on the graph.

Example

The ordered pair (4, 2) is the absolute maximum of the graph of the function $f(x) = -\frac{1}{2}x^2 + 4x - 6$.

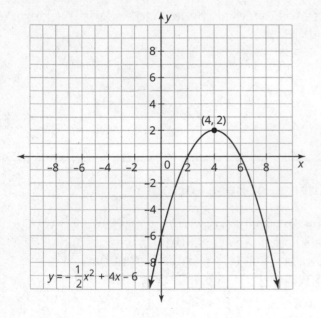

absolute minimum

A function has an absolute minimum if there is a point that has a y-coordinate that is less than the y-coordinates of every other point on the graph.

Example

The ordered pair (1, −4) is the absolute minimum of the graph of the function $y = \frac{2}{3}x^2 - \frac{4}{3}x - \frac{10}{3}$.

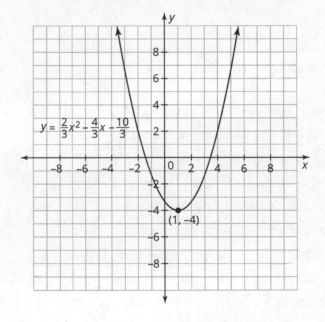

amplitude

The amplitude of a periodic function is half of the distance between the maximum and minimum values of the function.

Example

The function $y = \sin x$ has a maximum of 1 and a minimum of -1. The distance between the maximum and minimum is 2. So, the amplitude of $y = \sin x$ is 1.

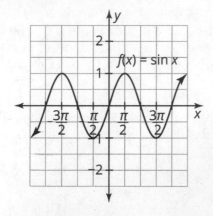

average rate of change

The average rate of change of a function is the ratio of the independent variable to the dependent variable over a specific interval. The formula for average rate of change is $\frac{f(b) - f(a)}{b - a}$. for an interval (a, b). The expression $a - b$ represents the change in the input of the function f. The expression $f(b) - f(a)$ represents the change in the function f as the input changes from a to b.

Example

Consider the function $f(x) = x^2$.

The average rate of change of the interval $(1, 3)$ is $\frac{3^2 - 1^2}{3 - 1} = \frac{9 - 1}{3 - 1} = \frac{8}{2} = 4$.

biased sample

A biased sample is a sample that does not accurately represent all of a population.

Example

A survey is conducted asking students their favorite class. Only students in the math club are surveyed. The sample of students is a biased sample.

Binomial Theorem

The Binomial Theorem states that it is possible to extend any power of $(a + b)$ into a sum of the form shown.

$$(a + b)^n = \binom{n}{0} a^n b^0 + \binom{n}{1} a^{n-1} b^1 + \binom{n}{2} a^{n-2} b^2$$

$$+ \dots + \binom{n}{n-1} a^1 b^{n-1} + \binom{n}{n} a^0 b^n$$

Example

Use the Binomial Theorem to find the third term of $(x + y)^{20}$.

$$(x + y)^{20} = \binom{20}{2} x^{20-2} y^2 = \frac{20!}{18!2!} x^{18} y^2$$

$$= \frac{20 \cdot 19}{2 \cdot 1} x^{18} y^2 = 190 \, x^{18} y^2$$

Change of Base Formula

The Change of Base Formula allows you to calculate an exact value for a logarithm by rewriting it in terms of a different base. It is especially helpful when using a calculator.

The Change of Base Formula states:

$\log_b (c) = \frac{\log_a (c)}{\log_a (b)}$, where $a, b, c > 0$ and $a, b \neq 1$.

Example

$$\log_4 (50) = \frac{\log 50}{\log 4}$$

$$\approx 2.821928095$$

characteristic of interest

A characteristic of interest is the specific question that you are trying to answer or specific information that a study is trying to gather.

Example

In a sample survey to determine teenagers' online habits, a characteristic of interest is the amount of time that a teenager spends online per day.

closed under an operation

A set is closed under an operation if the operation is performed on any of the numbers in the set and the result is a number that is also in the same set.

Example

The set of whole numbers is closed under addition. The sum of any two whole numbers is always another whole number.

cluster

A cluster is a sample of the population that contains the characteristics of the population.

Example

A city manager randomly selects one block in the city and surveys all of the residents of that block. Each block is considered a cluster.

cluster sample

A cluster sample is a sample obtained by creating clusters, with each cluster containing the characteristics of the population, and randomly selecting a cluster.

Example

If students in a high school are divided into clusters of 20 students based on their student I.D. number and then one cluster is randomly selected, this is a cluster sample.

coefficient of determination

The coefficient of determination (R^2) measures the "strength" of the relationship between the original data and its regression equation. The value of the coefficient of determination ranges from 0 to 1 with a value of 1 indicating a perfect fit between the regression equation and the original data.

common logarithm

A common logarithm is a logarithm with a base of 10. Common logarithms are usually written without a base.

Example

log (10x) or log x are examples of a common logarithm.

complex numbers

The set of complex numbers is the set of all numbers written in the form $a + bi$, where a and b are real numbers. The set of complex numbers consists of the set of imaginary numbers and the set of real numbers.

Example

The numbers $1 + 2i$, 7, and $-3i$ are complex numbers.

composition of functions

Composition of functions is the process of substituting one function for the variable in another function.

Example

If $f(x) = 3x - 5$ and $g(x) = x^2$, then the composition of the functions $f(g(x))$ can be written as $f(g(x)) = 3(x^2) - 5 = 3x^2 - 5$.

The composition of functions $g(f(x))$ can be written as $g(f(x)) = (3x + 5)^2$.

concavity of a parabola

The concavity of a parabola describes the orientation of the curvature of the parabola.

Example

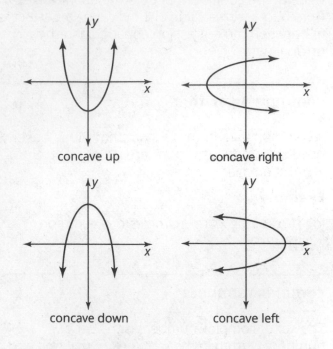

concave up

concave right

concave down

concave left

confidence interval

A confidence interval is an estimated range of values, based on the results of a sample survey, that will likely include the population proportion. Typically, a confidence interval of 95%, or 2 standard deviations from the mean, is used. The formula for calculating the confidence interval for proportions is $\sqrt{\frac{\hat{p}(1-\hat{p})}{n}}$, where $\hat{p}$ is the sample population and n is the sample size. The formula $\frac{s}{\sqrt{n}}$, where s is the standard deviation of the sample and n is the sample size, is used for continuous data.

Example

A survey of 2000 teenagers reports that 42% have a part-time job.

$$\sqrt{\frac{0.42(1-0.42)}{2000}}$$

$$\sqrt{\frac{0.42(0.58)}{2000}}$$

$$\approx 0.011$$

The interval from 40.9% to 43.1% represents a 95% confidence interval for the population proportion.

confounding

Confounding is the process of overlooking factors and situations that distort the final results when seeking to gather information or data.

Example

Suppose that a study is conducted to determine if there is a link between a certain type of insulin that some diabetic patients use and cancer. Confounding can occur due to the fact that there are other potential causes of cancer that could be involved in the sample.

continuous data

Continuous data are data that have an infinite number of possible values.

Example

The heights of students is an example of continuous data.

convenience sample

A convenience sample is a sample whose data are based on what is convenient for the person choosing the sample.

Example

If you choose the students sitting closest to you in math class as your sample, you have a convenience sample.

cosine function

The cosine function is a periodic function. It takes angle measures (θ values) as inputs and then outputs real number values which correspond to the coordinates of points on the unit circle.

Example

The function $h(\theta) = 4 \cos(\theta + \pi)$ is a cosine function.

cube root function

The cube root function is the inverse of the power function $f(x) = x^3$.

Example

The cube root function is $g(x) = \sqrt[3]{x}$.

cubic function

A cubic function is a function that can be written in the standard form $f(x) = ax^3 + bx^2 + cx + d$ where $a \neq 0$.

Example

The function $f(x) = x^3 - 5x^2 + 3x + 1$ is a cubic function.

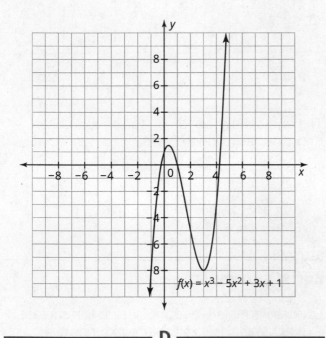

$f(x) = x^3 - 5x^2 + 3x + 1$

discontinuous function

A discontinuous function is a function that is not a continuous curve—it has points that are isolated from each other.

Example

The function $f(x) = \frac{1}{x}$ is a discontinuous function.

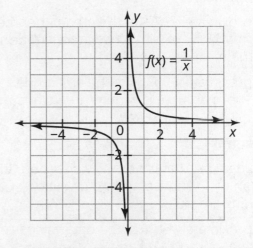

$f(x) = \frac{1}{x}$

discrete data

Discrete data are data that have a finite number of possible values.

Example

If you roll a number cube 10 times and record the results, the results are discrete data.

— **D** —

damping function

A damping function is a function that is multiplied to a periodic function to decrease its amplitude over time. It can be from a multitude of function families, including linear, quadratic, or exponential.

Example

In the function $f(x) = 2^x \cdot \sin x + 1$, the exponential function 2^x is the damping function.

Empirical Rule for Normal Distributions

The Empirical Rule for Normal Distributions states that:

- Approximately 68% of the area under the normal curve is within one standard deviation of the mean.
- Approximately 95% of the area under the normal curve is within two standard deviations of the mean.
- Approximately 99.7% of the area under the normal curve is within three standard deviations of the mean.

Example

For a data set that is normally distributed with a mean of 10 and a standard deviation of 1, the following are true:

- Approximately 68% of the data values are between 9 and 11.
- Approximately 95% of the data values are between 8 and 12.
- Approximately 99.7% of the data values are between 7 and 13.

end behavior

The end behavior of the graph of a function is the behavior of the graph as x approaches infinity and as x approaches negative infinity.

Example

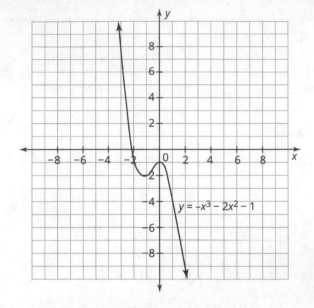

$$y = -x^3 - 2x^2 - 1$$

The end behavior of the graph shown can be described as follows:

As x approaches infinity, y approaches negative infinity.

As x approaches negative infinity, y approaches infinity.

Euclid's Formula

Euclid's Formula is a formula used to generate Pythagorean triples given any two positive integers. Given positive integers r and s, where $r > s$, Euclid's Formula is $(r^2 + s^2)^2 = (r^2 - s^2)^2 + (2rs)^2$.

Example

Let $r = 3$ and $s = 1$.

$$(3^2 + 1^2)^2 = (3^2 - 1^2)^2 + (2 \cdot 3 \cdot 1)^2$$
$$10^2 = 8^2 + 6^2$$

So, one Pythagorean triple is 6, 8, 10.

even function

An even function f is a function for which $f(-x) = f(x)$ for all values of x in the domain.

Example

The function $f(x) = x^2$ is an even function because $(-x)^2 = x^2$.

experiment

An experiment gathers data on the effect of one or more treatments, or experimental conditions, on the characteristic of interest.

Example

The following is an example of an experiment.

A sample of 200 asthma patients participated in the clinical trial for a new asthma drug. One hundred of the patients received a placebo treatment along with an inhaler, while the remaining 100 patients received the new drug along with an inhaler. Monthly blood and breathing tests were performed on all 200 patients to determine if the new drug was effective.

experimental unit

An experimental unit is a member of a sample in an experiment.

Example

Suppose that an experiment is conducted to test the effects of a new drug on a sample of patients. Each patient is an experimental unit in the experiment.

extraneous solution

Extraneous solutions are solutions that result from the process of solving an equation; but are not valid solutions to the equation.

Example

$$\log_2(x) + \log_2(x + 7) = 3$$
$$\log_2(x^2 + 7x) = 3$$
$$x^2 + 7x = 2^3$$
$$x^2 + 7x = 8$$
$$x^2 + 7x - 8 = 0$$
$$(x + 8)(x - 1) = 0$$
$$x + 8 = 0 \quad \text{or} \quad x - 1 = 0$$
$$x = -8 \qquad\qquad x = 1$$

The solution $x = -8$ is an extraneous solution because the argument of a logarithm must be greater than zero.

extrema

Extrema are the set of all relative maximums, relative minimums, absolute maximums, and absolute minimums for a graph.

Example

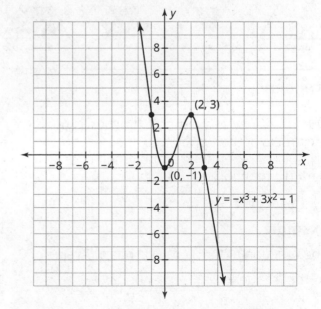

The graph shown has 2 extrema, a relative maximum at (2, 3) and a relative minimum at (0, −1).

F

Factor Theorem

The Factor Theorem states that a polynomial is divisible by $(x - r)$ if the value of the polynomial at r is zero.

Example

The polynomial $x^3 - 2x^2 + 2x - 1$ is divisible by $x - 1$ because $(1)^3 - 2(1)^2 + 2(1) - 1 = 0$.

factored form of a quadratic function

A quadratic function written in factored form is in the form $f(x) = a(x - r_1)(x - r_2)$, where $a \neq 0$.

Example

The function $h(x) = x^2 - 8x + 12$ written in factored form is $h(x) = (x - 6)(x - 2)$.

fractal

A fractal is a complex geometric shape that is constructed by a mathematical pattern. Fractals are infinite and self-similar.

Example

| Stage 0 | Stage 1 | Stage 2 | Stage 3 |

frequency

The frequency of a periodic function is the reciprocal of the period and specifies the number of repetitions of the graph of a periodic function per unit. It is calculated by the formula $\frac{|B|}{2\pi}$.

Example

The function $f(x) = 3 \cos (2x)$ has a B-value of 2, so the frequency is $\frac{|2|}{2\pi}$ or $\frac{1}{\pi}$ units.

function

A function is a relation such that for each element of the domain there exists exactly one element in the range.

Example

The equation $y = 2x$ is a function. Every x-value has exactly one corresponding y-value.

function notation

Function notation is a way of representing functions algebraically. The function $f(x)$ is read as "f of x" and indicates that x is the input and $f(x)$ is the output.

Example

The function $f(x) = 0.75x$ is written using function notation.

Fundamental Theorem of Algebra

The Fundamental Theorem of Algebra states that any polynomial equation of degree n must have exactly n complex roots or solutions; also, every polynomial function of degree n must have exactly n complex zeros. However, any root or zero may be a multiple root or zero.

Example

The polynomial equation $x^5 + x^2 - 6 = 0$ has 5 complex roots because the polynomial $x^5 + x^2 - 6$ has a degree of 5.

G

geometric series

A geometric series is the sum of the terms of a geometric sequence.

Example

The geometric series corresponding to the geometric sequence 2, 4, 8, 16 is $2 + 4 + 8 + 16$, or 30.

H

half-life

A half-life is the amount of time it takes a substance to decay to half of its original amount.

Example

The radioactive isotope strontium-90 has a half-life of about 30 years. A 1000-gram sample of strontium-90 will decay to 500 grams in 30 years.

Horizontal Line Test

The Horizontal Line Test is a test to determine if a function is one to one. To use the test, imagine drawing every possible horizontal line on the coordinate plane. If no horizontal line intersects the graph of a function at more than one point, then the function is one to one.

Example

The function $y = x$ passes the Horizontal Line Test because no horizontal line can be drawn that intersects the graph at more than one point. So, the function is one to one.

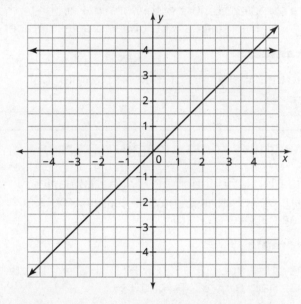

The function $y = x^2$ does not pass the Horizontal Line Test because a horizontal line can be drawn that intersects the graph at more than one point. So, the function is not one to one.

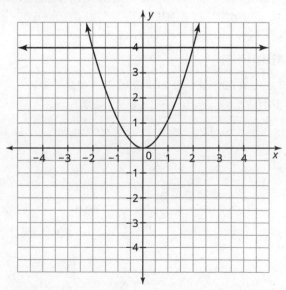

I

imaginary numbers

The set of imaginary numbers is the set of all numbers written in the form $a + bi$, where a and b are real numbers and b is not equal to 0.

Example

The numbers $2 - 3i$ and $5i$ are imaginary numbers. The number 6 is not an imaginary number.

imaginary part of a complex number

In a complex number of the form $a + bi$, the term bi is called the imaginary part of a complex number.

Example

The imaginary part of the complex number $3 + 2i$ is $2i$.

imaginary roots (imaginary zeros)

Equations and functions that have imaginary solutions requiring i have imaginary roots or imaginary zeros.

Example

The quadratic equation $x^2 - 2x + 2 = 0$ has two imaginary roots: $1 + i$ and $1 - i$.

initial ray of an angle

The initial ray of an angle in standard position is the ray with its endpoint at the origin and extending along the positive x-axis.

Example

The initial ray of the angle is labeled in the diagram.

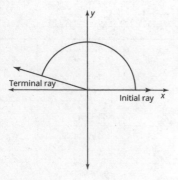

inverse cosine (cos⁻¹)

The $\cos^{-1}$ function is the inverse of the cosine function. The inverse cosine function is written as arccos or $\cos^{-1}$.

Example

$\cos(60°) = \frac{1}{2}$ so $\cos^{-1}\left(\frac{1}{2}\right) = 60°$

inverse of a function

The inverse of a one-to-one function is a function that results from exchanging the independent and dependent variables. A function $f(x)$ with coordinates $(x, f(x))$ will have an inverse with coordinates $(f(x), x)$.

Example

The inverse of the function $y = 2x$ can be found by exchanging the variables x and y.

The inverse of $y = 2x$ is $x = 2y$.

inverse sine (sin⁻¹)

The $\sin^{-1}$ function is the inverse of the sine function. The inverse sine function is written as arcsin or $\sin^{-1}$.

Example

$\sin(30°) = \frac{1}{2}$ so $\sin^{-1}\left(\frac{1}{2}\right) = 30°$

inverse tangent (tan⁻¹)

The $\tan^{-1}$ function is the inverse of the tangent function. The inverse tangent function is written as arctan or $\tan^{-1}$.

Example

$\tan(45°) = 1$ so $\tan^{-1}(1) = 45°$

invertible function

An invertible function is a function whose inverse exists. It is one-to-one and passes the Horizontal Line Test, so its inverse will also be a function.

Example

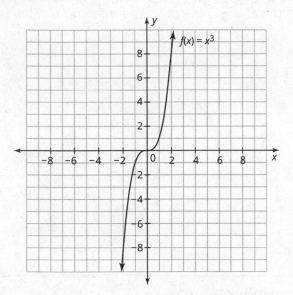

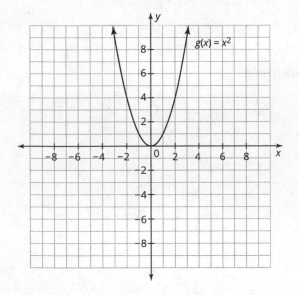

The graph of $f(x) = x^3$ is an invertible function because it is one-to-one and passes the Horizontal Line Test. Therefore its inverse will also be a function.

The graph of $g(x) = x^2$ is not an invertible function because it does not pass the Horizontal Line Test. Its inverse does not exist.

iterative process

An iterative process is one in which the output from one iteration is used as the input for the next iteration.

Example

A recursive sequence uses an iterative process to generate its terms.

$$a_n = 3a_{n-1} + 1$$

$$a_1 = 2$$

Begin with the first term, which is 2, and substitute it into the sequence to get the next term.

$$a_2 = 3a_1 + 1$$
$$= 3(2) + 1$$
$$= 7$$

Then substitute a_2 into the sequence to produce a_3, and so on.

——————— L ———————

logarithm

The logarithm of a positive number is the exponent to which the base must be raised to result in that number.

Example

Because $10^2 = 100$, the logarithm of 100 to the base 10 is 2.

$$\log 100 = 2$$

Because $2^3 = 8$, the logarithm of 8 to the base 2 is 3.

$$\log_2 (8) = 3$$

logarithm with same base and argument

The logarithm of a number, with the base equal to the same number, is always equal to 1.

$$\log_b (b) = 1$$

Example

$$\log_4 (4) = 1$$

logarithmic equation

A logarithmic equation is an equation that contains a logarithm.

Example

The equation $\log_2(x) = 4$ is a logarithmic equation.

logarithmic function

A logarithmic function is a function involving a logarithm.

Example

The function $f(x) = 3 \log x$ is a logarithmic function.

— M —

margin of error

The margin of error expresses the maximum expected difference between the true population data and the sample estimate of the data.

Example

In a poll of 1100 registered voters, 54% said they would vote to re-elect the current mayor. The margin of error for the poll is ± 3%, which means that somewhere between 51% (54% − 3%) and 57% (54% + 3%) will actually vote to re-elect the current mayor.

mean (μ)

The mean of a data set is the sum of all of the values of the data set divided by the number of values in the data set. The mean is also called the average.

Example

The mean of the numbers 7, 9, 13, 4, and 7 is $\frac{7 + 9 + 13 + 4 + 7}{5}$, or 8.

The mean of a set of normally distributed data is aligned with the peak of the normal curve.

midline

The midline of a periodic function is a reference line whose equation is the average of the minimum and maximum values of the function.

Example

In the graph of $g(x) = -2 \cos x + 3$ the midline occurs at $y = 3$ because the maximum value is 5 and the minimum value is 1.

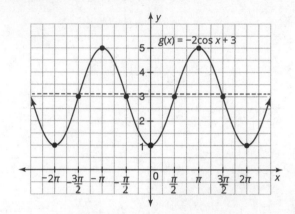

multiplicity

Multiplicity is how many times a particular number is a zero for a given function.

Example

The equation $x^2 + 2x + 1 = 0$ has a double root at $x = -1$. The root −1 has a multiplicity of 2.

$$x^2 + 2x + 1 = 0$$
$$(x + 1)(x + 1) = 0$$
$$x + 1 = 0 \quad \text{or } x + 1 = 0$$
$$x = -1 \quad \text{or} \quad x = -1$$

— N —

natural base e

The natural base e is an irrational number equal to approximately 2.71828.

Example

$e^2 \approx 2.7183^2 \approx 7.3892$

natural logarithm

A natural logarithm is a logarithm with a base of e. Natural logarithms are usually written as ln.

Example

$\log_e (x)$ or $\ln x$ is a natural logarithm.

normal curve

A normal curve is a curve that is bell-shaped and symmetric about the mean.

Example

A normal curve is shown.

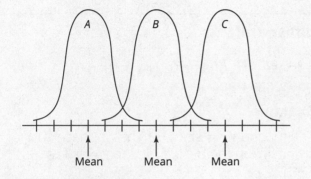

normal distribution

A normal distribution, or normal probability distribution, describes a continuous data set that can be modeled using a normal curve.

Example

Adult IQ scores, gas mileage of certain cars, and SAT scores are all continuous data that follow a normal distribution.

O

observational study

An observational study gathers data about a characteristic of the population without trying to influence the data.

Example

The following is an example of an observational study. New research funded by a pediatric agency found that nearly 70% of in-house day care centers show as much as 2.5 hours of television to the children in the center per day. The study examined 132 day care programs in 2 Midwestern states.

odd function

An odd function f is a function for which $f(-x) = -f(x)$ for all values of x in the domain.

Example

The function $f(x) = x^3$ is an odd function because $(-x)^3 = -x^3$.

P

parameter

When data are gathered from a population, the characteristic used to describe the population is called a parameter.

Example

If you wanted to find out the average height of the students at your school, and you measured every student at the school, the characteristic "average height" would be a parameter.

percentile

A percentile is a data value for which a certain percent of the data is below the data value in a normal distribution.

period

A period of a periodic function is the length of the smallest interval over which the function repeats.

Example

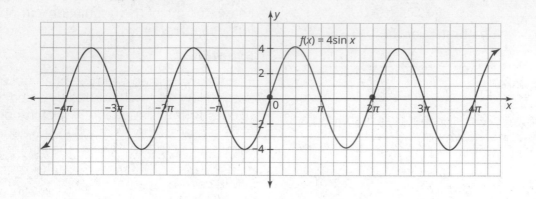

periodic function

A periodic function is a function whose graph consists of repeated instances of a portion of the graph.

Example

The function $f(x) = \sin x$ is a periodic function. The portion of the graph between $x = 0$ and $x = 2\pi$ repeats.

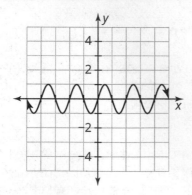

periodicity identity

A periodicity identity is a trigonometric identity based on the period of the trigonometric functions.

Example

The six periodicity identities are:

$\sin(x + 2\pi) = \sin x$; $\cos(x + 2\pi) = \cos x$

$\sec(x + 2\pi) = \sec x$; $\csc(x + 2\pi) = \csc x$

$\tan(x + \pi) = \tan x$; $\cot(x + \pi) = \cot x$

phase shift

A phase shift of a periodic function is a horizontal translation.

Example

The function $y = \sin(x - \pi)$ has a phase shift of π units from the basic function $y = \sin x$.

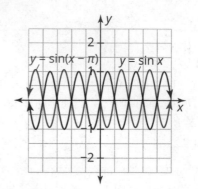

polynomial function

A polynomial function is a function that can be written in the form

$p(x) = \blacksquare x^n + \blacksquare x^{n-1} + \cdots + \blacksquare x^2 + \blacksquare x + \blacksquare$,

where the coefficients, represented by each $\blacksquare$, are complex numbers and the exponents are nonnegative integers.

Example

The function $f(x) = 5x^3 + 3x^2 + x + 1$ is a polynomial function.

© Carnegie Learning, Inc.

polynomial long division

Polynomial long division is an algorithm for dividing one polynomial by another of equal or lesser degree.

Example

$$
\begin{array}{r}
4x^2 - 6x + 3 \\
2x + 3 \overline{\smash{\big)}\, 8x^3 + 0x^2 - 12x - 7} \\
\underline{-(8x^3 + 12x^2)} \\
-12x^2 - 12x \\
\underline{-(-12x^2 - 18x)} \\
6x - 7 \\
\underline{-(6x + 9)} \\
\text{Remainder } -16
\end{array}
$$

population

The population is the entire set of items from which data can be selected. When you decide what you want to study, the population is the set of all elements in which you are interested. The elements of that population can be people or objects.

Example

If you wanted to find out the average height of the students at your school, the number of students at the school would be the population.

population proportion

A population proportion is the percentage of an entire population that yields a favorable outcome in an experiment.

Example

In an election, the population proportion represents the percentage of people in the entire town who vote to re-elect the mayor.

power function

A power function is a function of the form $P(x) = ax^n$ where n is a non-negative integer.

Example

The functions $f(x) = x$, $f(x) = x^2$, and $f(x) = x^3$ are power functions.

Power Rule of Logarithms

The Power Rule of Logarithms states that the logarithm of a power is equal to the product of the exponent and the logarithm of the base of the power.

$$\log_b (x)^n = n \cdot \log_b (x)$$

Example

$\ln (x)^2 = 2 \ln x$

Product Rule of Logarithms

The Product Rule of Logarithms states that the logarithm of a product is equal to the sum of the logarithms of the factors.

$$\log_b (xy) = \log_b (x) + \log_b (y)$$

Example

$\log (5x) = \log 5 + \log x$

pure imaginary number

A pure imaginary number is a number of the form bi, where b is not equal to 0.

Example

The imaginary numbers $-4i$ and $15i$ are pure imaginary numbers.

Pythagorean identity

A Pythagorean identity is a trigonometric identity based on the Pythagorean Theorem.

Example

The three Pythagorean identities are:

$\sin^2 x + \cos^2 x = 1$

$1 + \tan^2 x = \sec^2 x$

$1 + \cot^2 x = \csc^2 x$

Quadratic Formula

The Quadratic Formula $x = \dfrac{-b \pm \sqrt{b^2 - 4ac}}{2a}$, can be used to calculate the solutions to any quadratic equation of the form $ax^2 + bx + c$, where a, b, and c represent real numbers and $a \neq 0$.

quartic function

A quartic function is a polynomial function with a degree of four.

Examples

The function $f(x) = 3x^4 - 2x + 5$ is a quartic function.

quintic function

A quintic function is a polynomial function with a degree of five.

Examples

The function $f(x) = 5x^5 + 3x^4 + x^3$ is a quintic function.

Quotient Rule of Logarithms

The Quotient Rule of Logarithms states that the logarithm of a quotient is equal to the difference of the logarithms of the dividend and the divisor.

$\log_b \left(\dfrac{x}{y}\right) = \log_b (x) - \log_b (y)$

Examples

$\log \left(\dfrac{x}{2}\right) = \log x - \log 2$

radians

A radian is a unit of measurement for an angle in standard position. The ratio of the intercepted arc length of a central angle to the length of the radius is the measure of the central angle in radians.

Example

The angle shown has a radian measure of π radians.

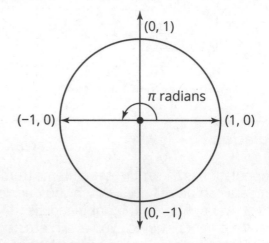

radical function

A radical function is a function that contains one or more radical expressions.

Example

The function $f(x) = \sqrt{3x + 5}$ is a radical function.

random sample

A random sample is a method of collecting data in which every member of a population has an equal chance of being selected.

Example

Choosing 100 fans at random to participate in a survey from a crowd of 5000 people is an example of a random sample.

rational equation

A rational equation is an equation that contains one or more rational expressions.

Example

The equation $\frac{1}{x-1} + \frac{1}{x+1} = 4$ is a rational equation.

rational function

A rational function is any function that can be written as the ratio of two polynomial functions. A rational function can be written in the form $f(x) = \frac{P(x)}{Q(x)}$ where $P(x)$ and $Q(x)$ are polynomial functions, and $Q(x) \neq 0$.

Example

The function $f(x) = \frac{1}{x-1} + \frac{1}{x+1}$ is a rational function.

real part of a complex number

In a complex number of the form $a + bi$, the term a is called the real part of a complex number.

Example

The real part of the complex number $3 + 2i$ is 3.

regression equation

A regression equation is a function that models the relationship between two variables in a scatter plot.

Example

The regression equation
$y = -0.41x^3 + 3.50x^2 - 4.47x + 8.44$ models the relationship between time and the number of vehicles.

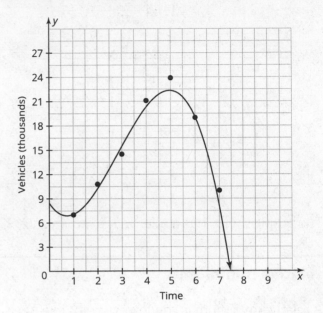

relation

A relation is the mapping between a set of input values called the domain and a set of output values called the range.

Example

The set of points {(0, 1), (1, 8), (2, 5), (3, 7)} is a relation.

relative maximum

A relative maximum is the highest point in a particular section of a graph.

Example

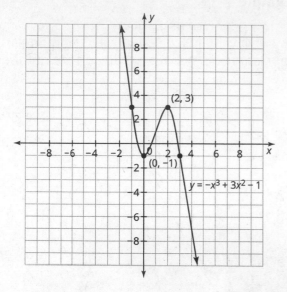

The graph shown has a relative maximum at (2, 3).

relative minimum

A relative minimum is the lowest point in a particular section of a graph.

Example

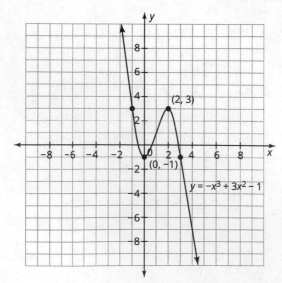

The graph shown has a relative minimum at (0, −1).

Remainder Theorem

The Remainder Theorem states that the remainder when dividing a polynomial by $(x - r)$ is the value of the polynomial at r.

Example

The value of the polynomial $x^2 + 5x + 2$ at 1 is $(1)^2 + 5(1) + 2 = 8$. So, the remainder when $x^2 + 5x + 2$ is divided by $x - 1$ is 8.

$$
\begin{array}{r}
x + 6 \\
x - 1 \overline{)x^2 + 5x + 2} \\
\underline{x^2 - x} \\
6x + 2 \\
\underline{6x - 6} \\
8
\end{array}
$$

removable discontinuity

A removable discontinuity is a single point at which the graph of a function is not defined.

Example

The graph of the function $f(x) = \frac{x^2}{x}$ has a removable discontinuity at $x = 0$.

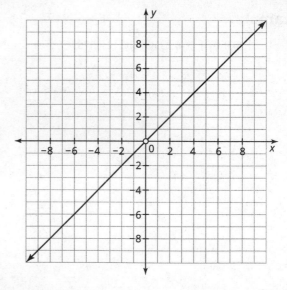

S

sample

Where data are collected from a selection of the population, the data are called a sample.

Example

If you wanted to find out the average height of the students in your school, you could choose just a certain number of students and measure their heights. The heights of the students in this group would be the sample.

sample proportion

A sample proportion is the percentage of a sample that yields a favorable outcome in an experiment. This is often used to make predictions about a population.

Example

In an election, a sample of townspeople is surveyed. The sample proportion represents the percentage of the survey results that indicate that they will vote to re-elect the mayor.

sample survey

A sample survey poses a question of interest to a random sample of the targeted population.

Example

The following is an example of a sample survey.

A recent survey of nearly 1200 young people from across the U.S. shows that 40% of 16- to 20-year-olds who have a driver's license admit to texting on a regular basis while they are driving.

sampling distribution

A sampling distribution consists of every possible sample of equal size from a given population. A sampling distribution provides an estimate for population parameters. The mean or proportion of a sampling distribution is estimated by the mean or proportion of a sample. For categorical data, the standard deviation of a sampling distribution is estimated by calculating $\sqrt{\frac{\hat{p}(1-\hat{p})}{n}}$ where $\hat{p}$ (p-hat) is the sample proportion and n is the sample size. For continuous data, the standard deviation of a sampling distribution is estimated by calculating $\frac{s}{\sqrt{n}}$ where s is the standard deviation of the original sample and n is the sample size.

Example

A sleep survey of 50 teens resulted in a sample mean of 7.7 hours and sample standard deviation of 0.8 hours.

The estimated mean of the sampling distribution is 7.7 hours. The estimated standard deviation of the sampling distribution is approximately 0.11 hours.

$$\frac{s}{\sqrt{n}} = \frac{0.8}{\sqrt{50}} \approx 0.11$$

self-similar

A self-similar object is exactly or approximately similar to a part of itself.

Example

A Koch snowflake is considered to be self-similar.

simple random sample

A simple random sample is a sample in which every member of the population has the same chance of being selected.

Example

Using a random number generator to select a sample is an example of simple random sampling.

sine function

The sine function is a periodic function. It takes angle measures (θ values) as inputs and then outputs real number values which correspond to the coordinates of points on the unit circle.

Example

The function $h(\theta) = -\sin(2\theta) + 1$ is a sine function.

square root function

The square root function is the inverse of the power function $f(x) = x^2$ when the domain is restricted to $x \geq 0$.

Example

The square root function is $g(x) = \sqrt{x}$.

standard deviation (σ)

Standard deviation is a measure of the variation of the values in a data set from the mean of the data. A lower standard deviation represents data that are more tightly clustered near the mean. A higher standard deviation represents data that are more spread out from the mean. Use the formula below to calculate standard deviation.

$$\text{standard deviation} = \sqrt{\frac{\sum_{i=1}^{n}(x_1 - \bar{x})^2}{n}}$$

where $\bar{x}$ is the mean and n is the number of data values in the data set $\{x_1, x_2, \ldots, x_n\}$.

Example

In the data set of test scores 60, 70, 80, 90, 100, the mean $\bar{x}$ is 80 and the number of data elements n is 5.

$$\sigma = \sqrt{\frac{\begin{array}{c}(60-80)^2 + (70-80)^2 + (80-80)^2 + \\ (90-80)^2 + (100-80)^2\end{array}}{5}}$$

$$= \sqrt{\frac{1000}{5}}$$

$$= \sqrt{200}$$

$$\approx 14.14.$$

standard form (general form) of a quadratic function

A quadratic function written in the form $f(x) = ax^2 + bx + c$, where $a \neq 0$, is in standard form, or general form.

Example

The function $f(x) = -5x^2 - 10x + 1$ is written in standard form.

standard normal distribution

The standard normal distribution is a normal probability distribution with the following properties:

- The mean is equal to 0.
- The standard deviation is 1.
- The curve is bell-shaped and symmetric about the mean.

Example

A standard normal distribution curve is shown.

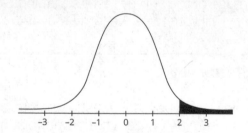

standard position of an angle

The standard position of an angle occurs when the vertex of the angle is at the origin and one ray of the angle is on the x-axis.

Example

The angle shown is in standard position.

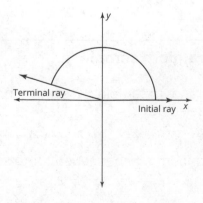

statistic

When data are gathered from a sample, the characteristic used to describe the sample is called a statistic.

Example

If you wanted to find out the average height of the students in your school, and you chose just a certain number of students randomly and measured their heights, the characteristic "average height" would be called a statistic.

statistically significant

A survey that has a result that is statistically significant indicates that the result did not likely occur by chance, but is likely linked to a specific cause. Typically, a result that is more than 2 standard deviations away from the mean is considered statistically significant.

Example

A survey of 2000 teenagers reports that 42% have a part-time job. The interval from 40.9% to 43.1% represents a 95% confidence interval for the population proportion. A survey that yields a report of 50% of teenagers with a part-time job would be considered statistically significant.

stratified random sample

A stratified random sample is a sample obtained by dividing the population into different groups, or strata, according to a characteristic, and randomly selecting data from each group.

Example

If students in a high school are divided by class, and random samples are then taken from each class, the result is a stratified random sample.

subjective sample

A subjective sample is a sample that is chosen based on some criteria, rather than at random.

Example

From a set of students, "choosing five students you know" is a subjective sample. In contrast, "choosing five students at random" is a random sample.

symmetric about a line

If a graph is symmetric about a line, the line divides the graph into two identical parts.

Example

The graph of $f(x) = x^2$ is symmetric about the line $x = 0$.

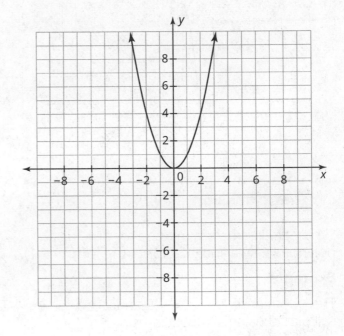

symmetric about a point

A function is symmetric about a point if each point on the graph has a point the same distance from the central point, but in the opposite direction.

Example

The graph of $f(x) = x^3$ is symmetric about the point $(0, 0)$.

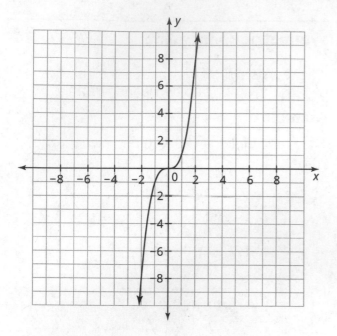

synthetic division

Synthetic division is a method for dividing a polynomial by a linear factor of the form $(x - r)$.

Example

The quotient of $2x^2 - 3x - 9$ and $x - 3$ can be calculated using synthetic division.

```
3 |  2   -3   -9
  |        6    9
  _____
     2    3  |  0
```

The quotient of $2x^2 - 3x - 9$ and $x - 3$ is $2x + 3$.

systematic sample

A systematic sample is a sample obtained by selecting every nth data in the population.

Example

If you choose every 12th student that walks into school, your sample is a systematic sample.

———————————— T ————————————

tangent function

The tangent function is a periodic function. It takes angle measures (θ values) as inputs and then outputs real number values which correspond to the coordinates of points on the unit circle.

Example

The function $f(\theta) = \tan\left(\frac{\theta}{2}\right)$ is a tangent function.

terminal ray of an angle

The terminal ray of an angle in standard position is the ray with its endpoint at the origin that is not the initial ray.

Example

The terminal ray of the angle is labeled in the diagram.

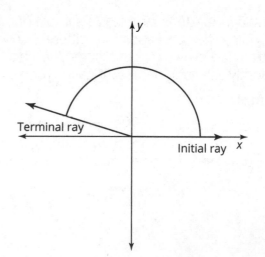

the number *i*

The number *i* is a number such that $i^2 = -1$.

theta (*θ*)

Theta is a symbol typically used to represent the measure of an angle in standard position.

Example

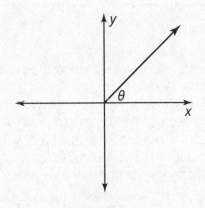

treatment

A treatment is a condition in an experiment.

Example

Suppose that an experiment is conducted to test the effects of a new drug on a sample of patients. The distribution of the drug to the patients is the treatment in the experiment.

trigonometric equation

A trigonometric equation is an equation that includes one or more trigonometric functions.

Example

The equation $\cos x = \frac{\sqrt{2}}{2}$ is a trigonometric equation.

trigonometric function

A trigonometric function is a periodic function that takes angle measures (*θ* values) as inputs and then outputs real number values which correspond to the coordinates of points on the unit circle.

Example

The function $g(x) = \sin x$ is a trigonometric function. The graph of the sine function $g(\theta) = \sin \theta$ is obtained by evaluating the *θ* values of the unit circle and graphing the coordinates.

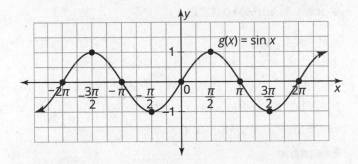

θ	$g(\theta) = \sin \theta$	$(\theta, g(\theta))$
0	$\sin(0) = 0$	$(0, 0)$
$\frac{\pi}{2}$	$\sin\left(\frac{\pi}{2}\right) = 1$	$\left(\frac{\pi}{2}, 1\right)$
π	$\sin(\pi) = 0$	$(\pi, 0)$
$\frac{3\pi}{2}$	$\sin\left(\frac{3\pi}{2}\right) = -1$	$\left(\frac{3\pi}{2}, -1\right)$
2π	$\sin(2\pi) = 0$	$(2\pi, 0)$

--- U ---

unit circle

A unit circle is a circle whose radius is one unit of distance.

Example

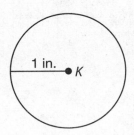

Circle *K* is a unit circle.

vertex form of a quadratic function

A quadratic function written in vertex form is in the form $f(x) = a(x - h)^2 + k$, where $a \neq 0$.

Example

The quadratic equation $y = 2(x - 5)^2 + 10$ is written in vertex form. The vertex of the graph is the point (5, 10).

vertical asymptote

A vertical asymptote is a vertical line that a function gets closer and closer to, but never intersects. The asymptote does not represent points on the graph of the function. It represents the output value that the graph approaches.

Example

The graph has two asymptotes: a vertical asymptote $x = 2$ and a horizontal asymptote $y = -1$.

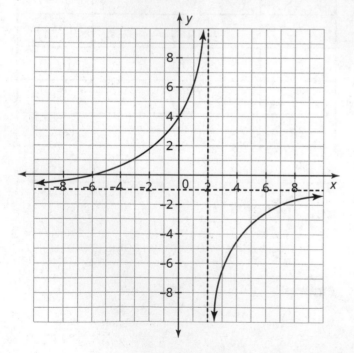

volunteer sample

A volunteer sample is a sample whose data consists of those who volunteer to be part of the sample.

Example

If you ask students in your school to complete and submit an optional survey so that you can collect data, your sample is a volunteer sample.

z-score

A z-score is a number that describes how many standard deviations from the mean a particular value is. The following formula can be used to calculate a z-score for a particular value, where z represents the z-score, x represents the particular data value, μ represents the mean, and σ represents the standard deviation.

$$z = \frac{x - \mu}{\sigma}$$

Example

Suppose that a set of data follows a normal distribution with a mean of 22 and a standard deviation of 2.4.

The z-score for a data value of 25 is
$z = \frac{25 - 22}{2.4} = 1.25$.

Zero Product Property

The Zero Product Property states: "If the product of two or more factors is equal to zero, then at least one factor must be equal to zero." This is also called the Converse of Multiplication Property of Zero.

Example

According to the Zero Product Property, if $(x - 2)(x + 3) = 0$ then $x - 2 = 0$ or $x + 3 = 0$.

Zero Property of Logarithms

The Zero Property of Logarithms states that the logarithm of 1, with any base, is always equal to 0.

$$\log_b (1) = 0$$

Example

$\log_3 (1) = 0$

Index

I

Identities
  periodicity, M4-44
  polynomial, M2-77–M2-86
  Pythagorean,
    M4-95–M4-101
Imaginary numbers, M1-97,
  M1-123
Imaginary part of a
  complex number,
  M1-97, M1-122
Imaginary roots, M1-97,
  M1-122
Imaginary zeros, M1-97,
  M1-122
Initial ray, M4-12, M4-84
Interpreting data, M5-121
Intervals
  confidence, M5-102–M5-
    103, M5-139
  of normal distributions,
    M5-25–M5-26
Inverse cosine ($\cos^{-1}$),
  M4-111, M4-156
Inverse of a function, M3-13,
  M3-81
Inverse, in solving
  trigonometric
  equations,
  M4-110–M4-111
Inverse sine ($\sin^{-1}$), M4-111,
  M4-156
Inverses of power function,
  M3-7–M3-16, M3-20
  by composition,
    M3-30–M3-31
  switching x and y,
    M3-9–M3-12
Inverse tangent ($\tan^{-1}$),
  M4-111, M4-156
Invertible function, M3-14,
  M3-81
Iterative process, defined,
  M3-278, M3-298

K

Koch, Helge von, M3-285
Koch Snowflake,
  M3-285–M3-289

L

Line, symmetric about a,
  M1-202, M1-298

Linear function
  building cubic function
    from, M1-162–M1-163
  vs. exponential function,
    M3-93–M3-104
Logarithmic equation
  applications of,
    M3-223–M3-234
  defined, M3-173, M3-237
  solving, M3-173–M3-175,
    M3-207–M3-220
  methods for,
    M3-211–M3-213
  with multiple logarithms,
    M3-214–M3-217
Logarithmic expressions,
  M3-171, M3-182
Logarithmic function,
  M3-125–M3-134
  defined, M3-129, M3-163
  graphing, M3-129–M3-131
Logarithmic functions,
  transformations of
  exponential and,
  M3-137–M3-156
Logarithmic model,
  solving problems with,
  M3-225–M3-226
Logarithm(s)
  applying, M3-132–M3-133
  are exponents,
    M3-127–M3-129
  of both sides of
    an equation,
    M3-201–M3-202
  common, M3-130, M3-163
  defined, M3-127, M3-162
  estimating with,
    M3-176–M3-180
  estimating with natural,
    M3-181
  natural, M3-130, M3-163
  properties of,
    M3-187–M3-190
    to rewrite expressions,
    M3-191–M3-192
  proportions of,
    M3-185–M3-194
Logarithm with Same Base
  and Argument,
  M3-239
Long division, polynomial,
  M2-26–M2-27

M

Margin of error, M5-96,
  M5-138
Maxima, of
  polynomial function,
  M1-228–M1-229
Mean, M5-14, M5-54
Menger, Karl, M3-283
Menger Sponge,
  M3-283–M3-284
Midline, M4-15
Model/modeling
  exponential, M3-98–M3-99
  linear, M3-98–M3-99
  motion with
    trigonometric function,
    M4-131–M4-138
  patterns of daylight,
    M4-124–M4-127
  with periodic functions,
    M4-119–M4-128
  with polynomial
    functions and data,
    M2-103–M2-114
  population change,
    M4-121–M4-123
  with e, M3-116–M3-117
  with problem situation,
    M1-131–M1-133
  process,
    M1-134–M1-135
  regression, M3-233
  solving problems with
    exponential,
    M3-227–M3-229
    logarithmic,
    M3-225–M3-226
    natural logarithmic,
    M3-230–M3-231
Modeling a situation,
  M1-131–M1-133
  with exponential function,
    M3-100–M3-103
  with rational function,
    M2-140–M2-141
Multiplication, of
  complex numbers,
  M1-100–M1-103
Multiplicity,
  M1-169, M1-187
Multiplying to create
  polynomials,
  M1-176–M1-178